G. D. Helming
1778 T St.
Lincoln
Nebr

Purchased from Mr Gouldin
Rec'd. Mch. 29. 1898
Home from February 20 until Mch. 27-18..
Elvira Egn Mch. 24. last.

# SHEPP'S GIANT LIBRARY

EIGHT
GREAT BOOKS
IN A
SINGLE
VOLUME

An Unrivalled
Compilation
of the
WORLD'S
BEST
LITERATURE
MUSIC
and ART

Masterpieces of
HISTORY
FICTION
POETRY
ORATORY
THE DRAMA
PAINTING
and MELODY

Profusely
Embellished with
the Choicest
Products of the
Illustrator's Art

PUBLISHED
BY

GLOBE
BIBLE
PUBLISHING
CO.

EDITED BY

DANIEL B. SHEPP, Author

of "Shepp's Photographs of the World,"
"Shepp's World's Fair Photographed,"
"Shepp's New York City Illustrated," etc.

723
Chestnut St.
Philadelphia, Pa.

PRESS OF
ALFRED M. SLOCUM CO.
PHILADELPHIA, PA.

# PREFACE.

" GREAT BOOK," said an ancient Greek philosopher, "is a great evil." Never were truer words. They must be properly interpreted, no doubt. Some books must of necessity be large, and yet are by no means evil. But when a book can be put into smaller compass, and yet is not, but is made bulky and voluminous, the evil is apparent. That which is good in the book is so hidden away that it cannot be found. Men cannot spare time to read so big a book, and thus they altogether fail to get the instruction and the entertainment that are buried within its pages. The light of truth is hidden beneath the bushel of useless verbiage.

The present work is the result of an earnest attempt to correct such ill conditions. How many are there, in these busy days, who can find time to read through the great masterpieces of fiction, the innumerable volumes of poetry, the sublime dramas of Shakespeare, the detailed history of the world? To do so would require that a man forsake all else and give his life up to this one task. Yet how dearly would every appreciative mind love to be stored with such intellectual treasures! And how desirable it is that such knowledge and entertainment should be placed within the reach of even the busiest man!

It is confidently believed that it is thus placed in "Shepp's Giant Library." With scholarly and reverential care, the best masterpieces of the world's literature have here been put into such compass as will make them universally accessible. They have not been dwarfed or mutilated. They have merely been freed from the superfluous wrappings that shut in the kernel of essential truth from the reach of the average reader. Of every one the full spirit is preserved in all its vital force, and with it far more of the letter than one man in a thousand is ever able to master and remember from the unabridged work.

Beginning with the Book of Books, the Bible, the complete story of Divine dealings with man is given in a simple, direct and convincing manner, from the creation of the world to the revelation of its end. In like manner, the general history of the world is rehearsed, down to the present day, with such mingled accuracy, conciseness, completeness and charm of narration as may nowhere else be found. A whole library of the masterpieces of fiction, in the literature of many lands, is also given, within the easy compass of a single volume. The tales of Shakespeare's greatest dramas form another volume of surpassing value. Under the head of "Famous Orations" will be found an authentic collection of those flights of oratory that have, in many lands and ages and on innumerable varying occasions, thrilled and convinced the minds of listening multitudes. Yet another volume presents the choicest gems of poetry, epic and lyric, in all the range of universal literature.

Nor are the other achievements of human genius forgotten. The divine art of music is represented in a whole library of selected compositions, for voice and instruments, including everything of assured merit from the best beloved folk-songs to the most sublime symphony. Pictorial art, too, has its place. By the side of the library is the gallery, in which are exhibited the most perfect reproductions ever made of the great paintings which adorn the walls of royal palaces and imperial museums. From Paris, from Dresden, from London, from Berlin, from every art centre in the world these lovely creations have been gathered with artistic discrimination. In addition to these latter, all the books of the Library are profusely and appropriately illustrated in the best manner of which artistic genius is capable.

Let it not be imagined that this is mere vainglorious boasting. The Library is open for actual inspection. It will be found to contain all that has been said, and far more. He who has it may be regardless of many another book. He will have in it all he could hope to get from years of delving in innumerable musty tomes, all he could hear in many seasons of operas and concerts, all he could see in years of wandering amid distant galleries of art. All this he may have at his own fireside, and find time to enjoy amid the busiest moments of the busiest day. It is with pardonable pride that such a work is laid before the public, and with ample confidence that those who look into it will testify that "the half was never told."

"Of making many books," said the Preacher, "there is no end, and much study is a weariness to the flesh." But here are many books combined in one, and here is that which will give all the advantages and benefactions of much study with no weariness to either mind or flesh. Such is "Shepp's Giant Library." Such only need be its introduction to the public.

# CONTENTS.

## Book I.—Stories of the Bible.

## Book II.—Tales from Shakespeare.

# Book III.—Treasury of Music.

## INSTRUMENTAL.

## VOCAL.—Sacred.

## VOCAL.—Secular.

# Book IV.—A Cluster of Fine Art.

## Book V.—Gems of Poetry.

# Book VI.—Famous Orations.

# Book VII.—Fiction.

Uncle Tom's Cabin.—By Harriet Beecher Stowe.

David Copperfield.—By Charles Dickens.

Twenty Thousand Leagues Under the Sea.—By Jules Verne.

Robinson Crusoe.—By Daniel Defoe.

Les Miserables.—By Victor Hugo.

Don Quixote.—By Miguel de Cervantes.

Eliza's Escape—Across the River to Freedom—The Baffled Trader—
Fighting for Freedom—Evangeline—Tom's New Master—Topsy—The
Little Evangelist—Death of Eva—Death of St. Clare—In the Slave
Market—Cassey—The Death of Tom—Emmeline's Escape.

The Visit to Yarmouth—"Barkis is Willin'"—School and Schoolmates
—Barkis Waiting—A Great Change—My Aunt Makes up Her Mind—
Early Loves—J. Steerforth—My Profession—"Wickfield and Heep"—
Dora—Out with the Tide—A Greater Loss—Betsy Trotwood's Story
—Mr. Spenlow—House-keeping Extraordinary—My Child-Wife—Little
Em'ly Again—The Home Coming—Heep—Death of Dora—Closing
Scenes.

# Book VIII.—History of the World.

## CHAPTER I.

## CHAPTER II.

## CHAPTER III.

## CHAPTER IV.

# Illustrations.

# BOOK I.

---

## STORIES OF THE BIBLE.

ADAM AND EVE

# Book I.

# Stories of the Bible.

---

## CHAPTER I.

### FROM EDEN TO EGYPT.

THE FALL OF MAN—CAIN AND ABEL—THE FLOOD—THE SONS OF NOAH—
SARAI AND HAGAR—THE CHILDREN OF ABRAHAM—ESAU AND
JACOB—THE FAMILY OF JACOB—ISRAEL IN EGYPT.

---

"IN the beginning"—majestic opening of majestic history—"in the beginning God created the heavens and the earth." In six days He created them, or six periods, in an order exactly coinciding with the scientific order of evolution. Genesis and geology agree with mathematical accuracy. First, the earth was without form and void, and dark ; primordial nebula. The Spirit of God moved upon it, and motion began. Then God said, "Let there be light," and there was light. Then the revolving nebula became divided into systems and worlds. This earth was transformed from a fluid into a solid mass. Dry land appeared, and vegetable life was created. Next the photosphere, or enveloping cloud of luminous gases around the earth, was absorbed and vanished, and the sun and moon and stars became visible. Pure atmospheric air having taken the place of the gaseous photosphere, the earth was fitted for animal life, and it accordingly appeared; first, molluscs ; then fishes, then birds, then reptiles, then mammals. Finally, in due course of time "God created man in His own image." Such was the work of creation, and after it "God rested." For since the creation of man there have been no more creative acts, no more perceptible processes of evolution. The age of man is the Sabbath of the universe.

### The Fall of Man.

God placed the man whom He had made in a garden in Eden, and created, from a rib taken from his side, a woman to be his wife. Adam and Eve were their names, "And God blessed them, and God said unto them, ' Be fruitful, and multiply and replenish the earth, and subdue it : and have dominion over the fish of the sea, and over the fowl of the air, and over every living thing that moveth upon the earth. Of every tree of the garden thou mayest freely eat: but of the tree of the knowledge of good and evil, thou shalt not eat of it: for in the day that thou eatest thereof thou shalt surely die.' " Then came the spirit of evil in the form of a serpent and tempted the woman to eat the forbidden fruit, telling her that if she did so she would become as wise as God Himself, and that she would not die, as God had threatened. "And when the woman saw that the tree was good for food, and that it was pleasant to the eye, and the tree to be desired to make one wise, she took of the fruit thereof, and did eat, and gave also unto her husband with her, and he did eat." Forthwith knowledge of evil came upon them. They sought to hide themselves from God, for they were ashamed to meet Him. But God called them, and convicted them of their sin. He cursed the serpent, and put everlasting enmity between him and the children of men, and He doomed Adam and Eve to pain and labor and final death, and drove them from the garden.

## Cain and Abel.

To Adam and Eve, after their departure from the garden, were born two sons, Cain and Abel. The one was a tiller of the ground, the other a keeper of sheep. The two brothers offered sacrifices to God, each of the products of his labor, and Abel's was accepted, but Cain's was not. Therefore Cain became angry with Abel and slew him. "And the Lord said unto Cain, 'Where is Abel, thy brother?' And he said: 'I know not: am I my brother's keeper?' And He said, 'What hast thou done? The voice of thy brother's blood crieth unto Me from the ground. And now art thou cursed from the earth, which hath opened her mouth to receive thy brother's blood from thy hand: a fugitive and a vagabond shalt thou be in the earth.'" And then God set a mark upon Cain by which all who saw him should know him, but which would prevent any one from killing him. Then Cain went to another country and took to himself a wife. Among his descendants were Jubal, the inventor of musical instruments, and Tubal-Cain, the first artificer in brass and iron.

After Cain and Abel, a third son was born to Adam and Eve, whom they named Seth, and through him descended a long line of patriarchs. These lived to a great age. Adam himself lived 930 years, Seth 912, and others for many generations lived to similar ages. Oldest of all was Methuselah, the seventh in direct line from Adam, who lived to the age of 969 years. The grandson of Methuselah was Noah, in whose time came a most stupendous change upon the world.

## The Flood.

As the human race grew in numbers, it became wicked and corrupt, and God determined to destroy it with a mighty flood. Noah and his family alone were righteous, and they alone were to be saved. So God commanded him to make a huge ark, into which he should take his wife, his sons, and his sons' wives, and a pair of every sort of animals, in order that they might survive the flood and after it repopulate the earth. Noah did so, and then came the flood which covered the earth with water and destroyed all life save that in the ark. For forty days and forty nights it rained, and after that the flood remained for 150 days upon the earth. Then the water began gradually to subside until the dry land again appeared. As the flood subsided, Noah sent out from the ark a raven, which did not return to him but flew about until the waters were dried up. He also sent out a dove which finding no ground to rest upon, returned to him. A second time he sent out the dove, and then it returned to him bearing an olive leaf, so that he knew the waters were abated from off the earth. Seven days later he sent forth the dove again, but it did not return to him. Then he waited a little longer and then, at the command of God, opened the ark and came forth with his family and all the animals.

Then Noah built an altar and worshipped God, and God said, "I will not again curse the ground any more for man's sake ; neither will I again smite any more every thing living, as I have done. While the earth remaineth, seed time and harvest, and cold and heat, and summer and winter, and day and night shall not cease." And God blessed Noah and his sons and said unto them, "Be fruitful and multiply and replenish the earth. And behold, I establish my covenant with you, and with your seed after you. I do set My bow in the cloud, and it shall be for a token of a covenant betveen Me and the earth. And I will look upon it and I will remember My covenant, and the waters shall no more become a flood to destroy all flesh."

## The Sons of Noah.

The sons of Noah were Shem, Ham and Japheth. From them descended the three great divisions of the human race, now called Semitic, Hamitic, and Japhetic. For a time all men spoke the same language. But then they determined to build a great city and a great tower, to be their capital and rallying place. At the building of it God sent upon them a diversity of languages, and so the city and tower were called Babel, or "Confusion." Then they scattered abroad, in various parts of the earth. Thereafter, the story of the Bible deals chiefly with the descendants of Shem, from whom came the Hebrew race.

Ninth in descent from Shem came Abram, who was destined to lead a great revolution in the affairs of men. He first dwelt in the land of the Chaldees. But God said to him, "Get thee out of thy country, and from thy kindred, and from thy father's house, unto a land that I will show thee : and I will make of thee a great nation, and I will bless thee, and make thy name great ; and thou shalt be a blessing : and I will bless them that bless thee, and curse him that cursest thee : and in thee shall all families of the earth be blessed." So Abram departed, and his nephew Lot went with him, and they settled in the land of Canaan, not far from where Jerusalem was afterward built. And God said to him, "Unto thy seed will I give this land." Abram also journeyed to Egypt and dwelt there for a time and became very rich in cattle, silver and gold. He also organized a fighting force, and became one of the most powerful chieftains in all the land.

## Sarai and Hagar.

The wife of Abram was named Sarai, and she was childless. So he took for a second wife Sarai's servant Hagar, who presently bore him a son. This aroused the jealousy and wrath of Sarai and she bitterly persecuted Hagar, and Hagar fled from her into the wilderness. But the Angel of the Lord commanded her to return, and she did so for a time. But again Sarai, to whom a son had now been born, persecuted her more bitterly and drove her forth from her home. So Hagar and her son, Ishmael, went out into the wilderness. And after a time they nearly perished of thirst. But God spoke to Hagar from the heavens and told her their lives should be spared, and showed her a well of water. And after that they prospered greatly. But according to the word of God, Ishmael became a wild man, whose hand was against every man and against whom every man's hand was turned.

About this time the cities of Sodom and Gomorrah became so wicked that God determined to destroy them and their inhabitants with fire. Abram, who was now called Abraham, pleaded with God that he would spare them, and God agreed to do so if ten righteous men could be found in them. But Abraham could not find so many, but only one, his nephew Lot. So Lot and his wife and two daughters were warned by an angel and they fled from Sodom to the city of Zoar, where they would be safe. But Lot's wife looked back longingly and was turned into a pillar of salt. Then God rained fire upon the cities and they were utterly destroyed, and the place where they were was covered with the Dead Sea.

### The Children of Abraham.

The faith of Abraham in God was wonderfully tested when God commanded him to offer up his son as a sacrifice. Abraham prepared to do it, but just as he was about to slay the lad God stayed his hand, and then repeated the promise to Abraham that he should be the father of a great nation. Abraham's son was named Isaac, and when he was grown to manhood Abraham determined to choose a suitable wife for him from among his own kindred. So he sent a servant to visit his neighbor and kinsman, Bethuel, who had a beautiful daughter named Rebecca. He found Rebecca at the well drawing water, and she graciously offered to draw water for the camels in his train. Then she invited him into her father's house and gave hospitable entertainment. The man was charmed with her beauty and grace, and was convinced that she was designed to be the wife of Isaac. So he made her rich presents and asked for her hand for Isaac. Her father and her brother, Laban, consented and she returned with the messenger to Abraham's house, where she became Isaac's wife, and through those two came the children in whom the promise to Abraham was to be fulfilled.

### Esau and Jacob.

To Isaac and Rebecca were born twin sons, Esau and Jacob. The former grew up to be a hunter, the latter a farmer. Esau was Isaac's favorite, but Rebecca preferred Jacob. One day Esau came home from the hunt hungry and tired, and asked Jacob for food. Jacob refused to give him any unless Esau would give him in turn his right to the inheritance of their father. Esau agreed, and thus practically disinherited himself. Afterward, when Isaac was very old and blind, he asked Esau to get some venison for him, and Esau went out to do so. But in the meantime Rebecca directed Jacob to offer his father food and thus to get from him a blessing. Jacob did so, disguising himself so as to seem to be Esau to the groping hands of his father. So Isaac bestowed upon Jacob his blessing, supposing him to be Esau.

EXPULSION OF HAGAR

Then Esau came and the trick was discovered, but the blessing could not be recalled from Jacob. So enmity arose in the heart of Esau against Jacob, and Jacob fled for his life. One night, during his exile, as he lay asleep he had a vision of Heaven opened and angels descending and ascending on a great ladder ; and God spoke to him and renewed to him the covenant he had made with Abraham and Isaac. In the morning Jacob built there an altar, and consecrated his life to the service of God, and went on his way encouraged and rejoicing.

## The Family of Jacob.

Jacob soon came to the home of his uncle Laban, who had two daughters, Leah and Rachel. Jacob became enamored of Rachel, and agreed to work in Laban's service for seven years if Laban would give her to him for his wife. But at the end of the seven years Laban insisted that Jacob should marry Leah instead, because she was the elder. Jacob agreed to this, but asked to have Rachel also, for whom he would serve Laban seven years longer. Thus he secured his two cousins for his wives, and he took two other wives also. To him they bore a number of sons : Reuben, Simeon, Levi, Judah, Dan, Nephtali, Gad, Asher, Issachar, Zebulun, Joseph, and Benjamin. These were the sons of Jacob. Then Jacob, who had grown richer in cattle and goods than Laban, took his departure and returned to his old home. On the way he met his brother Esau and became reconciled with him. Soon after the aged Isaac died, and Jacob succeeded to his possessions.

Joseph, the next to the youngest of Jacob's sons, was his father's favorite. He was also a dreamer of dreams, and in some of these dreams he was represented as superior to his brothers. Therefore his brothers hated him, and one day planned to kill him. But Reuben persuaded them merely to imprison him in a pit, and then to sell him as a slave to some Egyptian traders. Then they reported to Jacob that Joseph had been killed by a wild beast, and Jacob mourned for him as one dead. Joseph was, however, sold to Potiphar, an officer of the court of Pharaoh, the King of Egypt. He proved himself a faithful and capable servant, and was soon advanced to be manager of Potiphar's whole estate. Then Potiphar's wife tempted him to sin, and on his refusal to do as she wished, had him cast into prison. There he won the favor of the prison keeper, and became noted as an interpreter of dreams. Pharaoh, the King, having a strange dream, which none of his men could interpret, Joseph was sent for. He interpreted the dream and was taken into Pharaoh's favor and made the chief minister of Pharaoh's court.

## Israel in Egypt.

After this there came a great famine upon the country where Jacob dwelt, and the sons of Jacob went down to Egypt to buy grain, where it was plentiful. They did not know Joseph, but he knew them, and on a pretence that they were spies he threw them into prison and refused to release them until they had sent for their youngest brother, Benjamin, who had remained at home with his father. Then he released them, and they all started home with an abundant supply of grain. But he stopped them, and revealed to them who he was, and bade them remain in Egypt and prosper, and send for their father and all his household to come there too.   So Jacob, who was now called Israel, and all his family, settled in Egypt and greatly prospered.   He adopted as his own his two grandsons, Manasseh and Ephraim, the sons of Joseph who had been born in Egypt, and then he blessed them all and died. Joseph bore his body back to his old home and buried it there, and then returned to Egypt and died.   But his brothers and all their households remained in Egypt.

# CHAPTER II.

------

## FROM EGYPT TO JERUSALEM.

THE PLAGUES OF EGYPT—THE EXODUS—IN THE WILDERNESS—THE GIVING OF
THE LAW—THE TABERNACLE—NUMBERING THE TRIBES—SPYING OUT THE
LAND—BALAK AND BALAAM—REACHING THE PROMISED LAND—THE
DEATH OF MOSES—OVER JORDAN—THE SIN OF ACHAN—THE
CONQUEST OF CANAAN—THE JUDGES—ABIMELECH—
JEPHTHAH—SAMSON—RUTH—SAMUEL—SAUL—
DAVID AND GOLIATH—THE PASSING OF
SAUL—DAVID, KING OF ISRAEL.

------

AFTER the death of Joseph another king came to the throne in Egypt, who was jealous of the prosperity of the Israelites and began to persecute and oppress them. First he made them slaves, and then commanded all their male children to be put to death. One of the sons of Levi and his wife had a son whom they sought to preserve by placing him in a little boat hidden in the rushes in the margin of the river Nile. There the child was found by the daughter of Pharaoh, and she named him Moses, and adopted him and had him brought up as her own. But when Moses was grown, and saw how his kinsmen were oppressed, he refused to be known as the son of Pharaoh's daughter, but departed from the court and cast in his lot with the Children of Israel.

While Moses was tending the flocks of his father-in-law, God appeared to him in a vision at Mount Horeb, as a flame of fire in a bush, though the bush was not consumed. And God told him he would make him the deliverer of the Israelites from Egyptian bondage, and the leader of them into the land of Canaan, which he would deliver into their hands. So Moses and Aaron his brother returned to their oppressed kinsmen in Egypt, to begin the work of deliverance. They found the persecutions greatly increased. The Israelites were compelled to make bricks for the building of Pharaoh's palaces, though the necessary materials for making the bricks were not furnished to them, and when they failed to make the required number they were cruelly beaten with whips.

## The Plagues of Egypt.

Moses and Aaron went before Pharaoh and demanded that he should release the Israelites from their bondage and let them depart from Egypt. Pharaoh asked for a sign of their divine mission, whereupon Aaron threw his staff upon the ground and it became a serpent. The Egyptian priests did the same with their rods, which also became serpents. But Aaron's rod swallowed up all the others. Pharaoh's heart was hardened, however, and he refused to let the Israelites go. So at the word of Moses the waters of the river were turned into blood. This was the first of the plagues of Egypt. Pharaoh was still stubborn, and a second plague was sent upon the land, in the form of swarms of frogs, which were regarded by the Egyptians as unclean. Then Pharaoh consented to let them go, and the plague was abated. Again he hardened his heart and refused to let them go, and another plague, of lice, was sent upon the land. That was followed with a plague of flies, and then Pharaoh relented and promised to let them go, only to break his word as soon as the plague was abated.

Next came a murrain, which destroyed all the cattle of Egypt, and then an epidemic of boils upon the people, and then a storm of hail and fire. Then Pharaoh once more pretended that he would release the Israelites, but did not, and a plague of locusts was sent. Next came a plague of darkness, so dense that it could be felt, and finally the first-born child of every Egyptian family was slain, and also the first-born of all beasts. From all these plagues the children of Israel were exempt. In the last plague the Israelites marked the doorposts of their houses with the blood of lambs, and the death which smote the first-born of the Egyptians passed over them and left them unharmed. Thus was established the feast of the Passover, which ever afterward was the chief of the feasts kept by the Children of Israel.

## The Exodus.

After this last and most dreadful plague, Pharaoh did let the Children of Israel go. The latter, under the command of God, before setting out borrowed from their Egyptian neighbors all the gold and gems and other valuable articles they could, and carried them away, partly to punish the Egyptians for their cruelty, and partly to reward the Israelites for their years of servitude. They marched toward Canaan, but not by the direct road, which would have led them through the land of the Philistines, a warlike people with whom they were ill prepared to cope. Instead they went toward the Red Sea, the Lord leading them in the form of a pillar of cloud by day, and a pillar of flame by night.

Then Pharaoh began to regret that he had let them go, and set out with an army to bring them back. He overtook them near the shore of the Red Sea, and they were in great distress for fear he would capture them before they could get across. At first there seemed no way for them to get across. But God sent a great wind which parted the waters of the Red Sea so that the Israelites could pass over on dry ground. The Egyptians followed them, but God delayed their pursuit until the Israelites were safely on the other side. Then he let the Egyptians come on to the middle of the sea and then let the waters rush back and drown them all. Thus were the Israelites led safely out of Egypt and they sang songs of praise to God for their deliverance.

## In the Wilderness.

The Israelites were now in the wilderness of Arabia Petræa. When they became weary of marching they murmured. When they found at Marah only bitter or brackish water to drink, they complained to Moses, and Moses prayed to God and made the water sweet for them. Then they ran short of food, and murmured again, and wished they were back in Egypt. So God sent great flocks of quail to them, and caused manna to grow on the grass, so that they were well fed. Again they came to a place where there was no water to drink, and murmured against Moses, until God enabled him to draw a plentiful stream of water from a rock by striking it with his staff.

Next they came to a hostile tribe known as the Amalekites, and Moses sent out the strongest of the Israelites under the leadership of a man named Joshua, to fight them. Moses himself went up on a hill overlooking the battle and prayed. As long as he held his hands up to Heaven the Israelites were victorious, but when his hands grew weary and fell they were defeated. So Aaron and Hur stood one at each side and held up his hands all day, until the complete victory was won.

## The Giving of the Law.

When the Israelites reached Mount Sinai, they encamped there, and Moses went up to the top of the mountain to commune with God. And the mountain was enveloped in clouds, and there were thunder and lightning and a great earthquake. In that most memorable interview God gave to Moses the great fundamental law known as the Ten Commandments, engraved on a tablet of stone. These were the Commandments:

" Thou shalt have no other gods before me.

" Thou shalt not make unto thee any graven image, or any likeness of anything that is in the Heaven above, or that is in the earth beneath, or that is in the water under the earth: Thou shalt not bow down thyself to them, nor serve them: For I the Lord thy God am a jealous God, visiting the iniquity of the fathers upon the children unto the third and fourth generation of them that hate me ; and showing mercy unto thousands of them that love me and keep my commandments.

" Thou shalt not take the name of the Lord thy God in vain ; for the Lord will not hold him guiltless that taketh His name in vain.

"Remember the Sabbath day, to keep it holy. Six days shalt thou labor, and do all thy work: But the seventh day is the Sabbath of the Lord thy God: In it thou shalt not do any work, thou, nor thy son, nor thy daughter, thy man-servant, nor thy maid-servant, nor thy cattle, nor the stranger that is within thy gates: For in six days the Lord made heaven and earth, the sea, and all that in them is, and rested the seventh day ; wherefore the Lord blessed the Sabbath day and hallowed it.

" Honor thy father and thy mother: That thy days may be long upon the land which the Lord thy God giveth thee.

" Thou shalt not kill.

" Thou shalt not commit adultery.

" Thou shalt not steal.

" Thou shalt not bear false witness against thy neighbor.

" Thou shalt not covet thy neighbor's house, thou shalt not covet thy neighbor's wife, nor his man servant, nor his maid servant, nor his ox, nor his ass, nor anything that is thy neighbor's."

And all the people saw the thunderings, and the lightnings, and the noise of the trumpet, and the mountain smoking. And when they saw it they were afraid and stood far off. And they said to Moses, "Speak thou with us, and we will hear. But let not God speak with us, lest we die." And Moses said to them, "Fear not ; for God is come to prove you, and that his fear may be before your faces, that ye sin not." So the people stood at a distance while Moses drew near to the dark cloud where God was.

## The Tabernacle.

God also commanded Moses to construct a tabernacle, or great tent, to serve as a place of worship. He gave minute directions as to the plan and building of it and the arrangement of its contents. In it was to be a wooden chest covered with gold, containing the tablet bearing the law and other objects, to be known as the Ark of the Covenant. Aaron and his sons were to be the priests who should have charge of the Tabernacle and minister at its altar, and the Tabernacle was to be carried by the people in all their wanderings until they reached a permanent home in the promised land of Canaan.

For forty days and nights Moses remained on the mountain, alone with God, receiving these instructions. Meanwhile the people grew impatient, and demanded some other god which they might worship. So they took the gold they had brought from Egypt and melted it and made of it an image of a calf, such as they had seen the Egyptians worship, and they began to worship it. When Moses came down from the mountain he found the people at their idolatrous practices, and was so enraged at them that he flung down the stone tablet bearing the law and broke it into pieces. Then he burned the image in fire, and ground it to powder, and mixed the powder with water and made the people drink it. Finally, he ordered the sons of Levi to put to death about three thousand of the idolators. After that, Moses made a new tablet of stone, and God wrote the Ten Commandments upon it, as before, and the people in their repentance went zealously to work and built the Tabernacle as they had been commanded.

## Numbering the Tribes.

After the Tabernacle was finished, and the elaborate ceremonial of the law put into practice, the word was given for the Children of Israel to break camp and march on ; for now, a year after leaving Egypt, they were still at Mount Sinai. First, there was a "numbering of the tribes." A census was taken, and all the people were divided into thirteen great companies. Each company consisted of the descendants of one of the sons of Jacob, or of one of the two sons of Joseph. As it would be necessary for them to fight for the land of Canaan, they also took a census of all the able-bodied men who could serve as soldiers. There were over six hundred thousand of these, not counting those of the tribe of Levi, who were set aside as priests and servants of the Tabernacle. Of these there were eight thousand five hundred and eighty.

On their journey the Israelites marched like an army, each of the thirteen tribes under its own leader. When they rested, they formed a huge camp, with the Tabernacle in the centre. Soon after they moved on from Mount Sinai they began murmuring again because they had only manna to eat, whereas they wanted meat. So God sent them vast flocks of quails, and compelled them to eat them until they grew sick of them. After this, Moses' sister, Miriam, found fault with Moses because he had married a woman who was not an Israelite, and also because he was the supreme leader of the people. For punishment she was smitten with leprosy, and was healed only when she repented and Moses prayed for her.

## Spying out the Land.

Now the great host came near the borders of the land of Canaan, which had been promised to them for their home. Twelve men, one from each tribe excepting the Levites, were sent forward as spies, to discover what kind of a land it was and what sort of people inhabited it. They spent forty days in so doing, and then reported that it was a rich country, in proof of which they brought back a bunch of grapes so large that it took two men to carry it. But they said the people were giants, and the cities were strongly fortified, and it would be impossible to subdue them, and so they all except two spoke against attempting to enter the promised land. The two were Joshua and Caleb. They had faith in God's promise to give them possession of the land, and they urged the Israelites to enter it at once.

After some consideration the people decided not to try to enter Canaan. At this Moses and Aaron, and Joshua and Caleb, were greatly distressed. The Lord was so displeased that he threatened to send a pestilence and destroy the people. At Moses' prayer the pestilence was averted, but God decreed that the people should go back and wander in the wilderness for forty years, until all the men who had refused to enter Canaan were dead. Then their children should enter the promised land, and Joshua and Caleb should live to go with them. So they were all turned back into the wilderness again, where they met with many vicissitudes, and often fell into sin and were severely punished by the judgments of the Lord.

On one occasion they clamored for water, and railed against Moses for bringing them into a desert to die of thirst, although it was their own fault that they were there. Moses was a very patient man, but at this his patience gave way, and in a fit of wrath he exclaimed, "Must we fetch you water out of this rock?" Then he struck the rock, and water gushed forth freely. But Moses sinned in speaking angrily, and in speaking as though it were through his own power that he made the water flow. For this God decreed that he should merely see, but should not enter, the promised land. Again the Israelites became rebellious, and God sent a plague of fiery serpents against them, the bite of which was death. Many men were thus slain, until Moses, authorized by the Lord, set up a serpent made of brass upon a pole, and all who looked upon it were healed.

### Balak and Balaam.

When the Israelites reached the land of Moab, the king of the country, Balak, was afraid of them and wished to drive them back.  So he hired one of the wise men of the land, named Balaam, to go out and curse them ; for Balaam professed to be a prophet and to have power with God.  Balaam set out on his mission riding on an ass, and God sent an angel to stop him.  The angel stood in the pathway and the ass saw him, but Balaam could not.  The ass turned out into the field to get past, and Balaam struck it and forced it back into the road.  This happened a second and a third time, and then God gave the ass power to speak like a man and to rebuke Balaam for striking him.  Then Balaam's eyes were opened and he saw the angel, and the angel commanded him to return to the king, but to speak only such words as should be given to him by the angel.

The King then took Balaam to a place overlooking the camp of the Israelites, and built seven altars and offered sacrifices thereon.  Then Balaam attempted to pronounce a curse upon the Israelites.  But the angel of God put words of blessing into his mouth instead.  Then the King took Balaam to another place, and built more altars and offered sacrifices.  But again Balaam spoke blessings when he tried to curse.  A third time they tried it, on the summit of Mount Peor, and again Balaam blessed instead of cursing Israel :  "How goodly are thy tents, O Jacob," he said, " and thy tabernacles, O Israel.  As the valleys are they spread forth, as gardens by the river's side, as the trees which the Lord hath planted, and as cedar trees beside the waters.  Blessed is he that blesseth thee, and cursed is he that curseth thee.  Who can count the dust of Jacob, and the number of the fourth part of Israel ?  Let me die the death of the righteous, and let my last end be like his.  I shall see him, but not now.  I shall behold him, but not nigh.  There shall come a Star out of Jacob, and a Sceptre shall rise out of Israel, and shall smite the corners of Moab, and destroy all the children of Sheth."  After this, the King despaired of turning back Israel, and Balaam rose up, and went and returned to his place ; and Balak also went his way.

### Reaching the Promised Land.

At last the years of wandering were done.  Of all who had set out from Egypt, only three were now alive, Moses, Joshua, and Caleb.  These, with all the great host of Israel, reached the eastern side of the River Jordan, and encamped there. Two of the tribes, Reuben and Gad, and half of the tribe of Manasseh, decided to remain on that side of the river, but the others prepared to cross over and conquer the Canaanites and take possession of the land.  Their years of wandering in the wilderness had made them hardy and brave, and they did not fear the people they would have to meet.  It was planned that a portion of the country should be assigned to each of the tribes, excepting the Levites, for whom the others should provide a number of cities for their homes.

JACOB'S DREAM

Now Moses knew the end of his life was near. So he spoke long and earnestly, and for the last time, to the people of whom he had so long been the leader. He reminded them of all that had happened to them since they left Egypt, and of the promise God had given them for the future. He exhorted them to keep the law, and to observe all things that God had commanded them. He also wrote down in a book all the laws which God had given. Then he sang a great song of thanksgiving and prophesy: "Give ear, O ye Heavens, and I will speak; and hear, O earth, the words of my mouth. My doctrine shall drop as the rain, my speech shall distill as the dew, as the small rain upon the tender herb, and as the showers upon the grass: Because I will publish the name of the Lord: Ascribe ye greatness unto our God. He is the Rock, His work is perfect: For all His ways are judgment: A God of truth and without iniquity, just and right is He. Remember the days of old, consider the years of many generations: Ask thy father, and he will show thee; thy elders, and they will tell thee. How should one chase a thousand, and two put ten thousand to flight, except their Rock had sold them, and the Lord had shut them up? Rejoice, O ye nations, with His people: For He will avenge the blood of His servants, and will render vengeance to His adversaries, and will be merciful unto His land, and to His people." And Moses made an end of speaking to Israel, and he said unto them, "Set your hearts unto all the words which I testify among you this day, which ye shall command your children to observe to do, all the words of this law. For it is not a vain thing for you; because it is your life."

## The Death of Moses.

Then God led Moses from the plain of Moab, where the Children of Israel were encamped, to the mountains of Nebo, and to the top of Mount Pisgah, from which he could look across the River Jordan and see the promised land into which he might not enter. And the Lord said unto him, "This is the land which I swear unto Abraham, unto Isaac, and unto Jacob, saying, I will give it unto thy seed. I have caused thee to see it with thy eyes, but thou shalt not go over thither." So Moses the servant of the Lord died there in the land of Moab, according to the word of the Lord. And he buried him in a valley in the Land of Moab, over against Beth-peor: But no man knoweth of his sepulchre unto this day. And Moses was a hundred and twenty years old when he died, and his eye was not dim, nor his natural force abated. And the Children of Israel wept for Moses in the plains of Moab thirty days. Then Joshua, who was full of the spirit of wisdom, and upon whom Moses had laid his hands, became the leader of Israel, and the Children of Israel hearkened unto him and did as they were commanded. But there never again arose a prophet in Israel like unto Moses, whom the Lord knew face to face.

## Over Jordan.

So Joshua succeeded Moses as the leader of Israel, and began forthwith to prepare for the crossing over into Canaan. First he sent two spies, who made their way to the city of Jericho. There the King of that place sought to kill them, but a woman named Rahab gave them shelter, and hid them underneath the bundles of flax which were drying upon the roof of her house, and so saved them. She told them that she knew who they were, and the wonders God had wrought since they left Egypt, and she begged them that when the Israelites came over and possessed the land they would remember her and save her and her family from destruction. The men promised her that this should be done, and then, at night, she lowered them out of an upper window of her house and they went on their way in safety.

Then the Israelites prepared to cross the river. First the priests took up the Ark of the Covenant and marched boldly into the river. The waters of the river were at that time very high, but they immediately receded before the priests and the bed of the river was made dry. So the priests went with the Ark to the centre of the river and stood there while all the great multitudes of the Israelites passed over in safety on dry ground. Then twelve men, one from each tribe, each took a stone from the bed of the river where the priests were standing and carried them over to the new camp and there built a monument of them as a memorial of the passage over Jordan. And when all the rest were safely over the priests came up out of the bed of the river with the Ark, and then the waters came together again and filled up the bed of the river, and the river flowed on as before.

The first camp was made at Gilgal, and then the supply of manna ceased and they began to feed upon the fruits of the land of Canaan. Next they went on to Jericho and found the city gates barred against them. They made no attack upon the city, but by the command of God marched around it each day, for seven days, blowing trumpets made of rams' horns, and bearing the Ark of the Covenant. And on the seventh day, at a blast of the trumpet, all the people shouted aloud, and the walls of the city fell down flat before them. Then they entered the city and captured it and destroyed it and all its inhabitants, excepting the woman Rahab and her household, whom they saved and took with them as their guests. All the gold and silver and other valuables which they found in the city were turned in to the treasury of the Tabernacle. The news of the capture of Jericho spread throughout the land and all the inhabitants were stricken with fear of the Israelites.

## The Sin of Achan.

The next city attacked was Ai. It was a small, weak place, but the Israelites were repulsed from it in a disastrous manner. Joshua in his distress turned to God for aid, whereupon it was revealed to him that some one in the camp of Israel had disobediently kept for himself some of the spoils of Jericho instead of turning them in to the treasury of the Lord, and this defeat was sent as a punishment for his sin. Then it was shown that a man named Achan was the guilty one. He had kept a beautiful garment, and some silver, and a wedge of gold, and had hidden them under his tent. So he and his family were put to death, and the city of Ai was then readily captured.

Then Joshua built an altar on Mount Ebal and he wrote upon the stones of it a copy of the law of Moses. And all Israel gathered about while he read the words of the law, the blessings and cursings, according to all that is written in the book of the law. There was not a word of all that Moses commanded which Joshua did not read to them.

## The Conquest of Canaan.

Thus the whole of the land was, piece by piece, subdued, by the Israelites, and most of its inhabitants destroyed. The people of the city of Gideon saved themselves by a trick. They disguised themselves as travelers from a far country, went to Joshua's camp, and asked him to make a league of peace with them. Joshua was deceived, and granted their request, and pledged himself not to destroy them. But three days later he found out who they were, and how they had deceived him. He could not break his word, which he had pledged to them, but he said to them: "Now ye are cursed, and there shall none of you be freed from being bondmen, and hewers of wood, and drawers of water for the house of my God." And they answered him and said: "Behold we are in thine hand. As it seemeth good and right unto thee to do unto us, do." And Joshua made them that day hewers of wood and drawers of water for the congregation and for the altar of the Lord; and so they remained.

Then the kings of five of the tribes in Canaan heard how the men of Gideon had made peace with Joshua, and were angry, and declared war against Gideon. Joshua went to meet them and defeated them, and God sent a storm of hail upon them, which killed a great multitude. And at Joshua's word the sun and moon stood still, and the day was thus doubled in length, to give more time for the battle and for the destruction of the enemies of Israel. The five kings fled and hid in a cave, but were captured and hanged. In like manner Joshua marched all over the land of Canaan, subduing it and destroying the inhabitants, after which it was divided among the tribes of Israel by lot. The tabernacle was set up at Shiloh, and that place was thus made the religious capital of the country. Six cities of refuge were established, into which persons who had unintentionally killed others might enter and be safe from vengeance, and forty-eight cities were apportioned to the Levites. Then Joshua called all the elders of all the tribes together at Schechem, and addressed them much as Moses had done in his last speech to them. He rewrote the law in a book, and set up a memorial of the promise of the people to keep it, and then he died and was buried.

## The Judges.

After Joshua's death the leadership of Israel fell to a succession of so-called Judges, of whom in three hundred years there were fifteen, one of them being a woman. The first was Othniel, Caleb's younger brother. After him came Ehud, a left-handed man. At this time the King of Moab made war against Israel, and Ehud, visiting him in friendly guise, stabbed him and killed him, and then rallied the Israelites and conquered the men of Moab. The third Judge, Shamgar, who led Israel against the Philistines, and with no weapon but an ox goad, slew six hundred men in one battle. The next was a woman, Deborah, who made a man named Barak commander of the army, and sent him to fight Sisera, the commander of the army of the King of Canaan. Barak defeated Sisera with great slaughter, and

Sisera fled and took refuge in the tent of a woman named Jael, who let him think she would save him. But while he slept she drove a great nail into his head, and thus murdered him.

After this the Midianites attacked Israel, and ravaged it, and drove the people out of the cities into woods and caves. Then arose a man named Gideon, a farmer, to whom the Lord appeared, to set the Children of Israel free. He rallied the Israelites and urged them to march against the Midianites, and by a series of miracles convinced them that God would give them the victory. But God was not willing to have the whole army of Israel go into battle for fear they would think they had won the victory through their own strength. So all who were afraid to fight were sent back. There were twenty-two thousand of them, and only ten thousand were left. Then all the men were led down to the river to drink, and only those who scooped up water in the palms of their hands and thus drank were chosen. There were only three hundred of them, but with that little company Gideon went against the vast multitude of the Midianites. To each man he gave a trumpet, and a lamp concealed inside a pitcher. At midnight they rushed up to the camp of the Midianites and broke the pitchers so that the light of the lamps suddenly flashed out. Then they blew the trumpets, and shouted: "The sword of the Lord and Gideon." And the Midianites fled in confusion, and fought among themselves, and were driven out of the land.

### Abimelech.

In all this time the Israelites frequently lapsed into sin, and worshipped idols, and did other evil things. After the death of Gideon they became worse than ever, and gave themselves up to the worship of Baal. Then Gideon's son, Abimelech, by persuasion and bribery, got them to make him their king, and he killed all his brothers, except the youngest, who fled from him, in order that they might not be his rivals in authority. But after he had reigned three years the people of Schechem rebelled against him, and there was war between him and them, in which he finally conquered and destroyed them. The last of them took refuge in the temple of their idol, and Abimelech and his followers piled wood around it and burned them all.

Then Abimelech went to Thebez and captured it. But there was a strong tower within the city and to it all the men and women fled and shut themselves in. Then Abimelech and his followers came up and were about to burn the tower and the people within it, as they had done at Schechem. But a woman, whose son he had killed, threw down from the top of the tower a piece of a millstone, and it struck Abimelech and broke his skull. Then he called upon the young man who was his armor-bearer and said to him, "Draw thy sword, and kill me, so that men will not be able to say that I was killed by a woman." And the young man thrust him through with his sword and he died.

### Jephthah.

After Abimelech, Tola was Judge, and after him Jair, of both of whom little is known. Then the Israelites fell into worse idolatry than ever, and were abandoned

JOSEPH SOLD BY HIS BRETHREN

by the Lord to their enemies, and were enslaved by the Philistines and Ammonites. In their distress they finally sent for Jephthah, a brave soldier whom they had once driven out of the land because he married a woman who did not belong to the congregation of Israel. They sent to him and asked him to return and be their leader and save them from the Ammonites. He reminded them that they had driven him out and ill-used him and asked them if they would make him their Judge, in case he did return and delivered them from the Ammonites. They promised that they would do so.

Then Jephthah sent to the King of the Ammonites, and remonstrated with him and urged him to cease from his unjust war against Israel, but the king refused and then Jephthah prepared to fight him. But Jephthah first vowed that if God would give him victory over the Ammonites he would sacrifice to God, as a burnt offering, whatsoever first came forth out of his house to meet him as he returned home in triumph. Then he fought the battle and won it, and completely subdued the Ammonites. But when he returned home his daughter, his only child, was the first to come out to meet him. This gave him unspeakable sorrow, but he kept his vow and sacrificed her. After him Ibzan and Elon and Abdon were successively Judges of Israel, and then the Israelites were conquered by the Philistines again.

## Samson.

There was a good man in Israel named Manoah, and he and his wife had no child. But the angel of God appeared to them and promised them a son, who should take the vow of a Nazarite. That is, he should never drink wine, nor cut his hair, and should be a servant of God all his life. So a son was born to them and they named him Samson. And when he was grown to be a man he loved a daughter of a certain Philistine and determined to marry her. On his way to be married he was attacked by a lion, which he caught in his hands and killed with ease. A few days later he found a swarm of bees had settled on the lion's body and made honey there, and he took some of the honey and ate it. Then he gave a marriage feast to thirty of the Philistines, which lasted seven days. He gave them a riddle to guess, and agreed that if they guessed it he should give each of them a suit of clothes, but if they could not guess it, each of them should give him a suit. The riddle was, "Out of the eater came forth meat, and out of the strong came forth sweetness." It referred to the honey he had taken from the body of the lion. They could not guess it, and at last went to Samson's wife and told her she must coax him to tell her the riddle and then come and tell them, and if she did not do so they would burn her to death. In her fear she did so, and they told Samson the answer, and he lost the wager. But he knew his wife had told them.

Then Samson began his warfare against the Philistines, to set Israel free. He went to the city of Askelon and slew thirty Philistines, and took their clothes to pay the forfeit of his riddle. Next he caught three hundred foxes and tied firebrands to their tails and turned them loose in the fields of the Philistines, and thus burned their orchards and vineyards. In revenge, the Philistines took his wife and her

3

father and burned them to death. Then the Israelites became afraid, and delivered Samson up to the Philistines. But in the midst of the camp of the Philistines he broke his bonds, and snatching up the jaw-bone of an ass he slew a thousand men and escaped. Next he went to Gaza, and the Philistines shut the city gates against him. But he took up the great gates and their posts upon his shoulders and carried them far away.

Unfortunately he next fell under the spell of a wicked woman named Delilah, whom the Philistines had bribed to betray him. She tried for a long time to find out the secret of his strength, but he would not tell her. Finally, however, she prevailed upon him and he confessed to her that if his hair should be cut he would lose his strength. Thereupon, when he next fell asleep, she cut off his hair, and his strength departed, and she delivered him up to the Philistines. They did not kill him, but put him in prison, made him blind, and set him to grinding corn in a mill. After a time he repented of his sin, and his hair grew, and his strength was restored to him, but he did not tell the Philistines of it. One day the Philistines made a great feast in honor of their god, Dagon, and brought Samson out of prison to make sport for them. They put him between the two great pillars of stone that supported the centre of the roof of the house in which were assembled all the great lords and ladies of Philistia. Then Samson grasped the pillars with his hands and prayed for strength, and dragged the pillars down, and the roof fell. And Samson himself and all the multitude of the Philistines were killed in the ruins.

### Ruth.

In the time of the Judges there was a famine in Canaan, and one of the Israelites went from his home at Bethlehem to live in the land of Moab till the famine was past. There he died, leaving his wife, Naomi, and his two daughters-in-law, Orpah and Ruth. When the famine was over, Naomi returned to Bethlehem, but asked her daughters-in-law if they would not rather stay in Moab, which had always been their home. Orpah decided that she would, but Ruth returned with Naomi, saying: "Entreat me not to leave thee, or to return from following after thee; for whither thou goest, I will go; and where thou lodgest, I will lodge; thy people shall be my people, and thy God my God. Where thou diest, will I die, and there will I be buried. The Lord do so to me, and more also, if aught but death part thee and me."

So Naomi and Ruth returned to Bethlehem, and Ruth went to glean in the cornfields of a rich kinsman of theirs named Boaz. And Boaz noticed her and inquired who she was, and when he found out that she was Naomi's daughter he gave her much grain, so that she prospered. And after a time he loved her and made her his wife. And they had a son, whom they called Obed.

### Samuel.

There was a man named Elkanah, whose wife was named Hannah, who went every year to Shiloh to offer sacrifices. But they were unhappy because they were childless. One day Hannah prayed long and earnestly for a son, and vowed that if she might have one she would make him a Nazarite, as Samson was. Her prayer was answered, and she called her son Samuel, and took him to Shiloh and left him with the High Priest, Eli, to be a servant of the Tabernacle. The boy grew up to be devout and pious, and was obedient to Eli. One night he heard a voice calling him by name, and arose and said to Eli, "Here am I"; for he supposed Eli had called him. But Eli had not. A second time it occurred, and a third, and then they knew it was God who was calling him. And God made him a prophet.

Now came on a war with the Philistines, and the Israelites were defeated. In their despair, they sent for the Ark of the Covenant, to carry it before their army, in hope that it would give them the victory. The two sons of Eli, who, though priests, were wicked men, went with it. It was an unlawful thing thus to take the Ark away from the Tabernacle, and it displeased God so that he caused the Israelites to be defeated. They were utterly routed, and thirty thousand of them slain, including the two sons of Eli, and the Ark was captured by the Philistines. And when Eli heard it, he fell down dead. The Philistines took the Ark to their city of Ashdod, and put it in the temple of Dagon. The next day they found the great image of Dagon had fallen down on its face before the Ark. They set it up again, and the next day it was not only fallen but broken. Then a great pestilence came upon them, and many died. So they knew it was because they had taken the Ark from the Israelites, and they wanted to get rid of it. Wherever they took it, evil came upon them. At last they put the Ark upon a cart, and hitched two cows before it, and let them go without a driver. And the cattle took it back to Israel.

## Saul.

Samuel succeeded Eli as High Priest and also as Judge over Israel, and he ruled righteously for many years. But when he became old, and his two sons proved themselves wicked men, the people clamored for a king. Samuel warned them that it would be a great mistake, but they persisted, so at last God commanded Samuel to chose a king for them. He sent to Samuel for that purpose a young man named Saul. Now Saul was the tallest and one of the handsomest men in all the land, and the people accepted him gladly, and Samuel anointed him king. Then the Ammonites attacked Israel, and Saul commanded every able-bodied man to come out and help repulse them. In that way he raised a great army, and destroyed the Ammonites. But his rule was so arbitrary that the people began to fear that Saul would be not only their king but their oppressor.

After a couple of years Saul formed a standing army, and made his son Jonathan one of its commanders. The Philistines came up, and defeated them, and Saul and Jonathan were put to flight. Then Saul sent for Samuel to come and offer sacrifices, to gain the favor of God. But Samuel was slow in coming, and Saul impatiently offered the sacrifices himself. That was unlawful, and Samuel rebuked him for it, and told him the Lord would deprive him of his kingdom for it. But still God gave the Israelites victory. Jonathan and a single follower entered the Philistine's camp and did great slaughter, and an earthquake threw the Philistine army into confusion, and Saul and his army came up and completed the victory.

## David and Goliath.

After this Saul sinned more and more, and at last God commanded Samuel to go to Bethlehem and find a man named Jesse, son of Obed, and anoint one of his sons to be king in Saul's place. Samuel did so and found Jesse and his seven sons. And the Lord said unto Samuel, " Look not on his countenance, or on the height of his stature : For the Lord seeth not as man seeth ; for man looketh on the outward appearance, but the Lord looketh on the heart." So Samuel would not choose any one of the seven, but asked Jesse if he had no other children. And Jesse said that he had another son, the youngest, who was in the fields watching the sheep. Samuel made him send for him, and when he came saw at once that it was he whom God intended for the next king of Israel. So he anointed the boy, whose name was David, and the spirit of the Lord came upon David from that day forward. But the spirit of the Lord departed from Saul and an evil spirit began to trouble him. His attendants told him that he could get relief from the evil spirits only by having some one play the harp before him. So Saul said to his servants, " Provide me now a man that can play well, and bring him to me." Then one of them said that David, the son of Jesse, was a fine player, and Saul bade them send for him. So David came to Saul and Saul was pleased with him and made him his armor-bearer. And it came to pass that when the evil spirit troubled Saul, David took a harp and played upon it, and the evil spirit was driven out and Saul was refreshed and made well. But Saul did not know that David had been anointed to be king in his place.

Now the Philistines came up again, led by a gigantic warrior named Goliath, who was much larger and stronger than any other man in all the land. This giant daily defied the Israelites to come out and fight him, and Saul and all Israel were afraid of him. For a time no one could be found who would attempt to cope with Goliath. But one day David visited the camp and asked what was the matter. And when he heard he said he would go out and fight the Philistine. Saul tried to dissuade him, but David told how he had killed a lion and a bear with his hands, and said he was able, with the strength of the Lord, to overthrow Goliath. Then Saul gave David his own armor and sword with which to fight, but David declined to use them. He took nothing but his staff and a sling and five smooth stones. When Goliath saw David come against him he scorned him and cursed him. But David defied him in the name of God, and put a stone in his sling, and slung it, and struck the Philistine on his forehead. And Goliath staggered and fell before the blow, and David ran up and drew Goliath's own sword from its scabbard and cut off his head with it. And when the Philistines saw that their champion was dead they fled in confusion, and Saul's army pursued them and routed them utterly.

## The Passing of Saul.

David now lived with Saul all the time, and became the closest friend of Jonathan. But it came to pass that when the army returned from the war the people cried aloud, "Saul hath slain his thousands, but David his ten thousands." This made Saul jealous and angry, to think that David should be praised more

PHARAOH'S RAGE ON LEARNING THE CHILDREN OF ISRAEL HAD FLED

highly than he. So the next time David came before him to play upon the harp Saul threw a spear at him and tried to kill him, but David escaped, and after that Saul pretended to be his friend again and gave him his daughter Michal for his wife. Then again Saul planned to kill David and commanded Jonathan to do the deed. But Jonathan would not and warned David of his danger, and helped him to escape. Again and again Saul tried to kill David, but in vain. David found refuge with the High Priest, and then Saul commanded that all the Priests should be slain. Then David went elsewhere and was pursued by Saul all over the land. Even in the wilderness Saul pursued him. And Saul even thought of killing his own son, Jonathan, because he was David's friend. On more than one occasion David had an opportunity to kill Saul as the latter lay asleep, but he refrained. But he let Saul know that he had spared him. At the cave of Adullam David gathered together a great number of lawless and discontented men and put himself at their head and raided about the country with them.

At last the Philistines rose in great force against Saul, and Saul was afraid of defeat. He called upon the Lord, but got no answer. So he disguised himself and went to a woman at Endor, who was a witch, and got her to call up the spirit of Samuel, who had been dead for some years. Saul asked Samuel for advice and help. But Samuel gave him none, but told him he would be defeated by the Philistines and would himself be killed. Then Saul went to battle and the Philistines defeated him and killed Jonathan and two of Saul's other sons, and Saul himself was wounded. Then, in order that he might not be captured or killed by the Philistines Saul took a sword and fell upon it and died. So the prophesy of Samuel was fulfilled, and David became king.

## David King of Israel.

David was far away, but the news soon came to him. He was greatly grieved to hear of the death of his dear friend Jonathan, and also of that of Saul, although the latter had been his bitter enemy.

He lamented over them with great lamentation, saying: "The beauty of Israel is slain upon the high places. How are the mighty fallen! Tell it not in Gath, publish it not in the streets of Askelon, lest the daughters of the Philistines rejoice. Saul and Jonathan were lovely and pleasant in their lives, and in their death they were not divided. They were swifter than eagles, they were stronger than lions. How are the mighty fallen in the midst of the battle! O Jonathan, thou wast slain in thine high places. I am distressed for thee, my brother Jonathan. Very pleasant hast thou been unto me. Thy love to me was wonderful, passing the love of women. How are the mighty fallen, and the weapons of war perished!" After this, at the command of God, David went up to the city of Hebron, and the men of the tribe of Judah gathered about him, and they anointed David King over Israel. But a son of Saul, named Ish-bosheth, arose and proclaimed himself king, and most of the tribes of Israel, excepting that of Judah, followed him. But two of David's captains went and slew him, and then all the tribes recognized David as king.

# CHAPTER III.

---

## FROM JERUSALEM TO BETHLEHEM.

ABSALOM—ACCESSION OF SOLOMON—GLORIES OF THE KINGDOM—THE QUEEN OF
SHEBA—DIVISION OF THE KINGDOM—ELIJAH, THE TISHBITE-NABOTH'S
VINEYARD—SENNACHERIB—IN CAPTIVITY—DANIEL AND THE
LIONS—THE RETURN TO JERUSALEM—ESTHER—
THE PROPHETS—THE APOCRYPHA.

---

AVID resolved to make Jerusalem the capital of his kingdom. So he engaged skilful builders in wood and stone from Hiram, King of Tyre, and built a fine palace. Then he brought the Ark of the Covenant thither from the city of Kirjath-jearim, where it had been since its return from the Philistines. He wished to build a fine temple in which to place the Ark, but God, through the prophet Nathan, forebade him, saying that privilege was to be reserved for David's son and successor. So the Ark had to be kept in a tent as before. David also remembered his dear friend Jonathan, and inquired whether any of his children were still living. Finding that one of them was, but was hopelessly lame, he sent for him and had him live at the Court in luxury all his life. David greatly beautified the city of Jerusalem and did much for the civilization of the Israelites. He was a fine musician, and also a great poet, and wrote many psalms or hymns.

But David was also guilty of evil deeds. He conceived an unlawful love for Bathsheba, the wife of Uriah, one of his army officers. In order that he might have her for himself, he contrived to have Uriah exposed to great danger and killed in battle, whereupon he took Bathsheba for his wife. Nathan, at God's command, administered a bitter rebuke to him for this, and made him realize his guilt. A son was born to David and Bathsheba, and David loved him greatly. But the child died, and David mourned him bitterly, saying "I shall go to him, but he shall not come back to me." Afterward another son was born to them, who was named Solomon, and who grew up to be David's successor on the throne.

### Absalom.

Another of David's sons was Absalom, who grew up to be a very handsome young man, and a great favorite with the people of Israel. But he was proud and self-willed, and presently quarreled with his father, and began to plot to overthrow him and gain the throne for himself. So strong a revolt did he arouse that David had to flee from Jerusalem for safety, and Absalom pursued him with an army, and would have killed him. But after a time David made a stand and gave battle, and defeated Absalom's army with great slaughter. He gave strict orders, however, that no one was for any consideration to do Absalom himself any harm. But as Absalom rode under a tree his long hair caught in a branch and he was dragged by it from the saddle and left hanging there. One of David's soldiers saw him and went and told Joab, the commander of the army. Joab asked him why he did not kill him, saying he would have given him a great reward for so doing. The man replied that he would not, for any reward, injure Absalom, because David had commanded that he should not be hurt. Thereupon Joab went himself and thrust three spears through Absalom and killed him.

When the news of this was brought to David the king went up to his private chamber and wept bitterly, and said: "O my son Absalom, my son, my son Absalom! Would God I had died for thee, O Absalom, my son, my son!" And so the victory was turned into mourning among all the people, for they heard how the king was grieved at the death of his son and they mourned with him.

After that David grew proud of his military prowess, and took a census of his fighting men, and found he had no less than 1,300,000 subjects able to bear arms. This displeased the Lord, and he sent a pestilence upon the nation. That made David realize his sinfulness, and he offered sacrifices on an altar on Mount Moriah, and prayed for mercy and forgiveness. He also bought the field on the mountain top, and brought thither material for the building of a great temple, but left the actual work of building it for his successor to perform.

## Accession of Solomon.

Finding himself growing old and near the end of life, David made his son Solomon his heir and successor, and had him proclaimed king. This he did before he died, because another son, Adonijah, was plotting to seize the throne. Then he gave Solomon minute directions for the building of the temple, and said to him: "I go the way of all the earth. Be thou strong therefore, and show thyself a man, and keep the charge of the Lord thy God, to walk in His ways, to keep His statutes and His commandments, and His judgments, and His testimonies, as it is written in the Law of Moses, that thou mayest prosper in all thou doest, and whithersoever thou turnest thyself; that the Lord may continue His work which He spake concerning me." So David died and was buried at Jerusalem, and Solomon reigned in his place.

Solomon was king over all Israel, and he obeyed the laws of God, and greatly prospered. He married a daughter of Pharaoh, king of Egypt, and became great and powerful among the rulers of the earth. One night at Gibeon, God appeared to him in a dream and bade him ask what he would and it should be granted unto him. And Solomon answered: "Give Thy servant an understanding heart to judge Thy people, that I may discern between good and bad." And the speech pleased the Lord, and God said unto him: "Because thou hast asked this thing, and hast not asked for thyself long life, neither hast asked riches for thyself, nor has asked the life of thine enemies, but hast asked for thyself understanding to discern judgment ; behold, I have done according to thy words. Lo, I have given thee a wise and an understanding heart, so that there was none like thee before thee, neither after thee shall any arise like unto thee. And I have also given thee that which thou hast not asked, both riches, and honor ; so that there shall not be any among the kings like unto thee all thy days. And if thou wilt walk in My ways, to keep My statutes and My commandments, as thy father David did walk, then I will lengthen thy days."

After this Solomon showed great wisdom in his government. There came to him one day two women, disputing over the ownership of a child. Each declared it was hers. Then Solomon said, "Bring me a sword." And they brought him a sword, and he said "Divide the living child in two, and give half to the one, and half to the other." Then spake the woman to whom the child really belonged, and said, "O my lord, give her the living child and in no wise slay it." But the other said, "Let it be neither mine nor thine, but divide it." Then the king answered and said, "Give her the living child and in no wise slay it. She is its mother." And all Israel heard of the judgment which the king had judged, and they feared the king, for they saw that the wisdom of God was in him.

### Glories of the Kingdom.

Very great and glorious was the kingdom of Solomon. The king had 40,000 stalls of horses for his chariots, and 12,000 horsemen. And God gave Solomon wisdom excelling the wisdom of all other men in the world, and his fame spread through all nations. He was the author of three thousand proverbs, and he wrote more than a thousand songs ; and wise men from all parts of the world came to visit him to learn of him.

Then Hiram, king of Tyre, sent to Solomon and offered to help him with workmen in the building of the Temple. Solomon accepted the offer and many thousands of men were set at work on the splendid edifice. It was built of stone and cedar wood, and all overlaid with gold. When it was finished, the Ark of the Covenant was placed in it and many sacrifices of thanksgiving were offered upon its altar.

### The Queen of Sheba.

Solomon also built a great navy, and sent his ships to all parts of the known world. Some of them went as far as Ophir, in South Africa, and brought back rich stores of gold. This attracted the attention of the Queen of Sheba, and she visited Jerusalem to see what manner of a king Solomon was. She came to Jerusalem with a great train of followers, and with camels bearing spices and gold and precious stones. And she talked with him and he revealed his wisdom unto her. And when she had talked with him, and learned his wisdom, and seen the splendor of his house and the Temple, she said : "It was a true report that I heard in mine own land of thy acts and of thy wisdom. Behold, the half was not told me. Thy wisdom and prosperity exceed the fame which I heard. Happy are thy men, happy are these thy servants, which stand continually before thee and that hear thy wisdom. Blessed be the Lord thy God, which delighteth in thee, to set thee on the throne of

Israel: Because the Lord loved Israel forever, therefore made He thee king, to do judgment and justice." Then the Queen and Solomon gave each other rich presents and she returned to her own country.

It is related that Solomon's throne was made of pure ivory covered with pure gold. All the vessels of his house and of the Temple were pure gold. None of them were of silver, for silver was not considered worthy of such use.

But in the later years of his life Solomon fell into evil ways. He married many wives, and forsook the faith of his fathers and became an idolator. Wherefore the Lord said unto Solomon, "For as much as this is done of thee, and thou hast not kept My statutes, I will surely rend the kingdom from thee, and will give it to thy servant. Notwithstanding in thy days I will not do it for David, thy father's sake; but I will rend it out of the hand of thy son. Howbeit I will not rend away all the kingdom, but will give one tribe to thy son for David My servant's sake, and for Jerusalem's sake, which I have chosen." Then there arose rebellions in the land, and Solomon died amid many troubles and forebodings, and Rehoboam, his son, reigned in his stead.

### Division of the Kingdom.

Rehoboam was a haughty and tyrannical king, and soon a great rebellion arose against him. The two tribes of Judah and Benjamin remained faithful to him, while the other ten tribes seceded, and chose for their king one Jeroboam. This was a young man whom a prophet, during the reign of Solomon, had declared should be king, and whom Solomon for that reason sought to kill. So there were two kingdoms, one of Judah, and one of Israel. Now God had promised Jeroboam that if he would observe the law and reign righteously his kingdom should be prosperous and permanently established. But Jeroboam was afraid that if his people went to Jerusalem to worship they would be won back to Rehoboam. So he built temples in his own kingdom and set up golden idols for the people to worship, and forbade the people to go to Jerusalem to worship in the temple there. In this way great sin came upon the land.

A long succession of kings reigned over each of the two kingdoms. Most of them were wicked men, and committed idolatries, and because of their sin many evils came upon the people.

### Elijah, The Tishbite.

The worst of all the kings of Israel was Ahab, and his wife Jezebel was equally wicked. So God sent a prophet, Elijah, the Tishbite, to rebuke him and to tell him that because of his sins there should be for three years no rain nor dew in all the land. Then, to escape the wrath of Ahab, Elijah fled to the wilderness and was fed with food brought to him by the ravens. After a time the brook by the side of which he dwelt dried up, and then God sent him to the house of a widow living at Zarephath, to live there. When he got there he found her suffering from the famine. She had no food left but a handful of meal and a little oil. But she received Elijah hospitably and he blessed her, so that the supply of meal and oil was not exhausted but was daily renewed to supply their wants as long as the famine lasted. After a time her only son died, and at Elijah's prayer was restored to life.

When the drought had lasted three years, and the land was solely famine-stricken, Elijah went to Ahab and rebuked him again for his sins and challenged him to bring the priests of Baal up to Mount Carmel, and summon all the people, and let it be decided who was at fault for the evils that had come upon the land. Ahab did so, and Elijah came before all the people at Mount Carmel, and said: "How long halt ye between two opinions? If the Lord be God, follow Him; but if Baal, then follow him." And the people answered him not a word. Then Elijah proposed that the priests of Baal should build an altar and offer a sacrifice upon it, but put no fire thereon, and he would do the same. Then they should pray to Baal, and he would pray to Jehovah, to send down fire and consume the sacrifice. "And the God that answereth by fire, let him be God." And all the people answered, and said: "It is well spoken." Then the prophets of Baal built an altar and killed a bullock, and laid it upon it, and began praying to Baal to send down fire. They prayed to him all day, and leaped upon the altar, and cut themselves with knives, according to their custom. And Elijah mocked them, and said: "Cry aloud, for he is a god. Either he is talking, or he is pursuing, or he is on a journey, or peradventure he sleepeth, and must be awaked." But the whole day passed, and evening came, and there was no answer to their prayers. Then Elijah called the people nearer to him, and he built an altar of twelve stones, according to the law. And he killed a bullock, and placed it thereon, and then drenched the whole with water, to prove that he had placed no fire underneath it. Then at the time for the evening sacrifice, Elijah stood by the altar and prayed: "Lord God of Abraham, Isaac, and of Israel, let it be known this day that Thou art God in Israel, and that I am Thy servant, and that I have done all these things at Thy word." Then the fire of the Lord fell, and consumed the burnt sacrifice, and the wood, and the stones, and the dust, and licked up the water that was in the trench. And when all the people saw it, they fell on their faces and said: "The Lord He is the God." And Elijah said unto them: "Take the prophets of Baal. Let not one of them escape." And they took them and slew them, every one. Then at the word of Elijah there came a great storm of rain upon the land.

## Naboth's Vineyard.

But Ahab did not turn from his evil ways. There was a man named Naboth who had a vineyard that Ahab coveted, but he would not give it nor sell it to Ahab. So Ahab, at Jezebel's suggestion, had Naboth falsely accused of crimes, and put to death. Then he seized the vineyard for his own. But Elijah came and rebuked him, and told him that ruin would come upon him, and that Jezebel should be killed and her body should be eaten by dogs. And in due time this prophesy was fulfilled.

After that Elijah chose Elisha to be his successor, and then was carried up to heaven in a chariot of fire, letting fall his mantle upon Elisha. Then Elisha became the chief prophet of Israel, and performed many miracles. At Shunem he restored a woman's son to life. He cured Naaman, the captain of the army of the King of Syria, of leprosy. When an army was sent to seize him at Dotham, he smote all the men with blindness, and led them far away, and then restored their sight. At God's command, he anointed Jehu to be King of Israel, and Jehu put to death all of Ahab's family, thus fulfilling the prophesy of Elijah. And after nineteen kings had ruled over Israel, in 254 years, the end came. The land was conquered by the Assyrians, and all the people were carried away into captivity.

## Sennacherib.

Among the kings of Judah some were good and some were bad  One of the best of them was Hezekiah. But during his reign many evils fell upon the land. At one time it was invaded by Sennacherib, king of Syria, who marched into it with a great army. Hezekiah prayed to God for help, and God answered him through the lips of the prophet Isaiah, promising him that no harm should come to him. And that night the angel of the Lord visited the camp of Sennacherib, and smote all his men, so that in the morning every one of them lay dead ; and Senna-cherib fled back to Syria. Unfortunately, after that Hezekiah grew proud, and boasted of his wealth, and one day showed all the riches of his treasury to some visitors from Syria. Thus he excited their covetousness and it was prophesied that Judah should fall before the Syrians and all the treasures be taken as spoils to Babylon.

Then Nebuchadnezzar, King of Babylon, marched into the country and laid siege to Jerusalem, and captured it, and plundered the temple, and carried all the people away captive to Babylon, just as the people of the Kingdom of Israel had been. At this time there was a great prophet named Jeremiah, who prophesied about the fall of Jerusalem. He was taken prisoner by the Chaldeans, but was treated kindly by them and was let go to live in the land of Judah. And Jeremiah wrote to his brethren who were in captivity, bidding them to be patient, for in seventy years, he told them, they should be allowed to return to Jerusalem.

## In Captivity.

So the Kingdom of Judah came to an end, after 388 years. While the people were in captivity in Babylon there arose among them a great prophet named Ezekiel, who saw visions and foretold what would happen in the future. And after telling of the woes that were to come upon the Jews, he also prophesied that one day they should be restored to Jerusalem.

Daniel was another prophet, who rose to high favor in the Court of Babylon, because he was able to interpret a striking dream which Nebuchadnezzar had. He had three friends, named Shadrach, Meshach, and Abednego, who were faithful to God and refused to join in the idolatrous worship of Babylon. So the king threw them into a furnace of fire, but they were not harmed. Thereupon the king declared that their God was the greatest of all gods, and decreed that He should be worshipped throughout the empire.

After Nebuchadnezzar died, his son Belshazzar reigned in his stead. He was an exceedingly wicked man. One night he gave a great feast, and while he feasted a hand of fire wrote words upon the wall, which none could read. So they sent for Daniel and told him that if he could read them and interpret them, he would be made the third ruler in the kingdom. And Daniel read the words, "Mene, mene, tekel, upharsin," and said they meant that Belshazzar had been weighed in God's balances and found wanting, wherefore his kingdom was to be taken from him. That very night Cyrus, with the army of the Medes and Persians, captured the city and Belshazzar was slain, and Darius the Mede became king in his place.

### Daniel and the Lions.

Darius made Daniel one of the chief rulers of the kingdom, second only to himself. This aroused the jealousy of the other princes and they conspired to get rid of Daniel. So they complained to Darius that Daniel broke the law by making daily prayers to God, and demanded that he be cast into a den of lions. Darius did not wish to punish Daniel, but had to do so because no exception could be made to the law. So Daniel was cast into the den.

Then the king went to his palace, and passed the night fasting, and he could not sleep. And very early in the morning he hastened to the den of lions and cried aloud with an anxious voice to Daniel, saying, "O Daniel, servant of the living God, is thy God, whom thou servest continually, able to deliver thee from the lions?" Then said Daniel unto the King, "O King, live forever. My God hath sent His angel, and hath shut the lions' mouths, and they have not hurt me." Then the king rejoiced exceedingly and had Daniel taken out of the den, and cast into the den in his place the men who had brought the accusation against him, and they were all killed by the lions. Then Darius wrote to all parts of his empire making a decree that all men should fear and do reverence to the God of Daniel. "For he is the living God, and steadfast forever, and His kingdom that which shall not be destroyed, and His dominion shall be even unto the end."

### The Return to Jerusalem.

After seventy years of captivity the Jews were allowed to go back to Judah, as Jeremiah had prophesied. Cyrus, the king of Persia, made a proclamation that all who wished to return might do so, and that the Persians should assist them by giving them money for the journey. About 50,000 decided to return, under the leadership of Zerubbabel, a prince descended from King David, and Cyrus gave them vast stores of gold and silver. They found Jerusalem in ruins, as Nebuchadnezzar had left it, and at once began to rebuild it, both the city and the temple.

Then the Samaritans began to trouble them. These were a people who had been settled in the kingdom of Israel after the Israelites had been taken into captivity. They succeeded in persuading Artaxerxes, Cyrus's successor, that the Jews were rebellious, and so had the work at Jerusalem stopped for a time. But when Artaxerxes died, a second Darius became king, and he permitted the work to be resumed. He also assisted the Jews with gifts of money. So the temple and

BIRTH OF CHRIST

the city were rebuilt. Then Ezra, a great prophet, arose at Babylon, and returned to Jerusalem with many more of the exiles. And he restored the worship of the temple, and made the people obey the laws that had been given to Moses.

## Esther.

Among the Jews who still remained in Persia, was one Mordecai, who had a niece named Esther. Mordecai had on one occasion saved the life of the king, Ahasuerus. It came to pass that the king quarreled with his queen, Vashti, and divorced her, and then sought another queen. Mordecai brought Esther to his notice, and he admired her above all other women, and married her.

Now the king's Prime Minister was Haman, who was a proud man and wanted every one to bow down before him. This Mordecai refused to do, and Haman in his wrath determined to kill Mordecai and all his race. So he told the king that there was a lot of alien people in the land, who would not obey the laws and were constantly making trouble, and so he got the king to make a decree that they should all be put to death. When Mordecai heard this he was in great distress, and all the Jews mourned and lamented. And they appealed to Queen Esther to save them. And she went to the king and got him to promise that he would grant her anything she asked. Then she asked him to invite Haman to a banquet which she would give the next day, at which she would make known her request. This the king did. Haman was pleased to get the invitation, yet at the same time vexed because Mordecai would not do him reverence. So, on the advice of his friends, he built a high gallows, and gave orders that Mordecai should be hanged thereon.

Now that night the king could not sleep. So, to pass away the time, he had the records of his reign read to him. When he heard how Mordecai had saved his life he asked what reward had been given to him, and the answer was, none. Just at that time Haman entered the palace, having come to get the king to sanction the hanging of Mordecai. The king at once asked him what should be done to the man whom the king delighted to honor. Haman thought that must refer to himself. So he said, "Let the royal apparel be brought which the king usually wears, and the horse that the king rides upon, and the royal crown from the king's head, and let the man whom the king delights to honor wear the robe and the crown and ride upon the horse, and thus be escorted about the city by one of the king's most noble princes, proclaiming that thus it is done to the man whom the king delighteth to honor."

Then the king commanded Haman to do all these things to Mordecai; and so Haman had to see his enemy honored and he himself had to lead his horse about the city and make the proclamation in his honor.

The next day Haman went to the banquet with the king and queen, and the king asked Esther what the request was which she wished to make of him, declaring that it should be granted, no matter what it might be. And she asked him to spare her life and the lives of her people. "For," she said, "we are sold, I and my people, to be destroyed, to be slain, and to perish." Then the king demanded, "Who is he, and where is he, that durst presume in his heart to do so?" And

Esther said, "The adversary and enemy is this wicked Haman." Then Haman was greatly afraid and prayed to the queen for mercy. But the king commanded him to be taken out and put to death. So they hanged Haman upon the very gallows that he had prepared for Mordecai.

But the decree for the destruction of the Jews could not be recalled. So the king made Mordecai Prime Minister in Haman's place, and through him issued another decree, warning the Jews of their peril and bidding them defend themselves. And the Jews did so, and were preserved, and the anniversary of their preservation has ever since been observed in the great Feast of Purim.

## The Prophets.

Another great prophet who went up from Persia to aid in the restoration of Jerusalem was Nehemiah. It was he who by his energy got the people to rebuild the city wall, and make Jerusalem strong against its enemies, and he did much to bring them back to the faithful observance of the law.

The prophet Jonah was sent by God to preach to the city of Nineveh. He did not want to do so, and went on board a ship bound for another place. Then God sent a great storm, so that the ship was in danger of destruction, and Jonah was compelled to confess to the sailors that he was disobeying the Lord and that the storm was sent on his account. So they threw him overboard, and the storm ceased And Jonah was swallowed by a great fish, and after three days was thrown out upon dry land again. After that he went to Nineveh, and preached, and the people repented of their sins.

Among the greatest of the prophets at and after the time of the captivity was Isaiah; and others were Hosea, Joel, Amos, Obadiah, Micah, Nahum, Habakkuk, Zephaniah, Haggai, Zechariah, and Malachi.

## The Apocrypha.

Between the story of the Old Testament and that of the New there is a considerable gap in history. This is largely covered by the books known as the Apocrypha, and also by the history of Josephus and various Jewish traditions. It appears that in about the year 331 B. C., Alexander the Great visited Jerusalem, when he was conquering Asia, to punish the Jews for refusing to transfer their allegiance to him, when he summoned them to do so during his siege of Tyre. As he approached Jerusalem the High Priest, clad in robes of purple and white, and accompanied by a train of priests and citizens clad in white, went out to meet him. Alexander was impressed by the spectacle, and did reverence to the High Priest and thereafter showed the Jews many favors. A few years later Palestine became a kind of neutral territory between the rival empires of Syria and Egypt, and enjoyed a considerable degree of independence. A great many of the Jews migrated to Egypt and formed an important colony at Alexandria.

From 223 to 198 B. C., Antiochus the Great alternately won and lost Palestine in a succession of wars with Egypt. He was finally successful in retaining possession of it and was hailed by the Jews as their deliverer from subjection to Egypt, and confirmed upon them all the privileges Alexander had granted.    Under Antiochus Epiphanes the priesthood was greatly corrupted.    Antiochus made use of his money and the power of his army to bribe the unscrupulous and put to death the faithful, until finally he established heathenism in the holy city.    He forbade the use of the Mosaic ritual, promulgated a series of infamous decrees, forbade the worship of God, burned all the books of the law, placed a statue of Jupiter on the most holy altar in the temple, and finally forced some of the Jews publicly to eat the flesh of swine, sacrificed on that altar in honor of Jupiter.    Many of the Jews refused and were put to death with horrible tortures.

Then Mathathias, a priest of the Hasmonæan family, at the city of Modin, with his five sons, raised their rebellion.    They threw down the heathen altar, fled to the mountains, and raised the standard of liberty.    His eldest son was named Judas Maccabæus.    Under him the insurgents were victorious.    Antiochus died, stricken by God with a terrible disease.    The Maccabees recovered Jerusalem, purified the temple, and restored its worship.    For a number of years they held sway over the country, but then were compelled to make terms with the Romans, under whose protection, however, they enjoyed considerable freedom.    Julius Caesar made a number of decrees in their favor, granting them a large measure of home rule and permitting them to retain and practice all their peculiar customs.    A Roman officer was, however, stationed at Jerusalem, to maintain the general political government. The man who held this office was Herod, the descendant of a Philistine slave.    He presently made himself nominally king of the Jews, though of course subject to Rome.    He was a heathen at heart, a savage in character, and a brute in passions. So he made use of his position to betray and degrade the country, to foster immorality, to corrupt the priesthood, and break down the Jewish religion.    He rebuilt the temple on a more splendid scale than ever before, intending it to be the proud monument of his dynasty.    But it was really the whitened sepulchre that concealed the foul impurity of his family and the loathsome corruption into which he had plunged his people.

The loss of political liberty drove the Jews to seek consolation in religious philosophy.    Accordingly several different sects arose among them and they began paying more attention than ever before to the minute details of the letter of the law. Such was the political and religious state of the country and the people at the time of the birth of Christ.

# CHAPTER IV.

## FROM BETHLEHEM TO CALVARY.

IN THE TEMPLE—JOHN THE BAPTIST—BAPTISM OF JESUS—CALLING THE DISCIPLES—
THE FIRST MIRACLE—CLEANSING THE TEMPLE—HEALING THE SICK—MATTHEW THE
PUBLICAN—SENDING FORTH APOSTLES—THE SERMON ON THE MOUNT—RAISING
THE DEAD—STILLING THE TEMPEST—FEEDING THE MULTITUDE—JESUS WALKS
ON THE SEA—THE TRANSFIGURATION—THE LAST VISIT TO JERUSALEM—AT
BETHANY—THE RAISING OF LAZARUS—HUMILITY TAUGHT—ENTERING
JERUSALEM—THE PLOT OF JUDAS—THE LAST SUPPER—PETER'S
WARNING—THE LORD'S SUPPER—GETHSEMANE—THE BETRAYAL
—THE TRIAL—PETER'S DENIAL—DEATH OF JUDAS—BEFORE
PILATE—THE CRUCIFIXION—THE BURIAL—THE RESUR-
RECTION—THE ASCENSION—PENTECOST—PERSECU-
TIONS—ST. PAUL—DEATH OF HEROD—PAUL AND
BARNABAS—PAUL AND SILAS—ON MARS
HILL—CORINTH AND EPHESUS—BEFORE
FELIX AND FESTUS—THE VOYAGE TO
ROME—ST. JOHN AT PATMOS.

IN the days of Cæsar Augustus, Emperor of Rome, there was peace in all the world. A general census and taxation of all the people was ordered in Palestine, and all flocked to the cities for the purpose. Among those who went to Bethlehem were Joseph, a carpenter, and Mary, his wife and they found the hotels so crowded that they had to seek shelter in a stable, where, that night, a son was born to them, according to a promise that had been made to them by an angel. That same night, outside the city, some shepherds were watching their sheep, when suddenly a bright light appeared, and they were frightened. Then an angel spake to them, telling them not to be afraid, for he brought them good tidings of great joy, that there was born in the city a Saviour, Christ the Lord. He told them how and where they might find Him; and then suddenly there was with the angel a multitude of the heavenly host, praising God, and saying, "Glory to God in the highest; and on earth peace, good will toward men." They found the stable without difficulty, and entering in, saw Joseph and Mary, with the Babe in the manger. They told them of all they had heard and seen, and then went back to their flocks, praising God.

Then there arrived in the city Wise Men, or Magi, from Arabia. These men had heard that a king of the Jews was expected; and one night as they were watching the heavens they saw a bright star, which was the sign of some great event, and made up their minds that it indicated the birth of the King of the Jews. They asked not *whether* the King of the Jews was born, but *where* He was born, and then told the people that they had seen His star in the East, and had come to worship Him.

TEMPTATION OF CHRIST

They unpacked their beasts, and, going into the house, fell down before Mary and the young Child, and worshipped Him. They then opened their treasures and presented their gifts—gold, frankincense and myrrh.

God appeared to Joseph in a dream, warning him that Herod the King meant to kill the Child, and told him to flee into Egypt. Then Herod ordered all the children in Bethlehem and its neighborhood, under two years old, to be put to death. But Joseph and Mary lived safely with their Child in Egypt for two years or more, until Herod died, when the Lord again appeared to Joseph in a dream, and told him to return to the land of Israel, where he settled in the town of Nazareth. Here Joseph plied his trade as a carpenter.

## In the Temple.

Luke tells us that "the Child grew, and waxed strong in spirit, filled with wisdom ; and the grace of God was upon Him." Every year His parents went up to Jerusalem to attend the Passover. But they did not take Him until He was twelve years old. On the way back home, after the festival, they missed Him, and went back to the Temple, where they found Him in one of the courts, surrounded by the doctors and rabbis. Jesus was putting questions to the learned men such as they had never been asked before ; and in His own answers to their questions was showing such knowledge that they wondered greatly. Mary addressed Him, "Son, why hast Thou so dealt with us ? Behold, Thy father and I have sought Thee sorrowing." He said, "How is it that ye sought me ? Knew you not that I must be about my Father's business ? " But they understood not what He meant.

## John the Baptist.

In the wilderness, somewhere on the eastern bank of the river Jordan, John the Baptist retired and lived away from the busy haunts of men. He was the cousin of our Lord. It was foretold that he would be the forerunner of the Saviour, that he would prepare the Jews for the coming of their Messiah. He lived in the wilderness, away from the towns, that he might the better contemplate his great work, and be fitted by God for it. Hence, his dress was coarse and his food simple. His coat was made of the shaggy hair of camels, woven into a rough cloth, and fastened in at the waist with a leathern girdle; his food was principally the locust and wild honey.

The Jews at Jerusalem, hearing of this wonderful preacher, sent messengers to ask him whether he was really the Saviour, and this thought also arose in the minds of many that heard him. But John told them who he was, that he was "the voice of one crying in the wilderness," as their prophet Isaiah had foretold. He further said that Christ was so mighty that he was not worthy to do the most humble service for Him—to unloose His shoes ; that he could only baptize with water, but that Christ would baptize those who accepted Him with the Holy Ghost, but those who rejected Him with fire.

## Baptism of Jesus.

Then Jesus came to John to be baptized; and afterward, when he was going up out of the water, the heavens were opened unto Him for His encouragement and

4

joy, and the Holy Spirit came down and brooded over him like a dove, which is always an emblem of gentleness, meekness, and purity. And then God's voice spoke: " This is my beloved Son, in whom I am well pleased."

Soon after this, Jesus retired into a desert place for meditation and prayer before he began his public ministry, and fasted forty days and forty nights. Then Satan came to Him, and tempting Him through His hunger, said: "If Thou be the Son of God, command that these stones be made bread." Jesus answered him by quoting from the Old Testament: " Man shall not live by bread alone, but by every word that proceedeth out of the mouth of God." Then the devil took Jesus to Jerusalem, and placed Him on a pinnacle of the Temple, and told Jesus to cast Himself down, and misapplied a text of Scripture to support his plea. But Jesus repelled the temptation by another text, and said: " Thou shalt not tempt the Lord, thy God." Again he took Jesus up into a high mountain, and offered Him all He could see if He would but worship him. But Jesus drove him from His presence, and said: " Get thee hence, Satan: for it is written, thou shalt worship the Lord, the God, and Him only shalt thou serve." The devil left Him, and angels at once came and ministered unto Him.

### Calling the Disciples.

One day John was with two of his disciples, when Jesus passed by, and he pointed Him out to them, saying: " Behold, the Lamb of God!" They at once left John and followed Jesus, who turned round and asked them what they sought. They replied: " Master, where dwellest Thou?" Jesus said: " Come and see." They spent the remainder of the day with Him, and he convinced them that He was the Messiah. One of them, Andrew, felt anxious that his brother Simon should share the privilege that he had enjoyed, and with true brotherly love brought him to Jesus.

On the next day, Jesus, on His way to Galilee, found Philip. He went with Jesus, but, like Andrew, did not wish alone to have the blessing, so went for Nathaniel, and told him that he had found Him of whom Moses and the prophets wrote, Jesus of Nazareth.

The partners of Simon, James and John, the sons of Zebedee, were also called. They were to give up their calling as fishermen and He would make them fishers of men.

### The First Miracle.

On the third day after our Lord's return into Galilee, there was a marriage at Cana, a small town a few miles north of Nazareth. Perhaps the bride or bridegroom was some relative of Mary's, as she was one of the chief guests. Jesus also was invited, and his disciples, Philip and Nathaniel, who was a resident of the town. The feast began and went on smoothly enough until the wine ran short, and it was evident that not enough had been provided. There were standing near six large waterpots. Jesus directed the servants to fill these vessels with water, and when they had done so, He said unto them, "Draw out now, and bear unto the governor of the feast." He tasted the wine, and at once perceived that it was far better than any previously used. This was the first miracle which Jesus did.

## Cleansing the Temple.

Next Jesus went to Jerusalem to keep the feast of the Passover. On entering the outer court of the Temple He was grieved to see that they had made a market of this part of God's house. Oxen, sheep and doves were needful for the sacrifices, and it was a convenience for those who came from a distance to be able to buy what they wanted at Jerusalem; but it was a desecration of the Temple to carry on sales within its court. Then there were money-changers, who seemed to have been allowed to place their tables in the court of the Gentiles. Jesus quickly made a whip of small cords and drove them all out of the Temple. The sheep and the oxen were driven out, the tables of the money-changers were thrown down, and the money scattered over the ground; and then, with words full of righteous indignation, He said, "Take these things hence; make not my Father's house a house of merchandise."

Jerusalem being now filled with people from all parts, Jesus took the opportunity of making himself known as the Messiah, and of working many miracles. Many believed on Him, and carried back with them the tidings of what they had seen and heard to remote parts of the country. But there was one more illustrious than the others, Nicodemus, a ruler of the Jews, who was convinced from the miracles that Jesus did, that he must be a teacher sent by God. He belonged to the Sanhedrim, or Jewish council, a court consisting of seventy-two members, chief priests, elders, and scribes, with the high priest at its head. Nicodemus, afraid or ashamed to have it known that he sought Jesus, came to him by night. Jesus unfolded to him the doctrines of the new birth: that we were born in sin, but that we must be born again of the Holy Spirit. Nicodemus was astonished, and thought Jesus referred to being born again into this life; but Jesus told him it was being born unto life eternal.

Not long after this, John the Baptist suffered for his faithful preaching. King Herod Antipas had fallen in love with Herodias, his brother Philip's wife, and had married her contrary to the law. For this, John reproved Herod, who, wishing to silence his accuser, had him seized and imprisoned in his castle of Macherus, east of the Dead Sea, and afterwards put him to death.

## Healing the Sick.

Jesus went to Galilee, where many that had seen him at Jerusalem flocked round him, anxious to see and hear all they could. Amongst others that had heard of the miracles was a nobleman living at Capernaum. He had a son lying dangerously ill. As soon as he heard of the arrival of Jesus at Cana, he hastened to Him, and besought Him that He would come down to his house and heal his son ere he died.

Jesus told him to go his way, assuring him that his son was healed. This was not the kind of answer the nobleman expected. He thought that Jesus should return with him in his chariot to his house, and then heal his son ; but on his way home he met some of his servants who had set out to meet their master, and tell him that his son was cured. He inquired at what hour his son began to get better. The servants' answer was : "Yesterday, at the seventh hour, the fever left him." So the father knew that it was just the exact hour of the day before when Jesus said : "Thy son liveth."

Jesus went to Nazareth, where He had been brought up, and where He now, no doubt, met many who had known Him in the days of His childhood and youth. But he was ill-received there, and so went on to Capernaum.

### Matthew, the Publican.

As Jesus was passing along, He saw a publican sitting at the roadside, attending to his duties of receiving taxes, and bade him rise and follow Him. Levi, or Matthew, for this was his name, immediately obeyed : he left his books and his weights and measures, and the money he had yet to collect ; he left all and followed Jesus.

After this there was a feast of the Jews, and Jesus went up to Jerusalem. Near the Temple was the Pool of Bethesda, appropriately called "The House of Mercy ;" around it were five porches, or covered walks, which were now crowded with poor people. Among the crowd that lay there was one poor man who had been afflicted thirty-eight years. Jesus tried to cheer him, and to see if he still had any hope left. He said : "Wilt thou be made whole ?" The man replied by relating his experience, that he had no one when the water was troubled to help him down into the pool ; that he was too infirm to get there quickly without assistance, and that every one seemed so intent himself on reaching the pool, that by the time he got there the waters were stilled, and were supposed then to have lost their healing power. Jesus said unto him : "Arise, take up thy bed, and walk !" He made the effort and was made whole.

### Sending Forth Apostles.

One morning He called unto Him His disciples, and selected from them twelve who were not only to accompany Him, but themselves become preachers of the word ; able to heal diseases, and to cast out devils.

Their names were Simon Peter, or Cephas, as our Lord called him from the first ; Andrew, his brother ; James and John, the sons of Zebedee and Salome ; Philip, who was an early friend of Simon and Andrew ; Bartholomew, who is supposed to be Nathaniel ; Matthew, who gave up his profitable office when Jesus called him ; Thomas, James, the son of Alphæus and Mary, surnamed "The Less," perhaps because low of stature ; Jude or Judas, who was surnamed Thaddæus and Lebbæus, the brother of James, the Less ; Simon, called Zelotes, or Zealot ; and Judas, named Iscariot, from Carioth, the place of his birth.

### The Sermon on the Mount.

That all might hear, He went up into a mountain, followed by His disciples and the people, and when He had found a convenient spot, He sat down. There was

CHRIST ON THE MOUNT

no fear of interruption from the Pharisees or scribes, so Jesus began to preach His sermon on the mount. He commenced by telling them who were the truly blessed, from which they saw that it depended not on belonging to any favored class, having any particular talent or possessions, but that these blessings were within their humble reach, to whatever nation or calling they might belong. He said : " After this manner, pray ye :

Our Father, which art in heaven, hallowed be Thy name ; Thy kingdom come. Thy will be done in earth, as it is in heaven. Give us this day our daily bread. And forgive us our debts, as we forgive our debtors. And lead us not into temptation, but deliver us from evil : for Thine is the kingdom, and the power, and the glory, for ever. Amen." Jesus talked to the people for a long time, giving them holy counsel, expounding the Law and the Prophets, and above all teaching the virtues of humility, love and charity.

### Raising the Dead.

On the following day, our Lord went out from Capernaum and crossed the plains of Esdraelon, towards Nain, then a small city. They met, near the gate, a great crowd, forming a funeral procession. The corpse of a young man was being carried out. He was "the only son of his mother, and she was a widow." Jesus went up to the bier and touched it, and said, addressing the corpse, " Young man, I say unto thee, Arise," when immediately he that had been dead and was to have been so soon buried, sat upright and began to speak.

### Stilling the Tempest.

Our Lord proposed to His disciples that they should cross the lake of Gennesareth. Soon after they had hoisted sail, Jesus retired to the stern of the ship, and soon fell into a sleep. Suddenly they were caught in a gale. The disciples, in fear, awoke Him with the cry, " Master, carest Thou not that we perish ? " But our Lord said to them, " Why are ye so fearful, O ye of little faith ? " and then to the sea, " Peace, be still." Then, in an instant, died the wind away ; and the water was still and tranquil.

About this time Herod Antipas, who was now living in the Golden House at Tiberias, heard of the fame of Jesus, and expressed a wish to see Him. When he inquired who this man was, of whom every one was speaking, some of his attendants told him that Elias had reappeared on earth : others again, said that John the Baptist, whom their master had put to death, had risen from the dead. Then fear fell upon Herod, for he believed the latter report, that John had indeed risen, and that judgment would soon visit him for the cruel murder that he had committed.

### Feeding the Multitude.

One day Jesus was followed by a great throng of people, who were without food. It was evening, and the disciples asked Jesus to send the people away. He told them that they need not depart ; and then, turning to Philip, asked how many loaves they had. Presently, Andrew, Simon Peter's brother, found a lad with five small barley loves and two small fishes, and that was all.

Jesus told His disciples to make the men sit down by fifties. When all were seated, Jesus looked up to heaven to direct them to their Father. He implored a blessing on the meal they were about to make, then brake the loaves and gave them to the disciples who distributed them in order to the multitude : and then the fishes in like manner, until, not only had they all partaken, but until they had had enough—the five thousand men besides the women and children. Then, that nothing might be lost, He told them to gather up the fragments : they filled twelve baskets. There was more left than there had been originally, and the lad was no worse off than before Andrew discovered his stock.

### Jesus Walks on the Sea.

The people, when they had seen the miracle which had been wrought for them, were convinced that Jesus was the Messiah ; and perceiving that they were likely to take Him by force and make him a king, He urged the disciples to get into their ship whilst he sent the multitude away. His disciples had entered their ship, and were making for Capernaum, when a sudden and violent storm came up. The vessel was tossed about at the mercy of the waves, and they were well-nigh exhausted in rowing, when in early morning, Jesus drew near unto them, walking on the sea. In the dim light they were afraid ; for they thought it was a spirit. Then Jesus spake to them, and said, " Be of good cheer, it is I, be not afraid." Peter, whose love was the most impulsive, said, " Lord, if it be Thou, bid me come unto Thee on the water." And the Lord bade him come. The boisterous wind and the rough sea took all the courage out of him. His heart sank, and then his body would have followed. He cried out, " Lord, save me ;" and immediately Jesus caught him and saved him, saying, " O thou of little faith, wherefore didst thou doubt ? "

### The Transfiguration.

After this, Jesus went with His disciples to Cæsarea Philippi. No crowd now attended Jesus, for He sought retirement, as He had somewhat of importance to tell His disciples concerning Himself. He asked them, " Whom do men say that I the Son of man am ? " They answered Him that some said He was John the Baptist, some that He was Elias, others that He was Jeremias or one of the prophets risen again. Then said He to them, " But whom say ye that I am ? " And Peter at once answered, " Thou art the Christ, the Son of the living God."

Six days afterwards, Jesus took with Him Peter and James and John up into a mountain to pray. As Jesus prayed, the fashion of His countenance was altered ; it shone as the sun in all its dazzling glory. His garments, which, no doubt, were travel-stained and worn, became as a raiment of light, and glistened as the mountain snow. But the disciples fell asleep. Then two other figures appeared, also radiant in glory : they were Moses and Elias ; the one representing the Law, and the other the Prophets. They talked with Jesus concerning His death at Jerusalem, which showed that in the eyes of neither of them was this coming degradation inconsistent with the glory which was then revealed in Jesus, and which, after His resurrection, should surround Him forever and ever.

At last the disciples awoke, and as they opened their eyes they could perceive that their Master was the centre of the light, and that by Him stood two others. After Moses and Elias had departed, Peter said, "Lord, it is good for us to be here; if Thou wilt, let us make three tabernacles, one for Thee and one for Moses, and one for Elias." While he was yet speaking, a bright cloud overshadowed them, and forth from it came a voice, saying, "This is My beloved Son, in whom I am well pleased: hear ye Him."

The disciples, in their fear, fell on the ground, and remained there until the glory had passed away. Then Jesus came and touched them, and bade them arise, and not be afraid. They looked, and saw no one but Jesus, and as they went down the mountain-side together, He charged them, saying, "Tell the vision to no man, until the Son of man be risen from the dead."

### The Last Visit to Jerusalem.

About this time the feast of Tabernacles was at hand, and His brethren besought Him that He would go up with them to Jerusalem. Jesus refused to go with them, sent them on before Him, and, after a time, set out quietly with His more immediate followers. Jesus was now taking this journey for the last time.

### At Bethany.

Returning from Jerusalem one day, Our Lord stopped at Bethany, a little village about two miles southeast of the city, the abode of His dear friend Lazarus, and his sisters Martha and Mary. On this occasion Martha, for her name implies that she was the lady or mistress of the house, received Him, and having welcomed Him, bustled off to prepare for entertaining Him, while her sister Mary, not sharing at all her trouble and anxieties, was sitting enjoying the sweet converse of her Lord, which she herself had often delighted in, for she was also His disciple. Vexed that just now she should have all the trouble and her sister all the enjoyment, she came to Jesus and said: "Lord, dost Thou not care that my sister hath left me to serve alone? Bid her therefore that she help me." Jesus answered Martha and said: "Martha, Martha, thou art careful and troubled about many things, but one thing is needful; and Mary hath chosen that good part, which shall not be taken away from her."

### The Raising of Lazarus.

One day Jesus went far away, when there a message came from Bethany. His friend Lazarus had been taken ill, and his sisters sent to tell the Lord so. The messenger returned; but before he got back, Lazarus, becoming alarmingly worse, had died. Meantime, Jesus abode two days where He was, and then He said to His disciples: "Let us go into Judea again. Our friend Lazarus sleepeth; but I go that I may awake him out of his sleep." They thinking that this was a favorable sign, replied that if he slept he should do well; but Jesus then told them plainly "Lazarus is dead. And I am glad for your sakes that I was not there, to the intent ye may believe; nevertheless, let us go unto him."

It was evening when they drew near to the village; they then heard that Lazarus had been dead four days, and that many had come to the sisters to mourn

with them.   Some of these friends told Martha that Jesus was coming.   She went
out to meet Him, and accosted Him with words of sorrowful reproach.   "Lord, if
Thou hadst been here my brother had not died."   Jesus said to her: "Thy
brother shall rise again."   Martha replied: "I know that he shall rise again in
the resurrection at the last day."   Then said Jesus: "I am the resurrection, and
the life; he that believeth in Me, though he were dead, yet shall he live; and whosoever liveth and believeth in Me shall never die."   Then said he: "Where have
ye laid him?" and they asked Him to follow them to the grave.   On his way there,
Jesus wept.   Jesus had come to the grave.   It was a cave hewn out of a rock, and
a heavy stone lay at the mouth.   Jesus said: "Take ye away the stone."   Then
Jesus cried with a loud voice: "Lazarus, come forth."   And immediately he who
had been dead four days came forth, bound round with the usual grave-clothes, and
his face covered with a napkin.   Jesus commanded them to loose Lazarus, which,
when they had done he retired with his sisters.

## Humility Taught.

One day, some women desired that their children should receive His blessing.
As the women came near with the children, the disciples tried to prevent their
approach.   When Jesus saw what His disciples were doing, He was much displeased.
He Himself called the children unto Him, and said: "Suffer the little children to
come unto me, and forbid them not; for of such is the Kingdom of God.   Verily I
say unto you:   Whosoever shall not receive the kingdom of God as a little child, he
shall not enter therein."

## Entering Jerusalem.

One Sunday, Jesus left Bethany with His disciples to go into Jerusalem.
When they had come to the Mount of Olives, many people who had come up to the
feast, and who had heard that Jesus had also come, went forth to meet Him with
palm-branches in their hands, and shouting, "Hosanna, blessed is the King of Israel
that cometh in the name of the Lord."   Then Jesus sent two of His disciples,
saying to them, "Go your way into the village over against you; and straightway ye shall find an ass tied, and a colt with her, loose them and bring them unto
me; and if any man say aught unto you, ye shall say, the Lord hath need of them;
and straightway he will send them."   This was done in fulfilment of a prophecy
spoken by Zechariah, four hundred years before.

The disciples found the colt as they had been told.   The owners inquired what
they were doing in loosing it; but when they said, "The Lord hath need of him,"
no further objection was raised.   They brought the ass and the colt to Jesus, and
when they had thrown some garments on the colt, Jesus sat thereon.   By this time
many more people had come out from Jerusalem, and had joined those who had
already surrounded Jesus.   On moved this wondrous procession.   The multitude
took off their garments and spread them in the way; others cut down branches
from the trees for Jesus to ride over.

Slowly the procession wound over the Mount of Olives; the people shouting
and praising God, saying, "Hosanna to the Son of David.   Blessed be the King

that cometh in the name of the Lord; peace in heaven, and glory in the highest." Then some of the Pharisees, who mingled with the crowd, indignant that such honor was given to Jesus, said to Him, "Master, rebuke Thy disciples." And He answered them, "I tell you that if these should hold their peace, the stones would immediately cry out."

## The Plot of Judas.

The Jewish council, or Sanhedrim, met at the palace of Caiaphas, the high-priest. They plotted how they might take Jesus by craft, and put Him to death, but they were yet afraid, lest the people should rescue him, and thus cause an uproar. While they were sitting, Judas Iscariot, one of His disciples, presented himself before them. He asked the council what they would give him if he delivered Jesus unto them. They knowing him to be a disciple, and thinking it likely that their end would be best served in this manner, were very glad, and readily promised him thirty pieces of silver—just the price of a common slave.

On the following day the disciples asked Jesus where they should eat the Passover together, and he sent Peter and John to get a room for them.

## The Last Supper.

When the even was come, Jesus left Bethany with His twelve disciples, and came to the upper chamber that had been prepared for them. Then as they sat at the table, Jesus was troubled in spirit as He said, "Verily, verily, I say unto you, that one of you which eateth with me shall betray me." With feelings of deep sorrow they then began, one by one, to say to Jesus, "Lord, is it I?" Jesus replied, "It is one of the twelve that dippeth with me in the dish."

Sitting next to Jesus and leaning on His bosom was His beloved disciple, John; Peter, beckoning to him, suggested that he might ask the Saviour quietly who was the betrayer. John took occasion to ask the question, and Jesus replied, "He it is, to whom I shall give a sop when I have dipped it." Then, taking up a piece of the bread, and dipping it into the thick sauce made of dates, figs, and vinegar, he gave it to Judas Iscariot. Judas then had the hardihood to ask if it were he, and Jesus said it was, adding, "That thou doest, do quickly." Judas went immediately out, and it was night.

## Peter's Warning.

When he had departed, Jesus continued His discourse with the other disciples.

He gave them the new commandment, that they should love one another, as He had loved them; then turning to Simon, He said to him, "Simon, Simon, behold Satan hath desire to have you, that he may sift you as wheat; but I have prayed for thee that thy faith fail not; and when thou art converted strengthen thy brethren."

Peter at once replied, "Lord, I am ready to go with Thee, both to prison and to death." But Jesus who knew his impetuous and presumptuous disciple better than he knew himself, said to him, "I tell thee, Peter, the cock shall not crow this day, before thou shalt thrice deny that thou knowest me."

### The Lord's Supper.

As an emblem of His body, which would so soon be broken on the cross, He took bread, and blessed it, and brake it, and gave it to the disciples, and said, "Take, eat, this is my body which is given for you: this do in remembrance of me."

Then he took the cup of wine and when he had given thanks, He gave it to them, saying, "Drink ye all of it: this is my blood of the new testament, which is shed for many for the remission of sins."

### Gethsemane.

Crossing over the brook Kedron, our Lord entered the garden of Gethsemane with His disciples, and said to them "Sit ye here, while I go and pray yonder;" and He took with Him, apart from the others, Peter, James and John. He said to the three, "My soul is exceeding sorrowful, even unto death; tarry ye here, and watch with me;" and then, feeling how severe was the trial through which He was passing, He told His disciples to pray that they might not enter into temptation. Jesus then withdrew Himself from them about a stone's throw, knelt down, fell on His face, and prayed, "O my Father, if it be possible, let this cup pass from me; nevertheless, not as I will, but as Thou wilt." He turned to His disciples, and found them asleep again, and this happened three times.

### The Betrayal.

Then a crowd of people entered the garden. Foremost was Judas, and with him a band of officers and men, with weapons and lanterns and torches. As the band drew near, Judas, by preconcerted signal, approached Jesus, and said, "Hail Master," and kissed Him. Then they came and laid hands on Jesus, and took Him.

### The Trial.

The officers having bound Jesus, led Him away from the garden to the palace of the high-priest, where the Sanhedrim was then sitting. Peter and John followed their Master afar off; not near enough to be observed. When the band had safely conducted Jesus to the palace, John drew near; and making use of the interest he had—for he was known to the high-priest—got admitted himself, and afterwards spoke to the young woman who kept the door, and got Peter admitted also. The servants had kindled a fire in the hall, for the night was chilly, and Peter sat down with them to warm himself whilst he waited to see the result of his Lord's examination by the Sanhedrim, some of whom were then assembled at the high-priest's palace.

The high-priest first asked Jesus concerning His disciples and His doctrine, to which he replied, "I spake openly to the world; I ever taught in the synagogue, and in the temple, whither the Jews always resort; and in secret have I said nothing. Why askest thou me? Ask them who heard me, what I have said unto them; behold, they know what I said."

At last two came forward, who sware they had heard Jesus say He was able to destroy the temple of God, and to build it in three days. The high-priest asked

Jesus if he had no reply to make, but Jesus remained silent. Again the high-priest asked Him, and said, "I adjure Thee by the living God that Thou tell us whether Thou be the Christ, the Son of God." Jesus then answered that he was, and said, "Hereafter shall ye see the Son of man sitting on the right hand of power, and coming in the clouds of heaven."

Then the high-priest said, "He hath spoken blasphemy; what further need have we of witnesses? Behold now ye have heard His blasphemy. What think ye?" And the members of the council agreeing with the high-priest, said He was guilty of death, and so condemned Him.

## Peter's Denial.

Peter waited with the expectation that his Master would either successfully oppose His enemies, or else miraculously deliver Himself from their power. But when he saw Jesus thus condemned, he began to fear for himself. As he sat warming himself, the maid who had had charge of the door said, "Thou also wast with Jesus of Nazareth." Peter denied his Master before them all, and said that he neither knew Him, nor understood what was said.

This drew on Peter the attention of all the group, and one said, "Did I not see thee in the garden?" Peter at once denied that he was there, and immediately the cock crew. About an hour after this, others said they were sure he was one of those with Jesus. Then began Peter to curse and to swear, saying, "I know not this man of whom ye speak." And while he thus spake the cock crew the second time.

Jesus turned His head and looked on him, and then Peter remembered how his Master had said, "Before the cock crew twice, thou shalt deny me thrice."

## Death of Judas.

When morning dawned, Judas appeared before the council. He brought back the thirty pieces of silver to the council, saying, "I have sinned, in that I have betrayed innocent blood." Casting down the money, to possess which he had so grievously sinned, he went out and hanged himself, but the rope breaking, he fell from some height, and burst asunder. The council took up the money, and being too mindful of the law to put any money into the treasury that had been the price of blood, they bought with it a piece of ground in which to bury strangers.

## Before Pilate.

Then the council rose, and led Jesus away, bound, to Pontius Pilate the governor. He asked them what accusation they brought against Jesus, and they began to accuse Jesus of disloyalty to Cæsar, of forbidding to give tribute to him, and of proclaiming Himself a King.

Pilate asked Him if He were the King of the Jews. Jesus answerd, "My kingdom is not of this world; if my kingdom were of this world, then would my servants fight, that I should not be delivered to the Jews: but now is my kingdom not from hence."

Pilate called to the chief priests and the rulers, and said to them, "I have found no fault in this Man touching those things whereof ye accuse Him. I will therefore chastise Him and release Him." But the chief priests and elders persuaded the multitude to demand the death of Jesus and the release of Barabbas, the latter being a robber who had committed murder to attain his end. When Pilate asked them which of the two he should release, they cried out, "Not this man, but Barabbas." Pilate asked what he should then do with Jesus, whom they called the King of the Jews; and they all said, "Crucify Him, crucify Him."

Pilate then took water and washed his hands saying, "I am innocent of the blood of this just person, see ye to it." And the people said, "His blood be on us and on our children."

Jesus was now in the custody of the Roman soldiers. They stripped off His robes, and put on a purple military cloak, plaited a crown of thorns, which they put on His head, and for a sceptre they placed a reed in His right hand. Then bowing the knee before Him, in derision and mockery, they hailed Him as King of the Jews.

## The Crucifixion.

After taking from Him the purple robe, and putting on His own clothes, they placed on Him the cross on which He was to suffer and led Him away. When they had come to Mount Calvary or Golgotha,—an eminence on the north-west of Jerusalem,—they crucified Jesus, nailing His hands and feet to the cross, and on either side was crucified a malefactor; thus fulfilling the words of Isaiah, "He was numbered with the transgressors." Pilate wrote a superscription and set it up over the cross, "Jesus of Nazareth, the King of the Jews;" it was written in Greek and Latin and Hebrew, so that all who were to Calvary were able to read it.

As Jesus hung on the cross he was reviled by all classes, the chief priests, the scribes, the rulers, the soldiers, the people, and even His fellow-sufferers, the thieves, all took it for granted that if He were what He pretended to be He would save Himself and come down from the cross.

One of the thieves said to Him, "If thou be the Christ, save Thyself and us ;" but the other, repenting of having at all reviled Jesus, rebuked his fellow, saying, "Dost not thou fear God, seeing thou art in the same condemnation ? and we indeed justly, for we receive the due reward of our deeds, but this man hath done nothing amiss. Lord, remember me when Thou comest into Thy kingdom."

Jesus heard his prayer, and comforted his dying moments with the blessed assurance, " To-day shalt thou be with me in paradise."

In His distress of soul, Jesus cried out, " My God, my God, why hast Thou forsaken me ? " as He realized by what an awful distance sin separates the creature from the Creator. He said, "I thirst ; " and some one ran, and filled a sponge with vinegar and putting it on the stalk of a hyssop plant held it to His mouth for Him to drink. When Jesus had drunk the vinegar, He said, "It is finished." Then cried Jesus with a loud voice, "Father, into Thy hands I commend my spirit ; " and having said this, He bowed His head and gave up the ghost.

BEHOLD, I STAND AT THE DOOR AND KNOCK

A fearful convulsion shook the earth and rent the rocks, in the midst of which tombs were opened, and after three days many of the saints rose from the dead, and going into the city appeared uuto many.

When the centurion, who was on duty in charge of the soldiers, heard the dying words of Jesus, and then felt the earthquake, he feared greatly, saying, "Truly this was the Son of God."

### The Burial.

Joseph of Arimathæa, a good man, possessed of riches, went to Pilate and asked him for the body of Jesus. Pilate consented, and then Joseph wrapped the body in a fine linen cloth. Near the place of crucifixion was a garden belonging to Joseph, in which he had hewn out of the solid rock a tomb that had never yet been used. In this they laid the body of Jesus ; and having rolled a great stone to the mouth of the sepulchre, they went their way.

The chief priests and Pharisees came to Pilate to have the sepulchre made secure, as they remembered that Jesus had said He would rise again after three days ; and they feared that His disciples might remove His body. Pilate placed a guard of soldiers to watch the sepulchre, and they sealed the stone that lay in front, for still further protection.

### The Resurrection.

But at night the angel of the Lord descended from heaven, the earth shook, and the stone that had been set against the door of the sepulchre was rolled back, and formed a seat on which the angel sat with a countenance like lightning, and with dazzling white raiments. The keepers trembled before him, and became as dead men.

As the two Marys and Salome journeyed to the garden, they saw the stone removed, and judging that the Jews had removed the body of Jesus, they were broken-hearted. Mary Magdalene, full of grief, went back, and told Peter and John what had happened ; but Mary and Salome desired to make further search.

Into the entrance of the sepulchre, Mary and Salome now went, and saw on the right hand side an angel sitting, clothed in a long white garment. The women drew back affrighted, but the angel said, "Fear not ye : for I know that ye seek Jesus, who was crucified. He is not here ; for He is risen, as He said. Come, see the place where the Lord lay. And go quickly, and tell His disciples that He is risen from the dead ; and, behold, He goeth before you into Galilee ; there shall ye see Him ; lo, I have told you."

### The Ascension.

After that Jesus appeared to the women and to the disciples several times, in various places. He said to them, "All power is given unto me in heaven and in earth. Go ye, therefore, and teach all nations, baptizing them in the name of the Father, and of the Son, and of the Holy Ghost ; teaching them to observe all things whatsoever I have commanded you : and, lo, I am with you alway, even unto the end of the world."

One day he led His disciples out in the direction of Bethany, whither they had often gone together. Some of them said to Him, "Lord, wilt Thou at this time restore again the kingdom to Israel ? " He answered them, " It is not for you to know the times or the seasons, which the Father hath put in His own power. But ye shall receive power, after that the Holy Ghost is come upon you : and ye shall be witnesses unto me both in Jerusalem, and in all Judea, and in Samaria, and unto the uttermost parts of the earth."

When Jesus had finished speaking, He lifted up His hands and blessed them. Whilst He was thus blessing them, behold, He was carried up into heaven, and a cloud received Him out of their sight.

### Pentecost.

After the ascension of Christ, at the suggestion of Peter, the Apostles chose Matthias to be one of their number in place of the traitor Judas. Not long after they met to celebrate the Day of Pentecost, and while they sat together the Holy Ghost came upon them and they all received power to use foreign languages, so that they might go about the world preaching in the tongues of whatever lands they entered. Peter was now the leader of them, and he preached several notable sermons, and thousands were converted and added to the church. The Christians then generally sold their property and turned the proceeds in to the common fund of the Church. But two, Ananias and his wife, Sapphira, kept back a part of their wealth, and tried to deceive the Apostles. But their lying was exposed, and they were struck dead.

### Persecutions.

The Apostles were soon subjected to persecutions at the hands of the Jews. They were first imprisoned, but an angel opened the prison doors and released them. Then Stephen, who had been made a deacon, was accused of blasphemy and stoned to death. After that there was a great persecution and the Christians were driven out of Jerusalem, and scattered in many lands, but wherever they went they preached the gospel, and made many converts. The most zealous among their persecutors was a scholarly young man named Saul, of Tarsus. He was present at the killing of Stephen, and he soon set out for Damascus to arrest some Christians, who had fled thither. On his way he was stricken down and made blind, and he was led to Damascus helpless. Meantime the Apostle Philip went toward Egypt, and met a eunuch who was the treasurer of the Queen of Ethiopia, and preached to him, and converted and baptized him.

### St. Paul.

When Saul reached Damascus he was visited by one of the Christians whom he had meant to slay, and was soon converted fully. Thereafter he was called Paul, and was the most zealous of all the Apostles. Another notable convert was Cornelius, a Roman Centurion at Cæsarea. He was led by a vision to send for Peter, and at the same time Peter was instructed in a vision to accept converts from the Gentile nations, as well as from the Jews. Some of the others murmured at this, but Peter told them of his vision, and convinced them that the gospel was for the Gentiles, as well as for the children of Israel. So began the preaching to the Gentiles.

## Death of Herod.

Soon after this King Herod began to persecute the Christians bitterly. He put James to death, and threw Peter into prison. But Peter was released by an angel again. Then Herod set himself up to be worshipped by the people as a God, but as he sat upon his throne he was stricken with a mortal illness, and fell dead.

## Paul and Barnabas.

Then Paul and Barnabas set out on the first of their great missionary journeys. They went first to Seleucia, thence to Cyprus, Salamir, Paphos, and Perga. At Antioch, in Pisidia, they were violently persecuted, and fled thence to Iconium. There again they were ill-treated, and fled to Lystra and Derbe. There they wrought miracles and made converts. But some of the people wanted to worship them as Gods, and then others persecuted them, so they presently returned to Antioch.

## Paul and Silas.

On his next journey Paul took Silas with him instead of Barnabas. They went through various parts of Asia Minor, establishing many churches. At Troas, Paul was bidden in a vision to go over into Macedonia and preach. They went and made many converts at Philippi. They were thrown into prison there on false charges, but at night there came an earthquake, which opened the prison doors, and set them free. At this the keeper of the prison believed their preaching, and was baptized with all his family.

## On Mars Hill.

After further journeyings, Paul reached Athens, then the most highly cultivated of cities. He was received with much curiosity, and the Athenians were eager to hear him. So he went up to a great public place called Mars Hill, and there expounded the gospel. He was listened to with interest until he spoke of the resurrection of the dead, but at that some began to mock him. Nevertheless, he made some converts in that city, including one member of the Supreme Court of the Areopagus.

## Corinth and Ephesus.

Paul next went to Corinth, and lived there for a year and a half, and went to Ephesus. After he had been at the latter place for some time, and had made many converts, one Demetrius, a maker of shrines and idols, found his trade injured, and accordingly raised a riot against Paul. For hours they raged about, crying "Great is Diana of the Ephesians!" So Paul left them, and went his way to other Greek cities, where his preaching met with great success. Then he was called by the Holy Spirit back to Jerusalem.

### Before Felix and Festus.

Here he was arrested, but was allowed to speak to the people in his own defence, and when he made it known that he was a free-born Roman citizen he was treated with respect by the officers and taken to Cæsarea, to be examined by Felix, the Roman governor. Felix was much impressed by Paul's defence of himself, and set him at liberty, though under the surveillance of an officer. More than once Felix sent for Paul fo expound the gospel to him, and trembled at his preaching, but does not appear to have been converted. Then Felix was succeeded by Festus, whom the Jews besought to have Paul sent back from Cæsarea to Jerusalem, so that they might waylay him and kill him. But Festus would not, but went down to Cæsarea to see Paul there. He gave Paul a hearing, and then suggested that he go up to Jerusalem and be tried there. But Paul refused, saying: "I have done the Jews no harm. I ought to be tried not by them, but at Cæsar's judgment-seat. I appeal unto Cæsar." This appeal could not be denied, so preparations were made for sending Paul to Rome. Meantime the Viceroy Agrippa came thither and examined him and found no fault in him. When Paul preached to him, Agrippa said: "Almost thou persuadest me to be a Christian." But as Paul had appealed to Cæsar, to Rome he had to go.

### The Voyage to Rome.

The journey to Rome was made in a ship, which was beaten about much by storms. One landing was made on the southern shore of Crete. Next, after two weeks of dreadful storms, they were shipwrecked on the coast of Malta. The islanders received them kindly, and built a great fire to warm and dry them. Out of a bundle of sticks a viper crawled, and bit Paul on the hand. When the people saw that Paul was not injured by the poison they took him to be a god. Other miracles were wrought there, and some converts made. After three months they were taken off by another ship, and carried to Rome, where Paul was allowed to live in a house of his own, and preach the gospel. He made many converts, and wrote epistles to the various churches he had founded. But after several years he suffered martyrdom in the great persecution which the Emperor Nero made against the Christians.

### St. John at Patmos.

The last survivor of the Apostles was John, who lived to be very old, and spent the closing years of his life in exile on the island of Patmos. There, one Lord's Day, he had a wondrous vision, in which he was taken up into heaven and made to see all that should happen until the ending of the world and the final judgment of mankind.

# BOOK II.

---

## TALES FROM SHAKESPEARE.

SHAKESPEARE

# Book II.

# Tales from Shakespeare.

### By Charles and Mary Lamb.

---

## ROMEO AND JULIET.

THE FEUD BETWEEN THE MONTAGUES AND CAPULETS—ROMEO IN DISGUISE GOES TO THE
CAPULETS' BALL, AND FALLS IN LOVE WITH JULIET AND SHE WITH HIM—THEIR
INTERVIEW ON HER BALCONY—PLANS FOR A SECRET MARRIAGE—TYBALT KILLS
MERCUTIO, AND ROMEO KILLS TYBALT—ROMEO IS BANISHED—THE CAPULETS
FORCE JULIET INTO A MATCH WITH PARIS—TO ESCAPE SHE TAKES A
SLEEPING POTION AND FEIGNS DEATH — ROMEO AND PARIS MEET
AT HER TOMB—THEY FIGHT, AND PARIS IS SLAIN—THINKING
JULIET DEAD, ROMEO KILLS HIMSELF, AND SHE, FINDING HIM
DEAD, KILLS HERSELF—THE MONTAGUES AND CAPULETS
ARE RECONCILED TO EACH OTHER OVER THE DEAD
BODIES OF THE UNFORTUNATE LOVERS.

---

THE two chief families in Verona were the rich Capulets and the Montagues. There had been an old quarrel between these families, which was grown to such a height, and so deadly was the enmity between them, that it extended to the remotest kindred, to the followers and retainers of both sides, insomuch that a servant of the house of Montague could not meet a servant of the house of Capulet, nor a Capulet encounter with a Montague by chance, but fierce words and sometimes bloodshed ensued; and frequent were the brawls from such accidental meetings, which disturbed the happy quiet of Verona's estate.

Old Lord Capulet made a great supper, to which many fair ladies and many noble guests were invited. All the admired beauties of Verona were present, and all comers were made welcome if they were not of the house of Montague. At this feast of Capulets, Rosaline, beloved of Romeo, son to the old Lord Montague, was present; and though it was dangerous for a Montague to be seen in this assembly, yet Benvolio, a friend of Romeo, persuaded the young lord to go to this assembly in the disguise of a mask, that he might see his Rosaline, and seeing her compare her with some choice beauties of Verona, who (he said) would make him think his swan a crow. Romeo had small faith in Benvolio's words; nevertheless, for the love of Rosaline, he was persuaded to go. For Romeo was a sincere and passionate lover, and one that lost his sleep for love, and fled society to be alone, thinking on Rosaline, who disdained him, and never requited his love with the least show of courtesy or affection ; and Benvolio wished to cure his friend of this love by showing him diversity of ladies and company. To this feast of Capulets then young Romeo with Benvolio and their friend Mercutio went masked. Old Capulet bid them welcome, and told them that ladies who had their toes unplagued with corns would dance with them. And the old man was lighthearted and merry, and said that he had worn a mask when he was young, and could have told a whispering tale in a fair lady's ear. And they fell to dancing, and Romeo was suddenly struck with the exceeding beauty of a lady that danced there, who seemed to him to teach the torches to burn bright, and her beauty to show by night like a rich jewel worn by a blackamoor : beauty too rich for use, too dear for earth ! like a snowy dove trooping with crows (he said), so richly did her beauty and perfections shine above the ladies her companions. While he uttered these praises, he was overheard by Tybalt, a nephew of Lord Capulet, who knew him by his voice to be Romeo. And this Tybalt, being of a fiery and passionate temper, could not endure that a Montague should come under cover of a mask, to fleer and scorn (as he said) at their solemnities. And he stormed and raged exceedingly, and would have struck young Romeo dead. But his uncle, the old Lord Capulet, would not suffer him to do any injury at that time, both out of respect to his guests, and because Romeo had borne himself like a gentleman, and all tongues in Verona bragged of him to be a virtuous and well-governed youth. Tybalt, forced to be patient against his will, restrained himself, but swore that this vile

Montague should at another time dearly pay for his intrusion.

The dancing being done, Romeo watched the place where the lady stood ; and under favor of his masking habit, which might seem to excuse in part the liberty, he presumed in the gentlest manner to take her by the hand, calling it a shrine, which if he profaned by touching it, he was a blushing pilgrim, and would kiss it for atonement. "Good pilgrim," answered the lady, "your devotion shows by far too mannerly and too courtly : saints have hands, which pilgrims may touch, but kiss not." "Have not saints lips, and pilgrims too ?" said Romeo. "Ay," said the lady, "lips which they must use in prayer." "O then, my dear saint," said Romeo "hear my prayer and grant it, lest I despair." In such like allusions and loving conceits they were engaged, when the lady was called away to her mother. And Romeo inquiring who her mother was, discovered that the lady whose peerless beauty he was so much struck with, was young Juliet, daughter and heir to the Lord Capulet, the great enemy of the Montagues ; and that he had unknowingly engaged his heart to his foe. This troubled him, but it could not dissuade him from loving. As little rest had Juliet, when she found that the gentleman that she had been talking with was Romeo and a Montague, for she had been suddenly smit with the same hasty and inconsiderate passion for Romeo, which he had conceived for her ; and a prodigious birth of love it seemed to her, that she must love her enemy, and that her affections should settle there, where family considerations should induce her chiefly to hate.

It being midnight Romeo with his companions departed ; but they soon missed him, for, unable to stay away from the house where he had left his heart, he leaped the wall of an orchard which was at the back of Juliet's house. Here he had not remained long, ruminating on his new love, when Juliet appeared above at a window, through which her exceeding beauty seemed to break like the light of the sun in the east ; and the moon, which shone in the orchard with a faint light, appeared to Romeo as if sick and pale with grief at the superior luster of this new sun. And she leaning her hand upon her cheek, he passionately wished himself a glove upon that hand, that he might touch her cheek. She, all this while thinking herself alone, fetched a deep sigh, and exclaimed, "Ah me!" Romeo was enraptured to hear her speak, and said softly, unheard by her, "O speak again, bright angel, for such you appear, being over my head like a winged messenger from heaven whom mortals fall back to gaze upon." She, unconscious of being overheard, and full of the new passion which that night's adventure had given birth to, called upon her lover by name (whom she supposed absent): "O Romeo, Romeo!" said she, "wherefore art thou, Romeo? Deny thy father, and refuse thy name, for my sake ; or if thou wilt not, be but my sworn love, and I no longer will be a Capulet." Romeo, having this encouragement, would fain have spoken, but he was desirous of hearing more ; and the lady continued her passionate discourse with herself (as she thought), still chiding Romeo for being Romeo and a Montague, and wishing him some other name, or that he would put away the hated name, and for that name, which was no part of himself, he should take all herself. At this loving word Romeo could no longer refrain, but taking up the dialogue as if her words had been addressed to him personally, and not merely in fancy, he bade her call him Love, or by whatever other name she pleased, for he was no longer Romeo, if that name was displeasing to her. Juliet, alarmed to hear a man's voice in the garden, did not at first know who it was, that by favor of the night and darkness had thus stumbled upon the discovery of her secret ; but when he spoke again, though her ears had not yet drunk a hundred words of that tongue's uttering, yet so nice is a lover's hearing, that she immediately knew him to be young Romeo, and she expostulated with him on the danger to which he had exposed himself by climbing the orchard walls, for if any of her kinsmen should find him there, it would be death to him, being a Montague. "Alack," said Romeo, "there is more peril in your eye, than in twenty of their swords. Do you but look kind upon me, lady, and I am proof against their enmity. Better my life should be ended by their hate, than that hated life should be prolonged, to live without your love." "How came you into this place," said Juliet, "and by whose direction?" "Love directed me," answered Romeo. "I am no pilot, yet wert thou as far apart from me as that vast shore which is washed with the farthest sea, I should adventure for such merchandise. A crimson blush came over the face of Juliet, yet unseen by Romeo by reason of the night, when she reflected upon the discovery which she had made, yet not meaning to make it, of her love to Romeo. She would fain have recalled her words, but that was impossible ; fain would she have stood upon form, and have kept her lover at a distance, as the custom of discreet ladies is, to frown and be perverse, and give their suitors harsh denials at first ; to stand off, and affect a coyness or indifference, where they most love, that their lovers may not think them too lightly or too easily won : for the difficulty of attainment increases the value of the object. But there was no room in her case for denials, or puttings off, or any of the customary arts of delay and protracted courtship. Romeo had heard from her own tongue, when she did not dream that he was near her, a confession of her love. So with an honest frankness, which the novelty of her situation excused, she confirmed the truth of what he had before heard, and addressing him by the name of *fair Montague* (love can sweeten a sour name), she begged him not to impute her easy yielding to levity or an unworthy mind, but that he must lay the fault of it (if it were a fault) upon the accident of the night which had so strangely discovered her thoughts. And, she added, that though her behavior to him might not be sufficiently prudent, measured by the custom of her sex, yet that she would prove more true than many whose prudence was dissembling, and their modesty artificial cunning.

Romeo was beginning to call the heavens to witness that nothing was farther from his thoughts than to impute a shadow of dishonor to such an honored lady, when she stopped him, begged him not to swear : for although she joyed in him, yet she had no joy of that night's contract ; it was too rash, too unadvised, too sudden. But he being urgent with her to exchange a vow of love with her that night, she said that she already had given him hers before he requested it ; meaning when he overheard her confession ; but she would retract what she then bestowed, for the pleasure of giving it again, for her bounty was as infinite as the sea, and her love as deep. From this loving conference she was called by her nurse, who slept with her, and thought it time for her to be in bed, for it was near to daybreak ; but hastily returning she said three or four words more to Romeo, the purport of which was, that if his love was indeed honorable, and his purpose marriage, she would send a messenger to him to-morrow, to appoint a time for their marriage, when she would lay all her fortunes at his feet, and follow him as her lord through the world. While they were settling this point, Juliet was repeatedly called for by her nurse, and went in and returned, and went and returned again, for she seemed as jealous of Romeo going from her, as a young girl of her bird, which she will let hop a little from her hand, and pluck it back with a silken thread ; and Romeo was as loath to part as she : for the sweetest music to lovers is the sound of each other's tougues at night. But at last they parted, wishing mutually sweet sleep and rest for that night.

The day was breaking when they parted, and Romeo, who was too full of thoughts of his mistress and that blessed meeting to allow him to sleep, instead of going home, bent his course

ROMEO AND JULIET

*Act 2d, Scene 2d.*

to a monastery hard by, to find Friar Lawrence. The good friar was already up at his devotions, but seeing young Romeo abroad so early, he conjectured rightly that he had not been abed that night, but that some distemper of youthful affection had kept him waking. He was right in imputing the cause of Romeo's wakefulness to love, but he made a wrong guess at the object, for he thought that his love for Rosaline had kept him waking. But when Romeo revealed his new passion for Juliet, and requested the assistance of the friar to marry them that day, the holy man lifted up his eyes and hands in a sort of wonder at the sudden change in Romeo's affections, for he had been privy to all Romeo's love for Rosaline, and his many complaints of her disdain ; and he said that young men's love lay not truly in their hearts, but in their eyes. But Romeo replying that he himself had often chidden him for doting on Rosaline, who could not love him again, whereas Juliet both loved and was beloved by him, the friar assented in some measure to his reasons ; and thinking that a matrimonial alliance between young Juliet and Romeo might happily be the means of making up the long breach between the Capulets and the Montagues, which no one more lamented than this good friar, who was a friend to both the families, and had often interposed his mediation to make up the quarrel without effect, partly moved by policy, and partly by his fondness for young Romeo, to whom he could deny nothing, the old man consented to join their hands in marriage.

Now was Romeo blessed indeed, and Juliet, who knew his intent from a mes-senger which she had dispatched according to promise, did not fail to be early at the cell of friar Lawrence, where their hands were joined in holy marriage; the good friar praying the heavens to smile upon that act, and in the union of this young Montague and young Capulet to bury the old strife and long dissensions of their families.

The ceremony being over, Juliet hastened home, where she stayed impatient for the coming of night, at which time Romeo promised to come and meet her in the orchard, where they had met the night before; and the time between seemed as tedious to her as the night before some great festival seems to an impatient child that has got new finery which it may not put on till the morning.

That same day, about noon, Romeo's friends, Benvolio and Mercutio, walking through the streets of Verona, were met by a party of the Capulets with the impetuous Tybalt at their head. This was the same angry Tybalt who would have fought with Romeo at old Lord Capulet's feast. He seeing Mercutio, accused him bluntly of associating with Romeo, a Montague. Mercutio, who had as much fire and youthful blood in him as Tybalt, replied to this accusation with some sharpness; and in spite of all Benvolio could say to moderate their wrath, a quarrel was beginning, when Romeo himself passing that way, the fierce Tybalt turned from Mercutio to Romeo, and gave him the disgraceful appellation of villain. Romeo wished to avoid a quarrel with Tybalt above all men, because he was a kinsman of Juliet, and much beloved by her; besides this, young Montague had never thoroughly entered into the family quarrel, being by nature wise and gentle, and the name of a Capulet, which was his dear lady's name, was now rather a charm to allay resentment than a watchword to excite fury. So he tried to reason with Tybalt, whom he saluted mildly by the name of *good Capulet,* as if he, though a Montague, had some secret pleasure in uttering that name: but Tybalt, who hated all Montagues as he hated hell, would hear no reason, but drew his weapon; and Mercutio, who knew not of Romeo's secret motive for desiring peace with Tybalt, but looked upon his present forbearance as a sort of calm dishonorable submission, with many disdainful words provoked Tybalt to the persecution of his first quarrel with him; and Tybalt and Mercutio fought, until Mercutio fell, receiving his death's wound while Romeo and Benvolio were vainly endeavoring to part the combatants. Mercutio being dead, Romeo kept his temper no longer, but returned the scornful appellation of villain which Tybalt had given him; and they fought till Tybalt was slain by Romeo. This deadly broil falling out in the midst ot Verona at noonday, the news of it quickly brought out a crowd of citizens to the spot, and among them the old lords Capulet and Montague, with their wives; and soon after arrived the prince himself, who being related to Mercutio, whom Tybalt had slain, and having had the peace of his government often disturbed by these brawls of Montagues and Capulets, came determined to put the law in strictest force, against those who should be found to be offenders. Benvolio, who had been eyewitness to the fray, was commanded by the prince to relate the origin of it, which he did, keeping as near to the truth as he could without in-

jury to Romeo, softening and excusing the part which his friends took in it. Lady Capulet, whose extreme grief for the loss of her kinsman Tybalt made her keep no bounds in her revenge, exhorted the prince to do strict justice upon his murderer, and to pay no attention to Benvolio's representation, who being Romeo's friend, and a Montague, spoke partially. Thus she pleaded against her new son-in-law, but she knew not yet that he was her son-in-law, and Juliet's husband. On the other hand was to be seen Lady Montague's pleading for her child's life, and arguing with some justice that Romeo had done nothing worthy of punishment in taking the life of Tybalt, which was already forfeited to the law by his having slain Mercutio. The prince, unmoved by the passionate exclamations of these women, on a careful examination of the facts, pronounced his sentence, and by that sentence Romeo was banished from Verona.

Heavy news to young Juliet, who had been but a few hours a bride, and now by this decree seemed everlastingly divorced! When the tidings reached her, she at first gave way to rage against Romeo, who had slain her dear cousin: she called him a beautiful tyrant, a fiend angelical, a ravenous dove, a lamb with a wolf's nature, a serpent-heart hid with a flowering face, and other like contradictory names, which denoted the struggles in her mind between her love and her resentment: but in the end love got the mastery, and the tears which she shed for grief that Romeo had slain her cousin, turned to drops of joy that her husband lived whom Tybalt would have slain. Then came fresh tears, and they were altogether of grief for Romeo's banishment. That word was more terrible to her than the death of many Tybalts.

Romeo, after the fray, had taken refuge in friar Lawrence's cell, where he was first made acquainted with the prince's sentence, which seemed to him far more terrible than death. To him it appeared there was no world out of Verona's walls, no living out of the sight of Juliet. Heaven was there where Juliet lived, and all beyond was purgatory, torture, hell. The good friar would have applied the consolation of philosophy to his griefs; but this frantic young man would hear of none, but like a madman he tore his hair, and threw himself all along upon the ground, as he said, to take the measure of his grave. From this unseemly state he was roused by a message from his dear lady, which a little revived him, and then the friar took the advantage to expostulate with him on the unmanly weakness which he had shown. He had slain Tybalt, but would he also slay himself, slay his dear lady who lived but in his life? The noble form of man, he said, was but a shape of wax, when it wanted the courage which should keep it firm. The law had been lenient to him, that instead of death, which he had incurred, had pronounced by the prince's mouth only banishment. He had slain Tybalt, but Tybalt would have slain him: there was a sort of happiness in that. Juliet was alive, and (beyond all hope) had become his dear wife, therein he was most happy. All these blessings, as the friar made them out to be, did Romeo put from him like a sullen misbehaved wench. And the friar bade him beware, for such as despaired (he said) died miserable. Then when Romeo was a little calmed, he counseled him that he should go that night and secretly take his leave of Juliet, and thence proceed straightways to Mantua, at which place he should sojourn, till the friar found a fit occasion to publish his marriage, which might be a joyful means of reconciling their families ; and then he did not doubt but the prince would be moved to pardon him, and he would return with twenty times more joy than he went forth with grief. Romeo was convinced by these wise counsels of the friar, and took his leave to go and seek his lady, purposing to stay with her that night, and by daybreak pursue his journey alone to Mantua ; to which place the good friar promised to send him letters from time to time, acquainting him with the state of affairs at home.

That night Romeo passed with his dear wife, gaining secret admission to her chamber from the orchard in which he had heard her confession of love the night before. That had been a night of unmixed joy and rapture ; but the pleasures of this night, and the delight which these lovers took in each other's society, were sadly allayed with the prospect of parting, and the fatal adventures of the past day. The unwelcome daybreak seemed to come too soon, and when Juliet heard the morning song of the lark, she would fain have persuaded herself that it was the nightingale, which sings by night ; but it was too truly the lark which sung, and a discordant and unpleasing note it seemed to her ; and the streaks of day in the east too certainly pointed out that it was time for these lovers to part. Romeo took his leave of his dear wife with a heavy heart, promising to write to her from Mantua every hour in the day, and when he had descended from her chamber-window, as he stood below her on the ground, in that sad foreboding state of mind, in which she was, he appeared to her eyes as one dead in the bottom of a tomb. Romeo's mind misgave him in like manner; but now he was forced hastily to depart, for it was death for him to be found within the walls of Verona after daybreak.

This was but the beginning of the tragedy of this pair of star-crossed lovers. Romeo had not been gone many days, before the old Lord Capulet proposed a match for Juliet. The husband he had chosen for her, not dreaming that she was married already, was Count Paris, a gallant, young, and noble gentleman, no unworthy suitor to the young Juliet if she had never seen Romeo.

The terrified Juliet was in a sad perplexity at her father's offer. She pleaded her youth unsuitable to marriage, the recent death of Tybalt, which had left her spirits too weak to meet a husband with any face of joy, and how indecorous it would show for the family of the Capulets to be celebrating a nuptial-feast, when his funeral solemnities were hardly over: she pleaded every reason against the match but the true one, namely, that she was married already. But Lord Capulet was deaf to all her excuses, and in a peremptory manner ordered her to get ready, for by the following Thursday she should be married to Paris: and having found her a husband rich, young, and noble, such as the proudest maid in Verona might joyfully accept, he could not bear that out of an affected coyness, as he construed her denial, she should oppose obstacles to her own good fortune.

In this extremity Juliet applied to the friendly friar, always her counselor in distress, and he asking her if she had resolution to undertake a desperate remedy, and she answering that she would go into the grave alive, rather than marry Paris, her own dear husband living; he directed her to go home, and appear merry, and give her consent to marry Paris, according to her father's desire, and on the next night, which was the night before the marriage, to drink off the contents of a phial which he then gave her, the effect of which would be, that for two-and-forty hours after drinking it she should appear cold and lifeless; that when the bridegroom came to fetch her in the morning, he would find her to appearance dead; that then she would be borne, as the manner in that country was, uncovered, on a bier, to be buried in the family vault; that if she could put off womanish fear, and consent to this terrible trial, in forty-two hours after swallowing the liquid (such was its certain operation) she would be sure to awake, as from a dream; and before she should awake, he would let her husband know their drift, and he should come in the night, and bear her thence to Mantua. Love, and the dread of marrying Paris, gave young Juliet strength to undertake this horrible adventure; and she took the phial of the friar, promising to observe his directions.

Going from the monastery, she met the young Count Paris, and modestly dissembling, promised to become his bride. This was joyful news to the Lord Capulet and his wife. It seemed to put youth into the old man; and Juliet, who had displeased him exceedingly by her refusal of the count, was his darling again, now she promised to be obedient. All things in the house were in a bustle against the approaching nuptials. No cost was spared to prepare such festival rejoicings as Verona had never before witnessed.

On the Wednesday night Juliet drank off the potion. She had many misgivings, lest the friar, to avoid the blame which might be imputed to him for marrying her to Romeo, had given her poison; but then he was always known for a holy man: then lest she should awake before the time that Romeo was to come for her; whether the terror of the place, a vault full of dead Capulets' bones, and where Tybalt, all bloody, lay festering in his shroud, would not be enough to drive her distracted: again she thought of all the stories she had heard of spirits haunting the places where their bodies were bestowed. But then her love for Romeo, and her aversion for Paris, returned, and she desperately swallowed the draught, and became insensible.

When young Paris came early in the morning with music, to awaken his bride, instead of a living Juliet, her chamber presented the dreary spectacle of a lifeless corpse. What death to his hopes! What confusion then reigned through the whole house!—poor Paris lamenting his bride, whom most detestable death had beguiled him of, had divorced from him even before their hands were joined. But still more piteous it was to hear the mournings of the old lord and lady Capulet, who having but this one, one poor loving child to rejoice and solace in, cruel death had snatched her from their sight, just as these careful parents were on the point of seeing her advanced (as they thought) by a promising and advantageous match. Now all things that were ordained for the festival were turned from their properties to do the office of a black funeral. The wedding cheer served

for a sad burial feast, the bridal hymns were changed to sullen dirges, the sprightly instruments to melancholy bells, and the flowers that should have been strewed in the bride's path, now served but to strew her corpse. Now instead of a priest to marry her, a priest was needed to bury her; and she was borne to church indeed not to augment the cheerful hopes of the living, but to swell the dreary numbers of the dead.

Bad news, which always travels faster than good, now brought the dismal story of his Juliet's death to Romeo at Mantua, before the messenger could arrive who was sent from friar Lawrence to apprise him that these were mock funerals only, and but the shadow and representation of death, and that his dear lady lay in the tomb but for a short while, expecting when Romeo should come to release her from that dreary mansion. Just before, Romeo had been unusually joyful and light-hearted. He had dreamed in the night that he was dead (a strange dream, that gave a dead man leave to think), and that his lady came and found him dead, and breathed such life with kisses in his lips, that he revived, and was an emperor! And now that a messenger came from Verona, he thought surely it was to confirm some good news which his dreams had presaged. But when the contrary to this flattering vision appeared, and that it was his lady who was dead in truth, whom he could not revive by any kisses, he ordered horses to be got ready, for he determined that night to visit Verona, and to see his lady in her tomb. And as mischief is swift to enter into the thoughts of desperate men, he called to mind a poor apothecary, whose shop in Mantua he had lately passed, and from the beggarly appearance of the man, who seemed famished, and the wretched show in his shop of empty boxes ranged on dirty shelves, and other tokens of extreme wretchedness, he had said at the time (perhaps having some misgivings that his own disastrous life might haply meet with a conclusion so desperate), "If a man were to need poison, which by the law of Mantua it is death to sell, here lives a poor wretch who would sell it him." These words of his now came into his mind, and he sought out the apothecary, who, after some pretended scruples, Romeo offering him gold which his poverty could not resist, sold him a poison, which, if he swallowed, he told him, if he had the strength of twenty men, would quickly dispatch him.

With this poison he set out for Verona, to have a sight of his dear lady in her tomb, meaning, when he had satisfied his sight, to swallow the poison, and be buried by her side. He reached Verona at midnight, and found the churchyard, in the midst of which was situated the ancient tomb of the Capulets. He had provided a light and a spade, and wrenching iron, and was proceeding to break open the monument, when he was interrupted by a voice, which by the name of *vile Montague*, bade him desist from his unlawful business. It was the young Count Paris, who had come to the tomb of Juliet at that unseasonable time of night, to strew flowers and to weep over the grave of her that should have been his bride. He knew not what an interest Romeo had in the dead, but knowing him to be a Montague, and (as he supposed) a sworn foe to all the Capulets, he judged that he was come by night to do some villainous shame to the dead bodies; therefore in angry tone he bade him desist; and as a criminal, condemned by the laws of Verona to die if he were found within the walls of the city, he would have apprehended him. Romeo urged Paris to leave him, and warned him by the fate of Tybalt, who lay buried there, not to provoke his anger, or draw down another sin upon his head, by forcing him to kill him. But the count in scorn refused his warning, and laid hands on him as a felon, which Romeo resisting, they fought, and Paris fell. When Romeo, by the help of a light, came to see who it was that he had slain, that it was Paris, who (he learned on his way from Mantua) should have married Juliet, he took the dead youth by the hand, as one whom misfortune had made a companion, and said that he would bury him in a triumphal grave, meaning in Juliet's grave, which he now opened; and there lay his lady, as one whom death had no power upon to change a feature or complexion in her matchless beauty, or as if death were amorous, and the lean abhorred monster kept her there for his delight; for she lay yet fresh and blooming, as she had fallen to sleep when she swallowed that benumbing potion; and near her lay Tybalt in his bloody shroud, whom Romeo seeing, begged pardon of his lifeless corpse, and for Juliet's sake called him *cousin*, and said that he was about to do him a favor by putting his enemy to death. Here Romeo took his last leave of his lady's lips, kissing them; and here he shook the burden of his cross stars from his weary body, swallowing that poison which the apothecary had sold him, whose operation was fatal and real, not like that dissembling potion which Juliet had swallowed, the effect of which was now nearly expiring, and she about to awake to complain that Romeo had not kept his time, or that he had come too soon.

For now the hour was arrived at which the friar had promised that she should awake; and he, having learned that his letters which he had sent to Mantua, by some unlucky detention of the messenger, had never reached Romeo, came himself, provided with a pickaxe and lantern, to deliver the lady from her confinement; but he was surprised to find a light already burning in the Capulet's monument, and to see swords and blood near it, and Romeo and Paris lying breathless by the monument.

Before he could entertain a conjecture, to imagine how these fatal accidents had fallen out, Juliet awoke out of her trance, and seeing the friar near her, she remembered the place where she was, and the occasion of her being there, and asked for Romeo: but the friar, hearing a noise, bade her come out of that place of death, and of unnatural sleep, for a greater power than they could contradict had thwarted their intents; and being frightened by the noise of people coming, he fled; but when Juliet saw the cup closed in her true love's hands, she guessed that poison had been the cause of his end, and she would have swallowed the dregs if any had been left, and she kissed his still warm lips to try if any poison yet did hang upon them: then hearing a nearer noise of the people coming, she quickly unsheathed a dagger which she wore, and stabbing herself, died by her true Romeo's side.

The watch by this time had come up

to the place. A page belonging to Count Paris, who had witnessed the fight between his master and Romeo, had given the alarm, which had spread among the citizens, who went up and down the streets of Verona confusedly, exclaiming, a Paris, a Romeo, a Juliet, as the rumor had imperfectly reached them, till the uproar brought Lord Montague and Lord Capulet out of their beds, with the prince, to inquire into the causes of the disturbance. The friar had been apprehended by some of the watch, coming from the churchyard, trembling, sighing, and weeping in a suspicious manner. A great multitude being assembled at the Capulet's monument, the friar was demanded by the prince to deliver what he knew of these strange and disastrous accidents.

And there, in the presence of the old lords Montague and Capulet, he faithfully related the story of their children's fatal love, the part he took in promoting their marriage, in the hope in that union to end the long quarrels between their families: how Romeo, there dead, was husband to Juliet; and Juliet, there dead, was Romeo's faithful wife: how before he could find a fit opportunity to divulge their marriage, another match was projected for Juliet, who to avoid the crime of a second marriage swallowed the sleeping draught (as he advised), and all thought her dead: how meantime he wrote to Romeo, to come and take her thence when the force of the potion should cease, and by what unfortunate miscarriage of the messenger the letters never reached Romeo: further than this the friar could not follow the story, nor knew more than that, coming himself to deliver Juliet from that place of death, he found the Count Paris and Romeo slain. The remainder of the transactions was supplied by the narration of the page who had seen Paris and Romeo fight, and by the servant who came with Romeo from Verona, to whom this faithful lover had given letters to be delivered to his father in the event of his death, which made good the friar's words, confessing his marriage with Juliet, imploring the forgiveness of his parents, acknowledging the buying of the poison of the poor apothecary, and his intent in coming to the monument, to die, and lie with Juliet. All these circumstances agreed together to clear the friar from any hand he could be supposed to have had in these complicated slaughters, further than as the unintended consequences of his own well-meant, yet too artificial and subtle contrivances.

And the prince, turning to these old lords, Montague and Capulet, rebuked them for their brutal and irrational enmities, and showed them what a scourge heaven had laid upon such offences, that it had found means even through the love of their children to punish their unnatural hate. And these old rivals, no longer enemies, agreed to bury their long strife in their children's graves; and Lord Capulet requested Lord Montague to give him his hand, calling him by the name of brother, as if in acknowledgement of the union of their families by the marriage of the young Capulet and Montague; and saying that Lord Montague's hand (in token of reconcilement) was all he demanded for his daughter's jointure: but Lord Montague said he would give him more, for he would raise her statue of pure gold, that while Verona kept its name, no figure should be so esteemed for its richness and workmanship as that of the true and faithful Juliet. And Lord Capulet in return said, that he would raise another statue to Romeo. So did these poor old lords, when it was too late, strive to outdo each other in mutual courtesies: while so deadly had been their rage and enmity in past times, that nothing but the fearful overthrow of their children (poor sacrifices to their quarrels and dissensions) could remove the rooted hates and jealousies of the noble families.

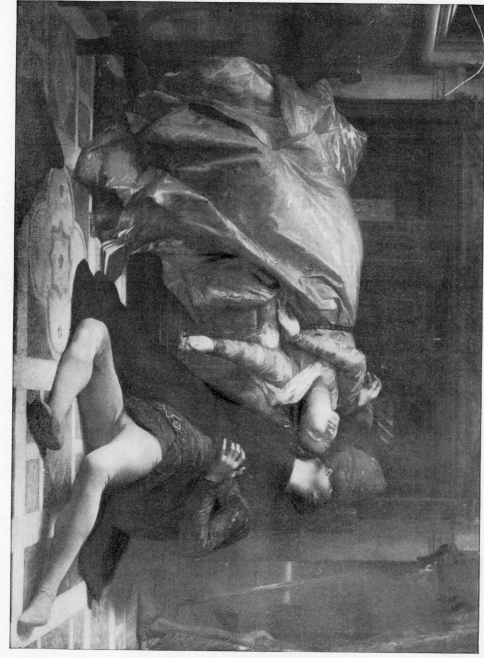

ROMEO AND JULIET

*Act 4th, Scene 5.*

# HAMLET.

---

THE GHOST APPEARS TO THE SENTRIES—HAMLET AND THE KING—HORATIO TELLS OF
THE GHOST—HAMLET SEES AND TALKS WITH IT—LAERTES AND OPHELIA DISCUSS
HAMLET'S LOVE FOR OPHELIA—HAMLET VOWS TO AVENGE HIS FATHER'S
MURDER—HE FEIGNS MADNESS—HE ENGAGES PLAYERS TO PRESENT A
PLAY PORTRAYING THE MURDER OF HIS FATHER—HE MAKES OPHELIA
THINK HIM MAD—THE PLAY IS GIVEN AND THE KING BETRAYED—
HAMLET KILLS OPHELIA'S FATHER, AND SHE GOES MAD AND
KILLS HERSELF—HER FUNERAL—THE KING PLOTS TO
HAVE HAMLET KILLED ON A JOURNEY TO ENG-
LAND—HAMLET ESCAPES—THE QUEEN IS POIS-
ONED WITH A DRINK MEANT FOR HAMLET—
HAMLET KILLS THE KING AND LAER-
TES, AND IS HIMSELF SLAIN.

---

GERTRUDE, Queen of Denmark, becoming a widow by the sudden death of King Hamlet, in less than two months after his death married his brother Claudius, which was noted by all people at the time for a strange act of indiscretion, or unfeelingness, or worse: for this Claudius did nowise resemble her late husband in the qualities of his person or his mind, but was as contemptible in outward appearance as he was base and unworthy in disposition; and suspicions did not fail to arise in the minds of some that he had privately made away with his brother, the late king, with the view of marrying his widow, and ascending the throne of Denmark, to the exclusion of young Hamlet, the son of the buried king, and lawful successor to the throne.

But upon no one did this unadvised action of the queen make such impression as upon this young prince, who loved and venerated the memory of his dead father almost to idolatry; and being of a nice sense of honor, and a most exquisite practicer of propriety himself, did sorely take to heart this unworthy conduct of his mother Gertrude: insomuch that, between grief for his father's death and shame for his mother's marriage, this young prince was overclouded with a deep melancholy, and lost all his mirth and all his good looks; all his customary pleasure in books forsook him; his princely exercises and sports, proper to his youth, were no longer acceptable; he grew weary of the world, which seemed to him an unweeded garden, where all the wholesome flowers were choked up, and nothing but weeds could thrive. Not that the prospect of exclusion from the throne, his lawful inheritance, weighed so much upon his spirits, though that to a young and high-minded prince was a bitter wound and a sore indignity; but what so galled him, and took away all his cheerful spirits, was that his mother had shown herself so forgetful to his father's memory: and such a father! who had been to her so loving and gentle a husband! and then she always appeared as loving and obedient a wife to him, and would hang upon him as if her affection grew to him: and now within two months, or, as it seemed to young Hamlet, less than two months, she had married again, married his uncle, her dead husband's brother, in itself a highly improper and unlawful marriage, from the nearness of relationship, but made much more so by the indecent haste with which it was concluded, and the unkingly character of the man whom she had chosen to be the partner of her throne and bed. This it was which, more than the loss of ten kingdoms, dashed the spirits, and brought a cloud over the mind of this honorable young prince.

In vain was all that his mother Gertrude or the king could do or contrive to divert him; he still appeared in court in a suit of deep black, as mourning for the king, his father's death, which mode of dress he had never laid aside, not even in complement to his mother on the day she was married, nor could he be brought to join in any of the festivities or rejoicings of that (as appeared to him) disgraceful day.

What mostly troubled him was an uncertainty about the manner of his father's death. It was given out by Claudius, that a serpent had stung him: but young Hamlet had shrewd suspicions that Claudius himself was the serpent; in plain English, that he had murdered him for his crown, and that the serpent who stung his father did now sit on his throne.

How far he was right in this conjecture, and what he ought to think of his mother—how far she was privy to this murder, and whether by her consent or knowledge, or without, it came to pass—were the doubts which continually harassed and distracted him.

A rumor had reached the ear of young Hamlet that an apparition exactly resembling the dead king his father had been seen by the soldiers upon watch, on the platform before the palace at midnight, for two or three nights successively. The figure came constantly clad in the same suit of armor, from head to foot, which the dead king was known to have worn: and they who saw it (Hamlet's bosom-friend Horatio was one) agreed in their testimony as to the manner and time of its appearance: that it came just as the clock struck twelve; that it looked pale, with a face more of sorrow than of anger; that its beard was grisly, and the color a *sable silvered*, as they had seen it in his life-time: that it made no answer when they spoke to it, yet once they thought it lifted up its head, and addressed itself to motion as if it were about to speak; but in that moment the morning cock crew, and it shrank in haste away, and vanished out of their sight.

The young prince, strangely amazed at their relation, which was too consistent and agreeing with itself to disbelieve, concluded that it was his father's ghost which they had seen, and determined to take his watch with the soldiers that night, that he might have a chance of seeing it: for he reasoned with himself that such an appearance did not come for nothing, but that the ghost had something to impart, and though it had been silent hitherto, yet it would speak to him. And he waited with impatience for the coming of night.

When night came he took his stand with Horatio and Marcellus, one of the guards, upon the platform where this apparition was accustomed to walk: and it being a cold night, and the air unusually raw and nipping, Hamlet and Horatio and their companion fell into some talk about the coldness of the night, which was suddenly broken off by Horatio announcing that the ghost was coming.

At the sight of his father's spirit, Hamlet was struck with a sudden surprise and fear. He at first called upon the angels and heavenly ministers to defend them, for he knew not whether it were a good spirit or bad: whether it came for good or for evil: but he gradually assumed more courage: and his father (as it seemed to him) looked upon him so piteously, and as it were desiring to have conversation with him, and did in all respects appear so like himself as he was when he lived, that Hamlet could not help addressing him: he called him by his name, Hamlet, King, Father! and conjured him that he would tell the reason why he had left his grave, where they had seen him quietly bestowed, to come again and visit the earth and the moonlight: and besought him that he would let them know if there was anything which they could do to give peace to his spirit. And the ghost beckoned to Hamlet, that he should go with him to some more removed place, where they might be alone: and Horatio and Marcellus would have dissuaded the young prince from following it, for they feared lest it should be some evil spirit, who

would tempt him to the neighboring sea, or to the top of some dreadful cliff, and there put on some horrible shape which might deprive the prince of his reason. But their counsels and entreaties could not alter Hamlet's determination, who cared too little about life to fear the losing of it; and as to his soul, he said, what could the spirit do to that, being a thing immortal as itself? And he felt as hardy as a lion; and bursting from them, who did all they could to hold him, he followed whithersoever the spirit led him.

And when they were alone together the spirit broke silence, and told him that he was the ghost of Hamlet, his father, who had been cruelly murdered, and he told the manner of it; that it was done by his own brother Claudius, Hamlet's uncle, as Hamlet had already but too much expected, for the hope of succeeding to his bed and crown. That as he was sleeping in his garden, his custom always in the afternoon, this treasonous brother stole upon him in his sleep, and poured the juice of poisonous henbane into his ears, which has such an antipathy to the life of man, that swift as quicksilver it courses through all the veins of the body, baking up the blood, and spreading a crust like leprosy all over the skin: thus sleeping, by a brother's hand he was cut off at once from his crown, his queen, and his life: and he adjured Hamlet, if he did ever his dear father love, that he would revenge his foul murder. And the ghost lamented to his son, that his mother should so fall off from virtue as to prove false to the wedded love of her first husband, and marry his murderer: but he cautioned Hamlet, howsoever he proceeded in his revenge against his wicked uncle, by no means to act any violence against the person of his mother, but to leave her to heaven and to the stings and thorns of conscience. And Hamlet promised to observe the ghost's direction in all things, and the ghost vanished.

And when Hamlet was left alone, he took up a solemn resolution that all he had in his memory, all that he had ever learned by books or observation, should be instantly forgotten by him, and nothing live in his brain but the memory of what the ghost had told him and enjoined him to do. And Hamlet related the particulars of the conversation which had passed to none but his dear friend Horatio; and he enjoined both to him and Marcellus the strictest secrecy as to what they had seen that night.

The terror which the sight of the ghost had left upon the senses of Hamlet, he being weak and dispirited before, almost unhinged his mind, and drove him beside his reason. And he, fearing that it would continue to have this effect, which might subject him to observation, and set his uncle upon his guard, if he suspected that he was meditating any thing against him, or that Hamlet really knew more of his father's death than he professed, took up a strange resolution, from that time to counterfeit as if he were really and truly mad; thinking that he would be less an object of suspicion when his uncle should believe him incapable of any serious project, and that his real perturbation of mind would be best covered and pass concealed under a disguise of pretended lunacy.

From this time Hamlet affected a certain wildness and strangeness in his apparel, his speech, and behavior, and did so excellently counterfeit the madman,

that the king and queen were both deceived, and not thinking his grief for his father's death a sufficient cause to produce such a distemper, for they knew not of the appearance of the ghost, they concluded that his malady was love, and they thought they had found out the object.

Before Hamlet fell into the melancholy way which has been related, he had dearly loved a fair maid called Ophelia, the daughter of Polonius, the king's chief councilor in affairs of state. He had sent her letters and rings, and made many tenders of his affection to her, and importuned her with love in honorable fashion : and she had given belief to his vows and importunities. But the melancholy which he fell into latterly had made him neglect her, and from the time he conceived the project of counterfeiting madness, he affected to treat her with unkindness, and a sort of rudeness ; but she, good lady, rather than reproach him with being false to her, persuaded herself that it was nothing but the disease in his mind, and no settled unkindness, which had made him less observant of her than formerly ; and she compared the faculties of his once noble mind and excellent understanding, impaired as they were with the deep melancholy that oppressed him, to sweet bells which in themselves are capable of most excellent music, but when jangled out of tune, or rudely handled, produce only a harsh and unpleasing sound.

Though the rough business which Hamlet had in hand, the revenging of his father's death upon his murderer, did not suit with the playful state of courtship, or admit of the society of so idle a

HAMLET

passion as love now seemed to him, yet it could not hinder but that soft thoughts of his Ophelia would come between ; and in one of these moments, when he thought that his treatment of this gentle lady had been unreasonably harsh, he wrote her a letter full of wild starts of passion and extravagant terms, such as agreed with his supposed madness, but mixed with some gentle touches of affection, which could not but show to this honored lady that a deep love for her yet lay at the bottom of his heart. He bade her to doubt the stars were fire, and to doubt that the sun did move, to doubt truth, to be a liar, but never to doubt that he loved her ; with more of such extravagant phrases. This letter Ophelia dutifully showed to her father, and the old man thought himself bound to communicate it to the king and queen, who from that time supposed that the true cause of Hamlet's madness was love. And the queen wished that the good beauties of Ophelia might be the happy cause of his wildness, for so she hoped that her virtues might happily restore him to his accustomed way again, to both their honors.

But Hamlet's malady lay deeper than she supposed, or than could be so cured. His father's ghost, which he had seen, still haunted his imagination, and the sacred injunction to revenge his murder gave him no rest till it was accomplished. Every hour of delay seemed to him a sin, and a violation of his father's commands. Yet how to compass the death of the king, surrounded as he constantly was with his guards, was no easy matter. Or if it had been, the presence of the queen, Hamlet's mother, who was generally with the king, was a restraint upon his purpose, which he could not break through. Besides, the very circumstance that the usurper was his mother's husband filled him with some remorse, and still blunted the edge of his purpose. The mere act of putting a fellow creature to death was in itself odious and terrible to a disposition naturally so gentle as Hamlet's was. His very melancholy, and the dejection of spirits he had so long been in, produced an irresoluteness and wavering of purpose, which kept him from proceeding to extremities. Moreover, he could not help having some scruples upon his mind, whether the spirit which he had seen was indeed his father, or whether it might not be the devil, who he had heard has power to take any form he pleases, and who might have assumed his father's shape only to take advantage of his weakness and his melancholy to drive him to the doing of so desperate an act as murder. And he determined that he would have more certain grounds to go upon than a vision or apparition, which might be a delusion.

While he was in this irresolute mind, there came to the court certain players, in whom Hamlet formerly used to take delight, and particularly to hear one of them speak a tragical speech, describing the death of old Priam, King of Troy, with the grief of Hecuba, his queen. Hamlet welcomed his old friends, the players, and remembering how that speech had formerly given him pleasure, requested the player to repeat it ; which he did in so lively a manner, setting forth the cruel murder of the feeble old king, with the destruction of his people and the city by fire, and the mad grief of the old queen, running barefoot up and down the palace, with a poor clout upon that head where a crown had been, and with nothing but a blanket upon her loins, snatched up in haste, where she had worn a royal robe, that it not only drew tears from all that stood by, who thought they saw the real scene, so lively was it represented, but even the player himself delivered it with a broken voice and real tears. This put Hamlet upon thinking, if that player could so work himself up to a passion by a mere fictitious speech, to weep for one that he had never seen, for Hecuba, that had been dead so many hundred years, how dull was he, who having a real motive and cue for passion, a real king and a dear father murdered, was yet so little moved that his revenge all this while had seemed to have slept in dull and muddy forgetfulness! And while he meditated on actors and acting, and the powerful effect which a good play, represented to the life, has upon the spectator, he remembered the instance of some murderer, who, seeing a murder on the stage, was by the mere force of the scene and resemblance of circumstances so affected, that on the spot he confessed the crime which he had committed. And he determined that these players should play something like the murder of his father before his uncle, and he would watch narrowly what effect it might have upon him, and from his looks he would be able to gather with more certainty if he were the murderer or not. To this effect he ordered a play to be prepared, to the representation of which he invited the king and queen.

The story of the play was of a murder done in Vienna upon a duke. The duke's name was Gonzago, his wife Baptista.

The play showed how one Lucianus, a near relation to the duke, poisoned him in his garden for his estate, and how the murderer in a short time after got the love of Gonzago's wife.

At the representation of this play, the king, who did not know the trap which was laid for him, was present, with his queen and the whole court; Hamlet sitting attentively near him to observe his looks. The play began with a conversation between Gonzago and his wife, in which the lady made many protestations of love, and of never marrying a second husband, if she should outlive Gonzago; wishing she might be accursed if ever she took a second husband, and adding that no woman ever did so but those wicked women who kill their first husbands. Hamlet observed the king, his uncle, change color at this expression, and that it was as bad as wormwood both to him and to the queen. But when Lucianus, according to the story, came to poison Gonzago sleeping in the garden, the strong resemblance which it bore to his own wicked act upon the late king, his brother, whom he had poisoned in his garden, so struck upon the conscience of this usurper, that he was unable to sit out the rest of the play, but on a sudden calling for lights to his chamber, and affecting or partly feeling a sudden sickness, he abruptly left the theatre. The king being departed, the play was given over. Now Hamlet had seen enough to feel satisfied that the words of the ghost were true, and no illusion; and in a fit of gayety, like that which comes over a man who suddenly has some great doubt or scruple resolved, he swore to Horatio that he would take the ghost's word for a thousand pounds.

But before he could make up his resolution as to what measures of revenge he should take, now he was certainly informed that his uncle was his father's murderer, he was sent for by the queen, his mother, to a private conference in her closet.

It was by desire of the king that the queen sent for Hamlet, that she might signify to her son how much his late behavior had displeased them both ; and the king, wishing to know all that passed at that conference, and thinking that the too partial report of a mother might let slip some part of Hamlet's words, which it might much import the king to know, Polonius, the old councilor of state, was ordered to plant himself behind the hangings in the queen's closet, where he might, unseen, hear all that passed. This artifice was particularly adapted to the disposition of Polonius, who was a man grown old in crooked maxims and policies of state, and delighted to get at the knowledge of matters in an indirect and cunning way.

Hamlet being come to his mother, she began to tax him in the roundest way with his actions and behavior, and she told him that he had given great offence to *his father*, meaning the king, his uncle, whom, because he had married her, she called Hamlet's father. Hamlet, sorely indignant that she should give so dear and honored a name as father seemed to him to a wretch who was indeed no better than the murderer of his true father, with some sharpness replied, "Mother, *you* have much offended *my father*." The queen said that was but an idle answer. "As good as the question deserved," said Hamlet. The queen asked him if he had forgotten who it was he was

speaking to. "Alas!" replied Hamlet, "I wish I could forget. You are the queen, your husband's brother's wife; and you are my mother; I wish you were not what you are." "Nay, then," said the queen, "if you show me so little respect, I will send those to you that can speak," and was going to send the king or Polonius to him. But Hamlet would not let her go, now he had her alone, till he had tried if his words could not bring her to some sense of her wicked life; and taking her by the wrist, he held her fast, and made her sit down. She, affrighted at his earnest manner, and fearful lest in his lunacy he should do her a mischief, cried out: and a voice was heard from behind the hangings, " Help, help, the queen! " which Hamlet hearing, and verily thinking it was the king himself there concealed, he drew his sword, and stabbed at the place where the voice came from, as he would have stabbed a rat that ran there, till the voice ceasing, he concluded the person to be dead. But when he dragged forth the body, it was not the king, but Polonius, the old officious councilor, that had planted himself as a spy behind the hangings. "O me!" exclaimed the queen, "what a rash and bloody deed you have done!" "A bloody deed, mother," replied Hamlet; "but not so bad as yours, who killed a king and married his brother." Hamlet had gone too far to leave off here. He was now in the humor to speak plainly to his mother, and he pursued it. And though the faults of parents are to be tenderly treated by their children, yet in the case of great crimes the son may have leave to speak even to his own mother with some harshness, so as that harshness is meant for her good, and to turn her from her wicked ways, and not done for the purpose of upbraiding. And now this virtuous prince did in moving terms represent to the queen the heinousness of her offence, in being so forgetful of the dead king, his father, as in so short a space of time to marry with his brother and reputed murderer: such an act as, after the vows which she had sworn to her first husband, was enough to make all vows of women suspected, and all virtue to be accounted hypocrisy, wedding contracts to be less than gamesters' oaths, and religion to be a mockery and a mere form of words. He said she had done such a deed that the heavens blushed at it, and the earth was sick of her because of it. And he showed her two pictures, the one of the late king, her first husband, and the other of the present king, her second husband, and he bade her mark the difference: what a grace was on the brow of his father, how like a god he looked! the curls of Apollo, the forehead of Jupiter, the eye of Mars, and a posture like to Mercury newly alighted on some heaven-kissing hill! this man *had been* her husband. And then he showed her whom she had got in his stead: how like a blight or a mildew he looked, for so he had blasted his wholesome brother. And the queen was sore ashamed that he should so turn her eyes inward upon her soul, which she now saw so black and deformed. And he asked her how she could continue to live with this man, and be a wife to him, who had murdered her first husband, and got the crown by as false means as a thief— And just as he spoke, the ghost of his father, such as he was in his lifetime, and such as he had lately seen it, entered the room, and

Hamlet, in great terror, asked what it would have; and the ghost said that it came to remind him of the revenge he had promised, which Hamlet seemed to have forgotten: and the ghost bade him speak to his mother, for the grief and terror she was in would else kill her. It then vanished, and was seen by none but Hamlet, neither could he by pointing to where it stood, or by any description, make his mother perceive it, who was terribly frightened all this while to hear him conversing, as it seemed to her, with nothing: and she imputed it to the disorder of his mind. But Hamlet begged her not to flatter her wicked soul in such a manner as to think that it was his madness, and not her own offences, which had brought his father's spirit again on the earth. And he bade her feel his pulse, how temperately it beat, not like a madman's. And he begged of her, with tears, to confess herself to heaven for what was past, and for the future to avoid the company of the king, and be no more as a wife to him: and when she should show herself a mother to him, by respecting his father's memory, he would ask a blessing of her as a son. And she promising to observe his directions, the conference ended.

And now Hamlet was at leisure to consider who it was that in his unfortunate rashness he had killed; and when he came to see that it was Polonius, the father of the Lady Ophelia, whom he so dearly loved, he drew apart the dead body, and, his spirits being a little quieter, he wept for what he had done.

This unfortunate death of Polonius gave the king a pretence for sending Hamlet out of the kingdom. He would willingly have put him to death, fearing him

# HAMLET

*Act 5th, Scene 1st.*

as dangerous ; but he dreaded the people, who loved Hamlet ; and the queen, who, with all her faults, doted upon the prince her son. So this subtle king, under pretence of providing for Hamlet's safety, that he might not be called to account for Polonius' death, caused him to be conveyed on board a ship bound for England, under the care of two courtiers, by whom he dispatched letters to the English court, which at that time was in subjection and paid tribute to Denmark, requiring, for special reasons there pretended, that Hamlet should be put to death as soon as he landed on English ground. Hamlet, suspecting some treachery, in the night-time secretly got at the letters, and skillfully erasing his own name, he in the stead of it put in the names of those two courtiers who had the charge of him to be put to death : then sealing up the letters, he put them into their place again. Soon after the ship was attacked by pirates, and a sea-fight commenced, in the course of which Hamlet, desirous to show his valor, with sword in hand singly boarded the enemy's vessel, while his own ship, in a cowardly manner, bore away, and, leaving him to his fate, the two courtiers made the best of their way to England, with those letters the sense of which Hamlet had altered to their own deserved destruction.

The pirates who had the prince in their power showed themselves gentle enemies ; and knowing whom they had got prisoner, in the hope that the prince might do them a good turn at court in recompense for any favor they might show him, they set Hamlet on shore at the nearest port in Denmark. From that place Hamlet wrote to the king, acquainting him with the strange chance which had brought him back to his own country, and saying that on the next day he should present himself before his majesty. When he got home a sad spectacle offered itself the first thing to his eyes.

This was the funeral of the young and beautiful Ophelia, his once dear mistress. The wits of this young lady had begun to turn ever since her poor father's death. That he should die a violent death, and by the hands of the prince whom she loved, so affected this tender young maid, that in a little time she grew perfectly distracted, and would go about giving flowers away to the ladies of the court, and saying that they were for her father's burial, singing songs about love and about death, and sometimes such as had no meaning at all, as if she had no memory of what happened to her. There was a willow which grew slanting over a brook, and reflected the leaves in the stream. To this brook she came one day when she was unwatched, with garlands she had been making, mixed up of daisies and nettles, flowers and weeds together, and clambering up to hang her garland upon the boughs of the willow, a bough broke and precipitated this fair young maid, garland, and all that she had gathered, into the water, where her clothes bore her up for a while, during which she chanted scraps of old tunes, like one insensible to her own distress, or as if she were a creature natural to that element : but long it was not before her garments, heavy with the wet, pulled her in from her melodious singing to a muddy and miserable death. It was the funeral of this fair maid which her brother Laertes was celebrating, the king and queen and whole court being present, when Hamlet arrived. He knew not what all this show imported, but stood on one side, not inclining to interrupt the ceremony. He saw the flowers strewed upon her grave, as the custom was in maiden burials, which the queen herself threw in ; and as she threw them she said, "Sweets to the sweet ! I thought to have decked thy bride-bed, sweet maid, not to have strewed thy grave. Thou shouldst have been my Hamlet's wife." And he heard her brother wish that violets might spring from her grave : and he saw him leap into the grave all frantic with grief, and bid the attendants pile mountains of earth upon him, that he might be buried with her. And Hamlet's love for this fair maid came back to him, and he could not bear that a brother should show so much transport of grief, for he thought that he loved Ophelia better than forty thousand brothers. Then discovering himself, he leaped into the grave where Laertes was, all as frantic or more frantic than he, and Laertes knowing him to be Hamlet, who had been the cause of his father's and his sister's death, grappled him by the throat as an enemy, till the attendants parted them : and Hamlet, after the funeral, excused his hasty act in throwing himself into the grave as if to brave Laertes ; but he said he could not bear that any one should seem to outgo him in grief for the death of the fair Ophelia, And for the time these two noble youths seemed reconciled.

But out of the grief and anger of Laertes for the death of his father and Ophelia, the king, Hamlet's wicked uncle, contrived destruction for Hamlet. He set on Laertes, under cover of peace and reconciliation, to challenge Hamlet to a friendly trial of skill at fencing, which Hamlet accepting, a day was appointed to try the match. At this match all the court was present, and Laertes, by direction of the king, prepared a poisoned weapon. Upon this match great wagers were laid by the courtiers, as both Hamlet and Laertes were known to excel at this swordplay, and Hamlet, taking up the foils, chose one, not at all suspecting the treachery of Laertes, or being careful to examine Laertes' weapon, who, instead of a foil or blunted sword, which the laws of fencing require, made use of one with a point, and poisoned. At first Laertes did but play with Hamlet, and suffered him to gain some advantages, which the dissembling king magnified and extolled beyond measure, drinking to Hamlet's success, and wagering rich bets upon the issue : but after a few passes, Laertes, growing warm, made a deadly thrust at Hamlet with his poisoned weapon, and gave him a mortal blow. Hamlet, incensed, but not knowing the whole of the treachery, in the scuffle exchanged his own innocent weapon for Laertes' deadly one, and with a thrust of Laertes' own sword repaid Laertes home, who was thus justly caught in his own treachery. In this instant the queen shrieked out that she was poisoned. She had inadvertently drunk out of a bowl which the king had prepared for Hamlet, in case that, being warm in fencing, he should call for drink : into this the treacherous king had infused a deadly poison, to make sure of Hamlet, if Laertes had failed. He had forgotten to warn the queen of the bowl, which she drank of, and immediately died, exclaiming with her last breath that she was poisoned. Hamlet, suspecting some treachery, ordered the doors to be shut, while he sought it out. Laertes told him to seek no further, for he was the traitor, and feeling his life go away with the wound which Hamlet had given him, he made confession of the treachery he had used, and how he had fallen a victim to it : and he told Hamlet of the envenomed point, and said that Hamlet had not half an hour to live, for no medicine could cure him ; and begging forgiveness of Hamlet he died, with his last words accusing the king of being the contriver of the mischief. When Hamlet saw his end draw near, there being yet some venom left upon the sword, he suddenly turned upon his false uncle, and thrust the point of it to his heart, fulfilling the promise which he had made to his father's spirit, whose injunction was now accomplished, and his foul murder revenged upon the murderer. Then Hamlet, feeling his breath fail and life departing, turned to his dear friend Horatio, who had been spectator of this fatal tragedy ; and with his dying breath requested him that he would live to tell his story to the world (for Horatio had made a motion as if he would slay himself to accompany the prince in death); and Horatio promised that he would make a true report as one that was privy to all the circumstances. And, thus satisfied, the noble heart of Hamlet cracked: and Horatio and the bystanders with many tears commended the spirit of their sweet prince to the guardianship of angels. For Hamlet was a loving and gentle prince, and greately beloved for his many noble and prince-like qualities, and if he had lived would no doubt have proved a most royal and complete king to Denmark.

# THE MERCHANT OF VENICE.

Portia's Suitors—Antonio Borrows Money from Shylock to Aid Bassanio in His Suit—Lorenzo and Jessica—Portia's Three Suitors Try Their Fate—Bassanio Wins and is Accepted—Lorenzo and Jessica Elope—Antonio Cannot Repay the Loan and Shylock Seeks to Make His Life Forfeit—The Trial—Portia, in Disguise, Defeats Shylock—Antonio's Fortunes are Restored—Marriage of Bassanio and Portia—Portia Plays a Trick upon Him, to His Great Embarrassment—Nerissa's Similar Trick upon Gratiano—The Tricks Confessed, and All Made Happy.

SHYLOCK, the Jew, lived at Venice; he was a usurer, who had amassed an immense fortune by lending money at great interest to Christian merchants. Shylock, being a hard-hearted man, exacted the payment of the money he lent with such severity that he was much disliked by all good men, and particularly by Antonio, a young merchant of Venice; and Shylock as much hated Antonio, because he used to lend money to people in distress, and would never take any interest for the money he lent; therefore there was great enmity between this covetous Jew and the generous merchant Antonio. Whenever Antonio met Shylock on the Rialto (or Exchange), he used to reproach him with his usuries and hard dealings; which the Jew would bear with seeming patience, while he secretly meditated revenge.

Antonio was the kindest man that lived, the best conditioned, and had the most unwearied spirit in doing courtesies; indeed, he was one in whom the ancient Roman honor more appeared than in any that drew breath in Italy. He was greatly beloved by all his fellow-citizens; but the friend who was nearest and dearest to his heart was Bassanio, a noble Venetian, who, having but a small patrimony, had nearly exhausted his little fortune by living in too expensive a manner for his slender means, as young men of high rank with small fortunes are too apt to do. Whenever Bassanio wanted money, Antonio assisted him; and it seemed as if they had but one heart and one purse between them.

One day Bassanio came to Antonio, and told him that he wished to repair his fortune by a wealthy marriage with a lady whom he dearly loved, whose father, that was lately dead, had left her sole heiress to a large estate; and that in her father's lifetime he used to visit at her house, when he thought he had observed this lady had sometimes from her eyes sent speechless messages, that seemed to say he would be no unwelcome suitor; but not having money to furnish himself with an appearance be-fitting the lover of so rich an heiress, he besought Antonio to add to the many favors he had shown him, by lending him three thousand ducats.

Antonio had no money by him at that time to lend his friend; but expecting soon to have some ships come home laden with merchandise, he said he would go to Shylock, the rich money-lender, and borrow the money upon the credit of those ships.

Antonio and Bassanio went together to Shylock, and Antonio asked the Jew to lend him three thousand ducats upon any interest he should require, to be paid out of the merchandise contained in his ships at sea. On this, Shylock thought within himself, "If I can once catch him on the hip, I will feed fat the ancient grudge I bear him; he hates our Jewish nation; he lends out money gratis; and among the merchants he rails at me and my well-earned bargains, which he calls interest. Cursed be my tribe if I forgive him!" Antonio, find-ing he was musing within himself and did not answer, and being impatient for money, said, "Shylock, do you hear? will you lend the money?" To this question the Jew replied, "Signor Anto-nio, on the Rialto many a time and often you have railed at me about my moneys and my usuries, and I have borne it with a patient shrug, for sufferance is the badge of all our tribe; and then you have called me unbeliever, cut-throat dog, and spit upon my Jewish garments, and spurned at me with your foot, as if I were a cur. Well, then, it now appears you need my help; and you come to me, and say, *Shylock, lend me moneys.* Has a dog money? Is it possible a cur

should lend three thousand ducats? Shall I bend low and say, Fair sir, you spat upon me on Wednesday last, another time you called me dog, and for these courtesies I am to lend you moneys?" Antonio replied, "I am as like to call you so again, to spit on you again, and spurn you too. If you will lend me this money, lend it not to me as to a friend, but rather lend it to me as to an enemy, that, if I break, you may with better face exact the penalty." "Why, look you," said Shylock, "how you storm! I would be friends with you, and have your love. I will forget the shames you have put upon me. I will supply your wants, and take no interest for my money." This seemingly kind offer greatly surprised Antonio; and then Shylock, still pretending kindness, and that all he did was to gain Antonio's love, again said he would lend him the three thousand ducats, and take no inter-est for his money; only Antonio should go with him to a lawyer, and there sign in merry sport a bond, that if he did not repay the money by a certain day, he would forfeit a pound of flesh, to be cut off from any part of his body that Shy-lock pleased.

"Content," said Antonio: "I will sign to this bond, and say there is much kindness in the Jew."

Bassanio said Antonio should not sign to such a bond for him; and still Anto-nio insisted that he would sign it, for that before the day of payment came his ships would return laden with many times the value of the money.

Shylock, hearing this debate, ex-claimed, "O father Abraham, what sus-picious people these Christians are! Their own hard dealings teach them to suspected the thoughts of others. I pray you tell me this, Bassanio: if he should break this day, what should I gain by the execution of the forfeiture? A pound of man's flesh, taken from a man, is not so estimable, nor profitable neither, as the flesh of mutton or of beef. I say, to buy his favor I offer this friendship: if he will take it, so; if not, adieu."

At last, against the advice of Bassanio, who, notwithstanding all the Jew had said of his kind intentions, did not like his friend should run the hazard of this shocking penalty for his sake, Antonio signed the bond, thinking it really (as the Jew said) merely in sport. The rich heiress that Bassanio wished to marry lived near Venice, at a place called Belmont: her name was Portia, and in the graces of her person and her mind she was nothing inferior to that Portia of whom we read, who was Cato's daughter, and the wife of Brutus.

Bassanio being so kindly supplied with money by his friend Antonio, at the hazard of his life, set out for Belmont with a splendid train, and attended by a gentleman of the name of Gratiano.

Bassanio proving successful in his suit, Portia in a short time consented to accept of him for a husband.

Bassanio confessed to Portia that he had no fortune, and that his high birth and noble ancestry was all that he could boast of; she, who loved him for his worthy qualities, and had riches enough not to regard wealth in a husband, answered with a graceful modesty, that she would wish herself a thousand times more fair, and ten thousand times more rich, to be more worthy of him; and then the accomplished Portia prettily dispraised herself, and said she was an unlessoned girl, unschooled, unpractised, yet not so old but that she could learn, and that she would commit her gentle spirit to be directed and governed by him in all things; and she said, "Myself and what is mine, to you and yours in now converted. But yesterday, Bassanio, I was the lady of this fair mansion, queen of myself, and mistress over these servants; and now this house, these servants and myself are yours, my lord; I give them with this ring," presenting a ring to Bassanio.

Bassanio was so overpowered with gratitude and wonder at the gracious manner in which the rich and noble Portia accepted of a man of his humble fortunes, that he could not express his joy and reverence to the dear lady who so honored him by anything but broken words of love and thankfulness; and taking the ring, he vowed never to part with it.

Gratiano and Nerissa, Portia's waiting-maid, were in attendance upon their lord and lady when Portia so gracefully promised to become the obedient wife of Bassanio; and Gratiano, wishing Bassanio and the generous lady joy, desired permission to be married at the same time.

"With all my heart, Gratiano," said Bassanio, "if you can get a wife."

Gratiano then said that he loved the lady Portia's fair waiting gentlewoman, Nerissa, and that she had promised to be his wife, if her lady married Bassanio. Portia asked Nerissa if this were true. Nerissa replied, "Madam, it is so, if you approve of it." Portia willingly consenting, Bassanio pleasantly said, "Then our wedding feast shall be much honored by your marriage, Gratiano."

The happiness of these lovers was sadly crossed at this moment by the entrance of a messenger, who brought a letter from Antonio containing fearful tidings. When Bassanio read Antonio's letter, Portia feared it was to tell him of the death of some dear friend, he looked so pale; and inquiring what was the news which had so distressed him, he said, "O sweet Portia, here are a few of the unpleasantest words that ever blotted paper: gentle lady, when I first imparted my love to you, I freely told you all the wealth I had ran in my veins; but I should have told you that I had less than nothing, being in debt." Bassanio then told Portia what has been here related, of his borrowing the money of Antonio, and of Antonio's procuring it of Shylock the Jew, and of the bond by which Antonio had engaged to forfeit a pound of flesh, if it was not repaid by a certain day; and then Bassanio read Antonio's letter, the words of which were—

"Sweet Bassanio, my ships are all lost, my bond to the Jew is forfeited, and since in paying it is impossible I should live, I could wish to see you at my death; notwithstanding, use your pleasure; if your love for me do not persuade you to come, let not my letter."

"Oh my dear love," said Portia, "dispatch the business and be gone; you shall have gold to pay the money twenty times over, before this kind friend shall lose a hair by my Bassanio's fault; and as you are so dearly bought, I will dearly love you." Portia then said she would be married to Bassanio before he set out, to give him a legal right to her money; and that same day they were married, and Gratiano was also married to Nerissa; and Bassanio and Gratiano, the instant they were married, set out in great haste for Venice, where Bassanio found Antonio in prison.

The day of payment being past, the cruel Jew would not accept of the money which Bassanio offered him, but insisted upon having a pound of Antonio's flesh. A day was appointed to try this shocking cause before the Duke of Venice, and Bassanio awaited in dreadful suspense the event of the trial.

When Portia parted with her husband, she spoke cheeringly to him, and bade him bring his dear friend along with him when he returned; yet she feared it would go hard with Antonio, and when she was left alone, she began to think and consider within herself, if she could by any means be instrumental in saving the life of her dear Bassanio's friend; and notwithstanding, when she wished to honor her Bassanio, she had said to him with such a meek and wife-like grace, that she would submit in all things to be governed by his superior wisdom, yet being now called forth into action by the peril of her honored husband's friend, she did nothing doubt her own powers, and by the sole guidance of her own true and perfect judgment, at once resolved to go herself to Venice, and speak in Antonio's defence.

Portia had a relation who was a counselor in the law; to this gentleman, whose name was Bellario, she wrote, and stating the case to him, desired his opinion, and that with his advice he would also send her the dress worn by a counselor. When the messenger returned, he brought letters from Bellario of advice how to proceed, and also everything necessary for her equipment.

Portia dressed herself and her maid Nerissa in men's apparel, and putting on the robes of a counselor, she took Nerissa along with her as her clerk; and setting out immediately, they arrived at Venice on the very day of the trial. The cause was just going to be heard before the duke and senators of Venice in the senate-house, when Portia entered this high court of justice, and presented a letter from Bellario, in which that learned counselor wrote to the duke, saying he would have come himself to plead for Antonio, but that he was prevented by sickness, and he requested that the learned young Doctor Balthasar (so he called Portia) might be permitted to plead in his stead. This the duke granted, much wondering at the youthful appearance of the stranger, who was prettily disguised by her counselor's robes and her large wig.

And now began this important trial. Portia looked around her, and she saw the merciless Jew, and she saw Bassanio, but he knew her not in her disguise. He was standing beside Antonio, in an agony of distress and fear for his friend.

The importance of the arduous task Portia had engaged in gave this tender lady courage, and she boldly proceeded in the duty she had undertaken to perform. And first of all she addressed herself to Shylock; and allowing that he had a right by the Venetian law to have the forfeit expressed in the bond, she spoke so sweetly of the noble quality of *mercy* as would have softened any heart but the unfeeling Shylock's; saying, that it dropped as the gentle rain from heaven upon the place beneath; and how mercy was a double blessing, it blessed him that gave, and him that received it; and how it became monarchs better than their crowns, being an attribute of God himself; and that earthly power came nearest to God's in proportion as mercy tempered justice: and she bid Shylock remember that as we all pray for mercy, that same prayer should teach us to show mercy. Shylock only answered her by desiring to have the penalty forfeited in the bond. "Is he not able to pay the money?" asked Portia. Bassanio then offered the Jew the payment of the three thousand ducats as many times over as he should desire; which Shylock refusing, and still insisting upon having a pound of Antonio's flesh, Bassanio begged the learned young counselor would endeavor to wrest the law a little to save Antonio's life. But Portia gravely answered, that laws once established must never be altered. Shylock hearing Portia say that the law might not be altered, it seemed to him that she was pleading in his favor, and he said: "A Daniel is come to judgment! O wise young judge, how I do honor you! How much elder are you than your looks!"

Portia now desired Shylock to let her look at the bond; and when she had read it, she said: "This bond is forfeited and by this the Jew may lawfully claim a pound of flesh, to be by him cut off nearest Antonio's heart." Then she said to Shylock, "Be merciful; take the money, and bid me tear the bond." But no mercy would the cruel Shylock show: and he said: "By my soul I swear there is no power in the tongue of man to alter me." "Why, then,

## MERCHANT OF VENICE
*Shylock and Jessica*

Antonio," said Portia, "you must prepare your bosom for the knife;" and while Shylock was sharpening a long knife with great eagerness to cut off the pound of flesh, Portia said to Antonio, "Have you anything to say?" Antonio, with a calm resignation, replied, that he had but little to say, for that he had prepared his mind for death. Then he said to Bassanio: "Give me your hand, Bassanio! Fare you well! Grieve not that I am fallen into this misfortune for you. Commend me to your honorable wife, and tell her how I have loved you!" Bassanio, in the deepest affliction, replied: "Antonio, I am married to a wife who is as dear to me as life itself; but life itself, my wife, and all the world, are not esteemed with me above your life: I would lose all; I would sacrifice all to this devil here to deliver you."

Portia hearing this, though the kind-hearted lady was not offended with her husband for expressing the love he owed to so true a friend as Antonio in these strong terms, yet could not help answering: "Your wife would give you little thanks if she were present to hear you make this offer." And then Gratiano, who loved to copy what his lord did, thought he must make a speech like Bassanio's, and he said, in Nerissa's hearing, who was writing in her clerk's dress by the side of Portia: "I have a wife, whom I protest I love; I wish she were in heaven, if she could but entreat some power there to change the cruel temper of this currish Jew." "It is well you wish this behind her back, else you would have but an unquiet house," said Nerissa.

Shylock now cried out impatiently: "We trifle time; I pray pronounce the sentence." And now all was awful expectation in the court, and every heart was full of grief for Antonio.

Portia asked if the scales were ready to weigh the flesh; and she said to the Jew: "Shylock, you must have some surgeon by, lest he bleed to death." Shylock, whose whole intent was that Antonio should bleed to death, said: "It is not so named in the bond." Portia replied: "It is not so named in the bond, but what of that? It were good you did so much charity." To this all the answer Shylock would make was: "I cannot find it; it is not in the bond." "Then," said Portia, "a pound of Antonio's flesh is thine. The law allows it, and the court awards it. And you may cut this flesh from off his breast. The law allows it, and the court awards it." Again Shylock exclaimed: "O wise and upright judge! A Daniel is come to judgment!" And then he sharpened his long knife again, and looking eagerly on Antonio, he said: "Come, prepare!"

"Tarry a little, Jew," said Portia; "there is something else. This bond here gives you no drop of blood; the words expressly are, 'a pound of flesh.' If in the cutting of the pound of flesh you shed one drop of Christian blood, your land and goods are by the law to be confiscated to the State of Venice." Now, as it was utterly impossible for Shylock to cut off the pound of flesh without shedding some of Antonio's blood, this wise discovery of Portia, that it was flesh and not blood that was named in the bond, saved the life of Antonio; and all admiring the wonderful sagacity of the young counselor who had so happily thought of this expedient, plaudits resounded from every part of the senate-house; and Gratiano exclaimed, in the words which Shylock had used, "O wise and upright judge! mark, a Jew, a Daniel has come to judgment!"

Shylock, finding himself defeated in his cruel intent, said with a disappointed look, that he would take the money; and Bassanio, rejoiced beyond measure at Antonio's unexpected deliverance, cried out, "Here is the money!" But Portia stopped him, saying, "Softly; there is no haste; the Jew shall have nothing but the penalty: therefore prepare, Shylock, to cut off the flesh; but mind you shed no blood; nor do not cut off more nor less than just a pound; be it more or less by one poor scruple, nay, if the scale turn but by the weight of a single hair, you are condemned by the laws of Venice to die, and all your wealth is forfeited to the senate." "Give me my money, and let me go," said Shylock. "I have it ready," said Bassanio; "here it is."

Shylock was going to take the money, when Portia again stopped him, saying, "Tarry, Jew; I have yet another hold upon you. By the laws of Venice, your wealth is forfeited to the State, for having conspired against the life of one of its citizens, and your life lies at the mercy of the duke; therefore down on your knees, and ask him to pardon you."

The duke then said to Shylock, "That you may see the difference of our Christian spirit, I pardon you your life before you ask it: half your wealth belongs to Antonio, the other half comes to the State."

The generous Antonio then said that he would give up his share of Shylock's wealth, if Shylock would sign a deed to make it over at his death to his daughter and her husband; for Antonio knew that the Jew had an only daughter, who had lately married against his consent to a young Christian, named Lorenzo, a friend of Antonio's, which had so offended Shylock that he had disinherited her.

The Jew agreed to this: and being thus disappointed in his revenge, and despoiled of his riches, he said, "I am ill. Let me go home; send the deed after me, and I will sign over half my riches to my daughter." "Get thee gone then," said the duke, "and sign it; and if you repent your cruelty and turn Christian, the State will forgive you the fine of the other half of your riches."

The duke now released Antonio, and dismissed the court. He then highly praised the wisdom and ingenuity of the young counselor, and invited him home to dinner. Portia, who meant to return to Belmont before her husband, replied, "I humbly thank your grace, but I must away directly." The duke said he was sorry he had not leisure to stay and dine with him; and turning to Antonio, he added, "Reward this gentleman; for in my mind you are much indebted to him."

The duke and his senators left the court; and then Bassanio said to Portia, "Most worthy gentleman, I and my friend Antonio have by your wisdom been this day acquitted of grievous penalties, and I beg you will accept of three thousand ducats due unto the Jew." "And we shall stand indebted to you over and above," said Antonio, "in love and service evermore."

Portia could not be prevailed upon to accept the money; but upon Bassanio still pressing her to accept of some reward, she said, "Give me your gloves; I will wear them for your sake;" and then Bassanio taking off his gloves, she espied the ring which she had given him upon his finger; now it was the ring the wily lady wanted to get from him, to make a merry jest when she saw Bassanio again, that made her ask him for his gloves; and she said, when she saw the ring, "And for your love I will take this ring from you." Bassanio was sadly distressed that the counselor should ask him for the only thing he could not part with, and he replied in great confusion, that he could not give him that ring, because it was his wife's gift, and he had vowed never to part with it; but that he would give him the most valuable ring in Venice, and find it out by proclamation. On this Portia affected to be affronted, and left the court, saying, "You teach me, sir, how a beggar should be answered."

"Dear Bassanio," said Antonio, "let him have the ring; let my love and the great service he has done for me be valued against your wife's displeasure." Bassanio, ashamed to appear so ungrateful, yielded, and sent Gratiano after Portia, with the ring; and then the *clerk* Nerissa, who had also given Gratiano a ring, she begged his ring, and Gratiano (not choosing to be outdone in generosity by his lord) gave it to her. And there was laughing among these ladies, to think, when they got home, how they would tax their husbands with giving away their rings, and swear that they had given them as a present to some woman.

Portia, when she returned, was in that happy temper of mind which never fails to attend the consciousness of having performed a good action; her cheerful spirit enjoyed everything she saw: the moon never seemed to shine so bright before; and when that pleasant moon was hid behind a cloud, then a light which she saw from her house at Belmont as well pleased her charmed fancy, and she said to Nerissa, "That light we see is burning in my hall; how far that little candle throws its beams; so shines a good deed in a naughty world;" and hearing the sound of music from her house, she said, "Methinks that music sounds sweeter than by day."

And now Portia and Nerissa entered the house, and dressing themselves in their own apparel they awaited the arrival of their husbands, who soon followed them with Antonio; and Bassanio presenting his dear friend to the Lady Portia, the congratulations and welcomings of that lady were hardly over, when they perceived Nerissa and her husband quarreling in a corner of the room. "A quarrel already?" said Portia. "What is the matter?" Gratiano replied, "Lady, it is about a paltry gilt ring that Nerissa gave me, with words upon it like the poetry on a cutler's knife: *Love me, and leave me not.*"

"What does the poetry or the value of the ring signify?" said Nerissa. "You swore to me, when I gave it to you, that you would keep it till the hour of death; and now you say you gave it to the lawyer's clerk. I know you gave it to a woman." "By this hand," replied Gratiano, "I gave it to a youth, a kind of boy, a little scrubbed boy no higher than yourself; he was clerk to the young counselor that by his wise pleading saved Antonio's life: this prating boy begged it for a fee, and I could not for my life deny him.' Portia said, "You were to blame, Gratiano, to part with your wife's first gift. I gave my Lord Bassanio a ring, and I am sure he would not part with it for all the world." Gratiano in excuse for his fault now said, "My Lord Bassanio gave his ring away to the counselor, and then the boy, his clerk, that took some pains in writing, he begged my ring."

Portia, hearing this, seemed very angry, and reproached Bassanio for giving away her ring; and she said Nerissa had taught her what to believe, and that she knew some woman had the ring. Bassanio was very unhappy to have so offended his dear lady, and he said with great earnestness, "No, by my honor, no woman had it, but a civil doctor, who refused three thousand ducats of me, and begged the ring, which when I denied him he went displeased away. What could I do, sweet Portia? I was so beset with shame for my seeming ingratitude, that I was forced to send the ring after him. Pardon me, good lady; had you been there, I think you would have begged the ring of me to give the worthy doctor."

"Ah!" said Antonio, "I am the unhappy cause of these quarrels."

Portia bid Antonio not to grieve at that, for that he was welcome notwithstanding; and then Antonio said, "I once did lend my body for Bassanio's sake, and but for him to whom your husband gave the ring, I should have now been dead. I dare be bound again, my soul upon the forfeit, your lord will never more break his faith with you." "Then you shall be his surety," said Portia; "give him this ring, and bid him keep it better than the other."

When Bassanio looked at this ring, he was strangely surprised to find it was the same he gave away; and then Portia told him how she was the young counselor, and Nerissa was her clerk; and Bassanio found, to his unspeakable wonder and delight, that it was by the noble courage and wisdom of his wife that Antonio's life was saved.

And Portia again welcomed Antonio, and gave him letters which by some chance had fallen into her hands, which contained an account of Antonio's ships, that were supposed lost, being safely arrived in the harbor. So these tragical beginnings of this rich merchant's story were all forgotten in the unexpected good fortune which ensued; and there was leisure to laugh at the comical adventures of the rings, and the husbands that did not know their own wives: Gratiano merrily swearing, in a sort of rhyming speech, that

——while he lived, he'd fear no other thing
So sore, as keeping safe Nerissa's ring.

## MERCHANT OF VENICE

*Act 4th, Scene 1st.*

# OTHELLO.

BRABANTIO, the rich senator of Venice, had a fair daughter, the gentle Desdemona. She was sought to by divers suitors, both on account of her many virtuous qualities and for her rich expectations. But among the suitors of her own clime and complexion she saw none whom she could affect: for this noble lady, who regarded the mind more than the features of men, with a singularity rather to be admired than imitated, had chosen for the object of her affections a Moor, a black whom her father loved, and often invited to his house.

Neither is Desdemona to be altogether condemned for the unsuitableness of the person whom she selected for her lover. Bating that Othello was black the noble Moor wanted nothing which might recommend him to the affections of the greatest lady. He was a soldier, and a brave one ; and by his conduct in bloody wars against the Turks had risen to the rank of general in the Venetian service, and was esteemed and trusted by the State.

He had been a traveler, and Desdemona (as is the manner of ladies) loved to hear him tell the story of his adventures, which he would run through from his earliest recollection ; the battles, sieges, and encounters which he had passed through; the perils he had been exposed to by land and by water : his hair-breadth escapes when he had entered a breach, or marched up to the mouth of a cannon, and how he had been taken prisoner by the insolent enemy, and sold to slavery : how he demeaned himself in that state, and how he escaped: all these accounts, added to the narration of the strange things he had seen in foreign countries, the vast wildernesses and romantic caverns, the quarries, the rocks and mountains, whose heads are in the clouds ; of the savage nations ; the cannibals who are man-eaters, and a race of people in Africa whose heads do grow beneath their shoulders: these trav-elers' stories would so enchain the atten-tion of Desdemona, that if she were called off at any time by household af-fairs, she would dispatch with all haste that business, and return, and with a greedy ear devour Othello's discourse. And once he took advantage of a pliant hour and drew from her a prayer, that he would tell her the whole story of his life at large, of which she had heard so much, but only by parts: to which he consented, and beguiled her of many a tear, when he spoke of some distressful stroke which his youth suffered.

His story being done, she gave him for his pains a world of sighs; she swore a pretty oath, that it was all passing strange, and pitiful, wondrous pitiful: she wished (she said) she had not heard it, yet she wished that Heaven had made her such a man: and she thanked him, and told him, if he had a friend who loved her, he had only to teach him how to tell his story, and that would woo her. Upon this hint, delivered not with more frankness than modesty, accompanied with a certain bewitching prettiness and blushes which Othello could not but understand, he spoke more openly of his love, and in this golden opportunity gained the consent of the generous Lady Desdemona privately to marry him.

Neither Othello's color nor his fortune was such that it could be hoped Brabantio would accept him for a son-in-law. He had left his daughter free; but he did expect that, as the manner of noble Venetian ladies was, she would choose ere long a husband of senatorial rank or expectations: but in this he was deceived; Desdemona loved the Moor, though he was black, and devoted her heart and fortunes to his valiant parts and qualities: so was her heart subdued to an implicit devotion to the man she had selected for a husband, that his very color, which to all but this discerning lady would have proved an insurmount-able objection, was by her esteemed above all the white skins and clear com-plexions of the young Venetian nobility, her suitors.

Their marriage, which though privately carried, could not long be kept a secret, came to the ears of the old man, Bra-bantio, who appeared in a solemn council of the Senate as an accuser of the Moor Othello, who by spells and witchcraft (he maintained) had seduced the affec-tions of the fair Desdemona to marry him, without the consent of her father, and against the obligations of hospitality.

At this juncture of time it happened that the State of Venice had immediate need of the services of Othello, news having arrived that the Turks with mighty preparation had fitted out a fleet, which was bending its course to the island of Cyprus, with intent to regain that strong post from the Venetians, who then held it: in this emergency the State turned its eyes upon Othello, who alone was deemed adequate to conduct the defence of Cyprus against the Turks. So that Othello, now summoned before the Senate, stood in their presence at once as a candidate for a great state employment, and as a culprit charged with offences which by the laws of Ven-ice were made capital.

The age and senatorial character of old Brabantio commanded a most patient hearing from that grave assembly; but the incensed father conducted his ac-cusation with so much intemperance, producing likelihoods and allegations for proofs that, when Othello was called upon for his defence he had only to relate a plain tale of the course of his love; which he did with such an artless eloquence, recounting the whole story of his wooing, as we have related it above, and delivered his speech with so noble a plainness (the evidence of truth), that the duke, who sat as chief judge, could not help confessing that a tale so told would have won his daughter too : and the spells and conjurations which Othello had used in his courtship plainly appeared to have been more than the honest arts of men in love : and the only witchcraft which he had used, the faculty of telling a soft tale to win a lady's ear.

This statement of Othello was confirmed by the testimony of the Lady Desdemona herself, who appeared in court, and professing a duty to her father for life and education, challenged leave of him to profess a yet higher duty to her lord and husband, even so much as her mother had shown in preferring him (Brabantio) above *her* father.

The old senator, unable to maintain his plea, called the Moor to him with many expressions of sorrow, and, as an act of necessity, bestowed upon him his daughter, whom, if he had been free to withhold her (he told him) he would with all his heart have kept from him ; adding, that he was glad at soul that he had no other child, for this behavior of Desdemona would have taught him to be a tyrant, and hang clogs on them for her desertion.

This difficulty being got over, Othello, to whom custom had rendered the hardships of a military life as natural as food and rest are to other men, readily under-

took the management of the wars in Cyprus : and Desdemona, preferring the honor of her lord (though with danger) before the indulgence of those idle delights in which new-married people usually waste their time, cheerfully consented to his going.

No sooner were Othello and his lady landed in Cyprus, than news arrived that a desperate tempest had dispersed the Turkish fleet, and thus the island was secure from any immediate apprehension of an attack. But the war which Othello was to suffer was now beginning ; and the enemies which malice stirred up against this innocent lady proved in their nature more deadly than strangers or infidels.

Among all the general's friends, no one possessed the confidence of Othello more entirely than Cassio. Michael Cassio was a young soldier, a Florentine, gay, amorous, and of pleasing address, favorite qualities with women ; he was handsome, and eloquent, and exactly such a person as might alarm the jealousy of a man advanced in years (as Othello in some measure was), who had married a young and beautiful wife ; but Othello was as free from jealousy as he was noble, and as incapable of suspecting, as of doing, a base action. He had employed this Cassio in his love affair with Desdemona, and Cassio had been a sort of go-between in his suit : for Othello, fearing that himself had not those soft parts of conversation which please ladies, and finding these qualities in his friend, would often depute Cassio to go (as he phrased it) a-courting for him : such innocent simplicity being an honor rather than a blemish to the character of the valiant Moor. So that no wonder if next to Othello himself (but at far distance, as beseems a virtuous wife) the gentle Desdemona loved and trusted Cassio. Nor had the marriage of this couple made any difference in their behavior to Michael Cassio. He frequented their house, and his free and rattling talk was no unpleasing variety to Othello, who was himself of a more serious temper: for such tempers are observed often to delight in their contraries, as a relief from the oppressive excess of their own: and Desdemona and Cassio would talk and laugh together, as in the days when he went a-courting for his friend.

Othello had lately promoted Cassio to be the lieutenant, a place of trust, and nearest to the general's person. This promotion gave great offence to Iago, an older officer, who thought he had a better claim than Cassio, and would often ridicule Cassio, as a fellow fit only for the company of ladies, and one that knew no more of the art of war, or how to set an army in array for battle, than a girl. Iago hated Cassio, and he hated Othello as well for favoring Cassio as for an unjust suspicion which he had lightly taken up against Othello, that the Moor was too fond of Iago's wife Emilia. From these imaginary provocations, the plotting mind of Iago conceived a horrid scheme of revenge, which should involve both Cassio, the Moor, and Desdemona in one common ruin.

Iago was artful, and had studied human nature deeply, and he knew that of all the torments which afflict the mind of man (and far beyond bodily torture), the pains of jealousy were the most intolerable, and had the sorest sting. If he could succeed in making Othello jealous of Cassio, he thought it would be an exquisite plot of revenge, and might end in the death of Cassio or Othello, or both; he cared not.

The arrival of the general and his lady in Cyprus, meeting with the news of the dispersion of the enemy's fleet, made a sort of holiday in the island. Everybody gave themselves up to feasting and making merry. Wine flowed in abundance, and cups went round to the health of the black Othello, and his lady, the fair Desdemona.

Cassio had the direction of the guard that night, with a charge from Othello to keep the soldiers from excess in drinking, that no brawl might arise, to fright the inhabitants, or disgust them with the new-landed forces. That night Iago began his deep-laid plans of mischief; under color of loyalty and love to the general, he enticed Cassio to make rather too free with the bottle (a great fault in an officer upon guard). Cassio for a time resisted, but he could not long hold out against the honest freedom which Iago knew how to put on, but kept swallowing glass after glass (as Iago still plied him with drink and encouraging songs), and Cassio's tongue ran over in praise of the lady Desdemona, who he again and again toasted, affirming that she was a most exquisite lady: until at last the enemy which he put into his mouth stole away his brains; and upon some provocation given him by a fellow whom Iago had set on, swords were drawn, and Montano, a worthy officer who interfered to appease the dispute, was wounded in the scuffle. The riot now began to be general, and Iago, who had set on foot the mischief, was foremost in spreading the alarm, causing the castle-bell to be rung (as if some dangerous

OTHELLO
*Act 5th, Scene 2d.*

mutiny, instead of a slight drunken quarrel, had arisen): the alarm-bell ringing awakened Othello, who, dressing, in a hurry, and coming to the scene of action, questioned Cassio of the cause. Cassio was now come to himself, the effect of the wine having a little gone off, but was too much ashamed to reply; and Iago, pretending a great reluctance to accuse Cassio, but as it were forced into it by Othello, who insisted to know the truth, gave an account of the whole matter (leaving out his own share in it, which Cassio was too far gone to remember) in such a manner, as while he seemed to make Cassio's offence less, did indeed make it appear greater than it was. The result was, that Othello, who was a a strict observer of discipline, was compelled to take away Cassio's place of lieutenant from him.

Thus did Iago's first artifice succeed completely : he had now undermined his hatred rival and thrust him out of his place : but a further use was hereafter to be made of the adventure of this disastrous night.

Cassio, whom this misfortune had entirely sobered, now lamented to his seeming friend Iago, that he should have been such a fool as to transform himself into a beast. He was undone, for how could he ask the general for his place again ! he would tell him he was a drunkard. He despised himself. Iago, affecting to make light of it, said that he, or any man living, might get drunk upon occasion ; it remained now to make the best of a bad bargain ; the general's wife was now the general, and could do anything with Othello ; that he were best to apply to the Lady Desdemona to mediate for him with her lord ; that she was of a frank, obliging disposition, and would readily undertake a good office of this sort, and set Cassio right again in the general's favor ; and then this crack in their love would be made stronger than ever. A good advice of Iago, if it had not been given for wicked purposes, which will after appear.

Cassio did as Iago advised him, and made application to the Lady Desdemona, who was easy to be won over in any honest suit ; and she promised Cassio that she would be his solicitor with her lord, and rather die than give up his cause. This she immediately set about in so earnest and pretty a manner, that Othello, who was mortally offended with Cassio, could not put her off. When he pleaded delay, and that it was too soon to pardon such an offender, she would not be beat back, but insisted that it should be the next night, or the morning after, or the next morning to that at farthest. Then she showed how penitent and humbled poor Cassio was, and that his offence did not deserve so sharp a check. And when Othello still hung back, "What ! my lord," said she, "that I should have so much to do to plead for Cassio, Michael Cassio, that came a-courting for you, and oftentimes when I have spoken in dispraise of you, has taken your part ? " I count this but a little thing to ask of you. When I mean to try your love indeed, I shall ask a weighty matter." Othello could deny nothing to such a pleader, and only requesting that Desdemona would leave the time to him, promised to receive Michael Cassio again into favor.

It happened that Othello and Iago had entered into the room where Desdemona was, just as Cassio, who had been imploring her intercession, was departing at the opposite door ; and Iago, who was full of art, said in a low voice, as if to himself, "I like not that." Othello took no great notice of what he said ; indeed, the conference which immediately took place with his lady put it out of his head : but he remembered it afterwards. For when Desdemona was gone, Iago, as if for mere satisfaction of his thought, questioned Othello whether Michael Cassio, when Othello was courting his lady, knew of his love. To this the general answering in the affirmative, and adding, that he had gone between them very often during the courtship, Iago knitted his brow, as if he had got fresh light of some terrible matter, and cried, "Indeed !" This brought into Othello's mind the words which Iago had let fall upon entering the room and seeing Cassio with Desdemona ; and he began to think there was some meaning in all this : for he deemed Iago to be a just man, and full of love and honesty, and what in a false knave would be tricks, in him seemed to be the natural workings of an honest mind, big with something too great for utterance : and Othello prayed Iago to speak what he knew, and to give his worst thoughts words. "And what," said Iago, "if some thoughts very vile should have intruded into my breast, as where is the palace into which foul things do not enter ?" Then Iago went on to say, what a pity it were if any trouble should arise to Othello out of his imperfect observations ; that it would not be for Othello's peace to know his thoughts ; that people's good names were not to be taken away for slight suspicions ; and when Othello's curiosity was raised almost to distraction with these hints and scattered words, Iago, as if in earnest care for Othello's peace of mind, besought him to beware of jealousy : with such art did this villain raise suspicions in the unguarded Othello, by the very caution which he pretended to give him against suspicion. "I know," said Othello, "that my wife is fair, loves company and feasting, is free of speech, sings, plays and dances well : but where virtue is these qualities are virtuous. I must have proof before I think her dishonest." Then Iago, as if glad that Othello was slow to believe ill of his lady, frankly declared that he had no proof, but begged Othello to observe her behavior well when Cassio was by ; not to be jealous nor too secure neither, for that he (Iago) knew the dispositions of the Italian ladies, his countrywomen, better than Othello could do; and that in Venice the wives let heaven see many pranks they dared not show their husbands. Then he artfully insinuated that Desdemona deceived her father in marrying with Othello, and carried it so closely, that the poor old man thought that witchcraft had been used. Othello was much moved with this argument, and brought the matter home to him, for if she had deceived her father, why might she not deceive her husband ?

Iago begged pardon for having moved him ; but Othello, assuming an indifference, while he was really shaken with inward grief at Iago's words, begged him to go on, which Iago did with many apologies, as if unwilling to produce anything against Cassio, whom he called his friend : he then came strongly to the point, and reminded Othello how Desdemona had refused many suitable matches of her own clime and complexion, and had married him, a Moor, which showed unnatural in her, and proved her to have a headstrong will : and when her better judgment returned, how probable it was she should fall upon comparing Othello with the fine forms and clear white complexions of the young Italians, her countrymen. He concluded with advising Othello to put off his reconcilement with Cassio a little longer, and in the meanwhile to note with what earnestness Desdemona should intercede in his behalf ; for that much would be seen in that. So mischievously did this artful villain lay his plots to turn the gentle qualities of this innocent lady into her destruction, and make a net for her out of her own goodness to entrap her : first setting Cassio on to entreat her mediation, and then out of that very mediation contriving stratagems for her ruin.

The conference ended with Iago's begging Othello to account his wife innocent until he had more decisive proof ; and Othello promised to be patient ; but from that moment the deceived Othello never tasted content of mind. Poppy, nor the juice of mandragora, nor all the sleeping potions in the world, could ever again restore to him that sweet rest which he had enjoyed but yesterday. His occupation sickened upon him. He no longer took delight in arms. His heart, that used to be roused at the sight of troops, and banners, and battle-array, and would stir and leap at the sound of a drum, or a trumpet, or a neighing war-horse, seemed to have lost all that pride and ambition which are a true soldier's virtue ; and his military ardor and all his old joys forsook him. Sometimes he thought his wife honest, and at times he thought her not so ; sometimes he thought Iago just, and at times he thought him not so ; then he would wish that he had never known of it ; he was not the worse for her loving Cassio, so long as he knew it not : torn in pieces with these distracting thoughts, he once laid hold on Iago's throat, and demanded proof of Desdemona's guilt, or threatened instant death for his having belied her. Iago, feigning indignation that his honesty should be taken for a vice, asked Othello, if he had not sometimes seen a handkerchief spotted with strawberries in his wife's hand. Othello answered, that he had given her such a one, and that it was his first gift. "That same handkerchief," said Iago, "did I see Michael Cassio this day wipe his face with." "If it be as you say," said Othello, "I will not rest till a wide revenge swallow them up : and first, for a token of your fidelity, I expect that Cassio shall be put to death within three days ; and for that fair devil [meaning his lady], I will withdraw and devise some swift means of death for her.

Trifles light as air are to the jealous proofs as strong as holy writ. A handkerchief of his wife's seen in Cassio's hand was motive enough to the deluded Othello to pass sentence of death upon them both, without once inquiring how Cassio came by it. Desdemona had never given such a present to Cassio, nor would this constant lady have wronged her lord with doing so naughty a thing as giving his presents to another man ; both Cassio and Desdemona were innocent of any offence against Othello ; but the wicked Iago, whose spirits never slept in contrivance of villany, had made his wife (a good, but a meek woman) steal this handkerchief from Desdemona, under pretence of getting the work copied, but in reality, to drop it in Cassio's way, where he might find it, and give a handle to Iago's suggestion that it was Desdemona's present.

Othello, soon after meeting his wife, pretended that he had a headache (as he might indeed with truth), and desired her to lend him her handkerchief to hold his temples. She did so. "Not this," said Othello, "but that handkerchief I gave you." Desdemona had it not about her (for indeed it was stolen as we have related). "How!" said Othello, "this is a fault indeed. That handkerchief an Egyptian woman gave to my mother; the woman was a witch, and could read people's thoughts: she told my mother, while she kept it, it would make her amiable, and my father would love her; but, if she lost it, or gave it away, my father's fancy would turn, and he would loathe her as much as he had loved her. She dying gave it me, and bade me, if I ever married, to give it to my wife. I did so; take heed of it. Make it a darling as precious as your eye." "Is it possible?" said the frightened lady. "'Tis true;" continued Othello; "it is a magical handkerchief; a sibyl that had lived in the world two hundred years, in a fit of prophetic fury worked it; the silk worms that furnished the silk were hallowed, and it was dyed in mummy of maidens' hearts conserved." Desdemona, hearing the wonderous virtues of the handkerchief, was ready to die with fear, for she plainly perceived she had lost it, and with it, she feared, the affections of her husband. Then Othello started, and looked as if he were going to do some rash thing, and still he demanded the handkerchief, which when she could not produce, she tried to divert her husband from too serious thoughts, and cheerfully told him, she saw all his talk about the handkerchief was only to put her off from her suit about Michael Cassio, whom she went on to praise (as Iago had foretold), till Othello in perfect distraction burst out of the room, and then Desdemona, though unwillingly, began to suspect her lord was jealous.

What cause she could have ministered to him she knew not, and then she accused herself for accusing the noble Othello, and thought to be sure that some untoward news from Venice, or some state troubles, had puddled his spirits, and made his temper not so sweet as formerly. And she said, "Men are not gods, and we must not look for that observance from them when they are married which they show us on the bridal day." And she beshrewed herself for so unkindly judging of his unkindness.

Again Othello and Desdemona met, and he accused her more plainly of being unfaithful, and of loving another man, but he did not name whom: and Othello wept, and Desdemona said, "Alas! the heavy day! why do you weep?" And Othello told her he could have borne all sorts of evils with fortitude—poverty, and disease, and disgrace; but her infidelity had broken his heart: and he called her a weed, that looked so fair, and smelled so sweet, that the sense ached at it; and wished she had never been born. And when he had left her, this innocent lady was so stupefied with wonder at her lord's untrue suspicion of her, that a weight-like sleep came over her, and she only desired her attendant to make her bed, and to lay her wedding sheets upon it, saying that when people teach their babes, they do it by gentle means and easy tasks, and Othello might have chid her so; for in good faith she was but a child when she was chidden. And this was all the complaint which this gentle lady made.

Desdemona being retired to bed, expecting her lord would follow her, soon fell into a slumber, the effect of her troubled spirits, when Othello entered the chamber, full of the black purpose which he had meditated of putting his lady to death. But when he saw her asleep, he thought he would not shed her blood, nor scar that white skin of hers, more white than alabaster. But he was resolved she should die, else (as he said) she would live to betray more men, as she had done him. Then he kissed her for the last time (as he said), and that kiss was so sweet, he must needs kiss her again; and he wept, but he said they were cruel tears.

Desdemona was awakened with his kisses, and she looked upon Othello, and she saw him gnaw his under lip, and roll his eyes, and she knew he was always fatal when he looked so: and he bade her prepare for death, and to say her prayers, for he would not kill her soul. And this innocent wife, as she lay at his mercy, begged for compassion, and to know her fault; and then he named Cassio, and the handkerchief which (he said) she had given him; and as the guiltless lady was proceeding to clear herself, he suddenly would hear no more, but covering her up in the bed clothes, stifled her till she died.

In this instant of time was brought into the house Cassio, wounded and bleeding, whom Iago had set one of his creatures on to assassinate; but the fellow not succeeding in his attempt to kill Cassio (whom he had wounded, but not mortally), and being himself killed by Iago to prevent discovery, in his pockets were found certain letters, which made the guilt of Iago, and the innocence of Cassio, clear beyond a doubt; and Cassio now came to beg pardon of Othello, and to ask wherein he had offended him, that he had employed Iago to murder him.

This discovery was as a thunderstroke to Othello, who now plainly saw that he was no better than a murderer, and that his wife (poor innocent lady) had been ever faithful to him; the extreme anguish of which discovery making life insupportable, he fell upon his sword, and throwing himself upon the body of his dear injured lady, expired.

These rash acts raised much passion of horror and amazement in the bystanders, for Othello had borne a fair reputation, and till he was wrought upon by the arts of a villain, which his own noble nature never gave him leave to suspect, he was a loving and a doting husband. He had loved, not wisely, but too well; and his manly eyes (when he learned his mistake), though not used to weep on every small occasion, dropped tears as fast as the Arabian trees their gum. And when he was dead all his former merits and his valiant acts were remembered. Nothing now remained for his successor but to put the utmost censure of the law in force against Iago, who was executed with strict tortures; and to send word to the State of Venice of the lamentable death of their renowned general.

# MACBETH.

---

THE THREE WEIRD SISTERS AND THEIR PROPHECY—MACBETH'S AMBITION—PART OF
THE PROPHECY FULFILLED—LADY MACBETH'S TEMPTATION—THE VISIT OF THE
KING TO MACBETH'S CASTLE—THE MURDER OF KING DUNCAN—THE KNOCK-
ING AT THE GATE—MACBETH HIRES MURDERERS TO SLAY BANQUO—THE
BANQUET—BANQUO'S GHOST APPEARS—THE WITCHES ON THE HEATH—
THE PROCESSION OF GHOSTS—REVOLT OF THE NOBLES—LADY
MACBETH'S SLEEP-WALKING AGONY — THE ATTACK UPON
MACBETH'S CASTLE—THE MOVING FOREST—DEATH
OF LADY MACBETH — THE BATTLE — MACBETH
AND MACDUFF FIGHT—MACBETH IS SLAIN
AND MACDUFF PROCLAIMED KING
OF SCOTLAND IN HIS PLACE.

---

WHEN Duncan the Meek reigned King of Scotland, there lived a great thane, or lord, called Macbeth. This Macbeth was a near kinsman to the king, and in great esteem at court for his valor and conduct in the wars; an example of which he had lately given, in defeating a rebel army assisted by the troops of Norway in terrible numbers.

The two Scottish generals, Macbeth and Banquo, returning victorious from this great battle, their way lay over a blasted heath, where they were stopped by the strange appearance of three figures like women, except that they had beards, and their withered skins and wild attire made them look not like any earthly creatures. Macbeth first addressed them, when they, seemingly offended, laid each one her choppy finger upon her skinny lips, in token of silence: and the first of them saluted Macbeth with the title of Thane of Glamis. The general was not a little startled to find himself known by such creatures; but how much more, when the second of them followed up that salute by giving him the title of Thane of Cawdor, to which honor he had no pretensions; and again the third bid him, "All hail! king that shall be hereafter!" Such a prophetic greeting might well amaze him, who knew that while the king's sons lived he could not hope to succeed to the throne. Then turning to Banquo, they pronounced him in a sort of riddling terms, to be *lesser than Macbeth and greater! not so happy, yet much happier!* and prophesied that though he should never reign, yet his sons after him should be kings in Scotland. They then turned into air and vanished; by which the generals knew them to be the weird sisters, or witches.

While they stood pondering on the

strangeness of this adventure, there ar-arrived certain messengers from the king, who were empowered by him to confer upon Macbeth the dignity of Thane of Cawdor. An event so miraculously cor-responding with the prediction of the witches astonished Macbeth, and he stood wrapped in amazement, unable to make reply to the messengers; and in that point of time swelling hopes arose in his mind, that the prediction of the third witch might in like manner have its ac-complishment, and that he should one day reign king in Scotland.

Turning to Banquo, he said, "Do you not hope that your children shall be kings, when what the witches promised to me has so wonderfully come to pass?" "That hope," answered the general, "might enkindle you to aim at the throne; but oftentimes these ministers of darkness tell us truths in little things to betray us into deeds of greatest con-sequence."

But the wicked suggestions of the witches had sunk too deep into the mind of Macbeth to allow him to attend to the warnings of the good Banquo. From that time he bent all his thoughts how to com-pass the throne of Scotland.

Macbeth had a wife, to whom he com-municated the strange prediction of the weird sisters, and its partial accomplish-ment. She was a bad, ambitious woman, and so as her husband and herself could arrive at greatness, she cared not much by what means. She spurred on the re-luctant purpose of Macbeth, who felt compunction at the thought of blood, and did not cease to represent the murder of the king as a step absolutely neces-sary to the fulfillment of the flattering prophecy.

It happened at this time that the king, who out of his royal condescension would oftentimes visit his principal nobility upon gracious terms, came to Macbeth's house, attended by his two sons, Malcolm and Donalbain, and a numerous train of thanes and attendants, the more to honor Macbeth for the triumphal success of his wars.

The castle of Macbeth was pleasantly situated, and the air about it was sweet and wholesome, which appeared by the nests which the martlet, or swallow, had built under all the jutting friezes and buttresses of the building, wherever it found a place of advantage: for where those birds most breed and haunt the air is observed to be delicate. The king en-tered well pleased with the place, and not less so with the attentions and re-spect of his honored hostess, Lady Mac-beth, who had the art of covering treach-erous purposes with smiles: and could look like the innocent flower, while she was indeed the serpent under it.

The king, being tired with his journey, went early to bed, and in his state-room two grooms of his chamber (as was the custom) slept beside him. He had been unusually pleased with his reception, and had made presents before he retired to his principal officers; and among the rest, had sent a rich diamond to Lady Macbeth, greeting her by the name of his most kind hostess.

Now was the middle of night, when over half the world nature seems dead, and wicked dreams abuse men's minds asleep, and none but the wolf and the murderer is abroad. This was the time when Lady Macbeth waked to plot the murder of the king. She would not have undertaken a deed so abhorrent to her sex, but that she feared her husband's nature, that it was too full of the milk of human kindness to do a contrived murder. She knew him to be ambitious, but withal to be scrupulous, and not yet prepared for that height of crime which commonly in the end accompanies inordinate ambition. She had won him to consent to the murder, but she doubted his resolution: and she feared that the natural tenderness of his disposition (more humane than her own) would come between, and defeat the purpose. So with her own hands armed with a dagger, she approached the king's bed; having taken care to ply the grooms of his chamber so with wine that they slept intoxicated and careless of their charge. There lay Duncan, in a sound sleep after the fatigues of his journey, and as she viewed him earnestly, there was something in his face, as he slept, which resembled her own father; and she had not the courage to proceed.

She returned to confer with her husband. His resolution had begun to stagger. He considered that there were strong reasons against the deed. In the first place, he was not only a subject, but a near kinsman to the king; and he had been his host and entertainer that day, whose duty, by the laws of hospitality, it was to shut the door against his murderers, not bear the knife himself. Then he considered how just and merciful a king this Duncan had been, how clear of offence to his subjects, how loving to his nobility, and in particular to him; that such kings are the peculiar care of Heaven, and of their subjects doubly bound to revenge their deaths. Besides, by the favors of the king, Macbeth stood high in the opinion of all sorts of men, and how would those honors be stained by the reputation of so foul a murder!

In these conflicts of the mind Lady Macbeth found her husband inclining to the better part, and resolving to proceed no further. But she being a woman not easily shaken from her evil purpose, began to pour in at his ears words which infused a portion of her own spirit into his mind, assigning reason upon reason why he should not shrink from what he had undertaken; how easy the deed was; how soon it would be over; and how the action of one short night would give to all their nights and days to come a sovereign sway and royalty! Then she threw contempt on his change of purpose, and accused him of fickleness and cowardice; and declared that she had given suck, and knew how tender it was to love the babe that milked her, but she would, while it was smiling in her face, have plucked it from her breast and dashed its brains out, if she had so sworn to do it, as he had sworn to perform that murder. Then she added, how practicable it was to lay the guilt of the deed upon the drunken, sleepy grooms. And with the valor of her tongue she so chastised his sluggish resolutions, that he once more summoned up courage to the bloody business.

So, taking the dagger in his hand, he softly stole in the dark to the room where Duncan lay; and as he went, he thought he saw another dagger in the air, with the handle toward him and on the blade and at the point of it drops of blood: but when he tried to grasp at it, it was nothing but air, a mere phantasm proceeding from his own hot and oppressed brain and the business he had in hand.

MACBETH

*Act 3d, Scene 4th.*

Getting rid of this fear, he entered the king's room, whom he dispatched with one stroke of his dagger. Just as he had done the murder, one of the grooms, who slept in the chamber, laughed in his sleep, and the other cried, "Murder," which woke them both; but they said a short prayer; one of them said, "God bless us!" and the other answered, "Amen;" and addressed themselves to sleep again. Macbeth, who stood listening to them, tried to say, "Amen" when the fellow said "God bless us!" but, though he had most need of a blessing, the word stuck in his throat, and he could not pronounce it.

Again, he thought he heard a voice which cried, "Sleep no more; Macbeth doth murder sleep, the innocent sleep, that nourishes life." Still it cried, "Sleep no more," to all the house. "Glamis hath murdered sleep, and therefore Cawdor shall sleep no more, Macbeth shall sleep no more."

With such horrible imaginations Macbeth returned to his listening wife, who began to think he had failed of his purpose, and that the deed was somehow frustrated. He came in so distracted a state, that she reproached him with his want of firmness, and sent him to wash his hands of the blood which stained them, while she took his dagger, with purpose to stain the cheeks of the grooms with blood, to make it seem their guilt.

Morning came, and with it the discovery of the murder, which could not be concealed; and though Macbeth and his lady made great show of grief, and the proofs against the grooms (the dagger being produced against them and their faces smeared with blood) were sufficiently strong, yet the entire suspicion fell upon Macbeth, whose inducements to such a deed were so much more forcible than such poor silly grooms could be supposed to have; and Duncan's two sons fled. Malcolm, the eldest, sought for refuge in the English court; and the youngest, Donalbain, made his escape to Ireland.

The king's sons, who should have succeeded him, having thus vacated the throne, Macbeth as next heir was crowned king, and thus the prediction of the weird sisters was literally accomplished.

Though placed so high, Macbeth and his queen could not forget the prophecy of the weird sisters, that, though Macbeth should be king, yet not his children, but the children of Banquo, should be kings after him. The thought of this, and that th.y had defiled their hands with blood, and done so great crimes, only to place the posterity of Banquo upon the throne, so rankled within them, that they determined to put to death both Banquo and his son, to make void the predictions of the weird sisters, which in their own case had been so remarkably brought to pass.

For this purpose they made a great supper, to which they invited all the chief thanes; and, among the rest, with marks of particular respect, Banquo and his son Fleance were invited. The way by which Banquo was to pass to the palace at night was beset by murderers appointed by Macbeth, who stabbed Banquo; but in the scuffle Fleance escaped. From that Fleance descended a race of monarchs who afterward filled the Scottish throne, ending with James the Sixth of Scotland and the First of England, under whom the two crowns of England and Scotland were united.

At supper the queen, whose manners were in the highest degree affable and royal, played the hostess with a gracefulness and attention which conciliated every one present, and Macbeth discoursed freely with his thanes and nobles, saying that all that was honorable in the country was under his roof, if he had but his good friend Banquo present, whom yet he hoped he should rather have to chide for neglect than to lament for any mischance. Just at these words the ghost of Banquo, whom he had caused to be murdered, entered the room, and placed himself on the chair which Macbeth was about to occupy. Though Macbeth was a bold man, and one that could have faced the devil without trembling, at this horrible sight his cheeks turned white with fear, and he stood quite unmanned with his eyes fixed upon the ghost. His queen and all the nobles, who saw nothing, but perceived him gazing (as they thought) upon an empty chair, took it for a fit of distraction ; and she reproached him, whispering that it was but the same fancy which had made him see the dagger in the air when he was about to kill Duncan. But Macbeth continued to see the ghost, and gave no heed to all they could say, while he addressed it with distracted words, yet so significant, that his queen, fearing the dreadful secret would be disclosed, in great haste dismissed the guests, excusing the infirmity of Macbeth as a disorder he was often troubled with.

To such dreadful fancies Macbeth was subject. His queen and he had their sleeps afflicted with terrible dreams, and the blood of Banquo troubled them not more than the escape of Fleance, whom now they looked upon as father to a line of kings, who should keep their posterity out of the throne. With these miserable thoughts they found no peace, and Macbeth determined once more to seek out the weird sisters, and know from them the worst.

He sought them in a cave upon the heath, where they, who knew by foresight of his coming, were engaged in preparing their dreadful charms, by which they conjured up infernal spirits to reveal to them futurity. Their horrid ingredients were toads, bats, and serpents, the eye of a newt and the tongue of a dog, the leg of a lizard and the wing of a night-owl, the scale of a dragon, the tooth of a wolf, the maw of the ravenous salt-sea shark, the mummy of a witch, the root of the poisonous hemlock (this to have effect must be digged in the dark), the gall of a goat, and the liver of a Jew, with slips of the yew tree that roots itself in graves, and the finger of a dead child : all these were set on to boil in a great kettle, or caldron, which, as fast as it grew too hot, was cooled with a baboon's blood : to these they poured in the blood of a sow that had eaten her young, and they threw into the flame the grease that had sweated from a murderer's gibbet. By these charms they bound the infernal spirits to answer their questions.

It was demanded of Macbeth, whether he would have his doubts resolved by them, or by their masters the spirits. He, nothing daunted by the dreadful ceremonies which he saw, boldly answered, "Where are they? let me see them." And they called the spirits, which were three. And the first arose in the likeness of an armed head, and he called Macbeth by name, and bid him beware of the Thane of Fife; for which caution Macbeth thanked him: for Macbeth had entertained a jealousy of Macduff, the Thane of Fife.

And the second spirit arose in the likeness of a bloody child, and he called Macbeth by name, and bid him have no fear, but laugh to scorn the power of man, for none of woman born should have power to hurt him; and he advised him to be bloody, bold, and resolute. "Then live, Macduff!" cried the king; "What need I fear of thee? but yet I will make assurance doubly sure. Thou shalt not live; that I may tell pale-hearted Fear it lies, and sleep in spite of thunder."

That spirit being dismissed, a third arose in the form of a child crowned, with a tree in his hand. He called Macbeth by name, and comforted him against conspiracies, saying, that he should never be vanquished, until the wood of Birnam to Dunsinane Hill should come against him. "Sweet bodements! good!" cried Macbeth; "who can unfix the forest, and move it from its earth-bound roots? I see I shall live the usual period of man's life, and not be cut off by a violent death. But my heart throbs to know one thing. Tell me, if your art can tell so much, if Banquo's issue shall ever reign in this kingdom?" Here the caldron sunk into the ground, and a noise of music was heard, and eight shadows, like kings, passed by Macbeth, and Banquo last, who bore a glass which showed the figures of many more, and Banquo all bloody smiled upon Macbeth, and pointed to them; by which Macbeth knew that these were the posterity of Banquo, who should reign after him in Scotland: and the witches, with a sound of soft music, and

with dancing, making a show of duty and welcome to Macbeth, vanished. And from this time the thoughts of Macbeth were all bloody and dreadful.

The first thing he heard when he got out of the witches' cave, was, that Macduff, Thane of Fife, had fled to England, to join the army which was forming against him under Malcolm, the eldest son of the late king, with intent to displace Macbeth, and set Malcolm, the right heir, upon the throne. Macbeth, stung with rage, set upon the castle of Macduff, and put his wife and children, whom the thane had left behind, to the sword, and extended the slaughter to all who claimed the least relationship to Macduff.

These and such-like deeds alienated the minds of all his chief nobility from him. Such as could, fled to join with Malcolm and Macduff, who were now approaching with a powerful army which they had raised in England; and the rest secretly wished success to their arms, though for fear of Macbeth they could take no active part. His recruits went on slowly. Everybody hated the tyrant, nobody loved or honored him, but all suspected him, and he began to envy the condition of Duncan, whom he had murdered, who slept soundly in his grave, against whom treason had done its worst: steel nor poison, domestic malice nor foreign levies, could hurt him any longer.

While these things were acting, the queen, who had been the sole partner in his wickedness, in whose bosom he could sometimes seek a momentary repose from those terrible dreams which afflicted them both nightly, died, it is supposed by her own hand, unable to bear the remorse of guilt, and public hate; by which event he was left alone, without a soul to love or care for him, or a friend to whom he could confide his wicked purposes.

He grew careless of life, and wished for death ; but the near approach of Malcolm's army roused in him what remained of his ancient courage, and he determined to die (as he expressed it) "with armor on his back." Besides this, the hollow promises of the witches had filled him with false confidence, and he remembered the sayings of the spirits, that none of woman born was to hurt him, and that he was never to be vanquished till Birnam Wood should come to Dunsinane, which he thought could never be. So he shut himself up in his castle, whose impregnable strength was such as defied a siege : here he sullenly awaited the approach of Malcolm. When, upon a day, there came a messenger to him, pale and shaking with fear, almost unable to report that which he had seen : for he averred that as he stood upon his watch on the hill, he looked toward Birnam, and to his thinking the wood began to move! "Liar and slave," cried Macbeth, "if thou speakest false thou shalt hang alive upon the next tree, till famine end thee. If thy tale be true, I care not if thou dost as much by me : " for Macbeth now began to faint in resolution, and to doubt the equivocal speeches of the spirits. He was not to fear till Birnam Wood should come to Dunsinane : and now a wood did move ! "However," said he, "if this which he avouches be true, let us arm and out. There is no flying hence, nor staying here. I begin to be weary of the sun, and wish my life at an end." With these desperate speeches he sallied forth upon the besiegers, who had now come up to the castle.

Then Macbeth remembered the words of the spirit, how none of woman born should hurt him ; and smiling confidently he said to Macduff, "Thou losest thy labor, Macduff. As easily thou mayest impress the air with thy sword, as make me vulnerable. I bear a charmed life, which must not yield to one of woman born." "Despair thy charm," said Macduff, "and let that lying spirit, whom thou hast served, tell thee that Macduff was never born of woman, never as the ordinary manner of men is to be born, but was untimely taken from his mother."

"Accursed be the tongue which tells me so," said the trembling Macbeth, who felt his last hold of confidence give way ; "and let never man in future believe the lying equivocations of witches and juggling spirits, who deceive us in words which have double senses, and while they keep their promise literally, disappoint our hopes with a different meaning. I will not fight with thee."

"Then live!" said the scornful Macduff ; "we will have a show of thee, as men show monsters, and a painted board, on which shall be written, 'Here men may see the tyrant!'"

"Never," said Macbeth, whose courage returned with despair ; "I will not live to kiss the ground before young Malcolm's feet, and to be baited with the curses of the rabble. Though Birnam Wood be come to Dunsinane, and thou opposed to me wast never born of woman, yet will I try the last." With these frantic words he threw himself upon Macduff, and cutting off his head, made a present of it to the young and lawful King Malcolm ; who took upon him the government.

# BOOK III.

---

## TREASURY OF MUSIC.

ST. CECILIA

# ALBUM LEAF.

E. GRIEG, Op. 12. No. 7.

# GOOD NIGHT.

LOESCHHORN.

# FROM VIENNA TO BERLIN.

## POLKA.

RICHARD EILENBERG.

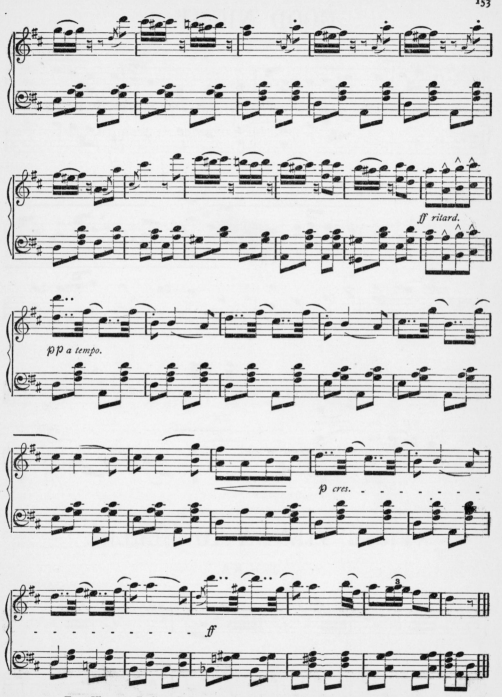

From Vienna to Berlin.  Polka.

# LOIN DU BAL.

ERNEST GILLET.

SONG OF LOVE

# SIMPLE AVEU.

FRANCIS THOMÉ. Op. 25.

*In a singing style.*

# ONE HEART, ONE SOUL.

## POLKA MAZURKA.

JOHANN STRAUSS.

# BRIDAL CHORUS.

WAGNER.

# MINUET.

## "FROM DON JUAN."

MOZART.

# LONGING.

JUNGMANN.

# MARCH MILITAIRE.

*Allegro Moderato.*

L. GOBBAERTS, Op. 50.

# LADY BETTY.

SEYMOUR SMITH.

# ANDANTE.

PAR BEETHOVEN.

A DANCING LESSON

# KISS WALTZ.

JOHANN STRAUSS.

# CAVALLERIA RUSTICANA.

## INTERMEZZO.

P. MASCAGNI.

Cavalleria Rusticana.

# WHATE'ER MY GOD ORDAINS IS RIGHT.

BEETHOVEN.

What-e'er my God or-dains is right, His will is ev-er just; How

e'er He or-ders now my cause, I will be still and trust.

He holds me that I shall not fall; Wherefore to Him I leave it all.

THE ZITHER PLAYER

# I'M BUT A STRANGER HERE.

THOMAS R. TAYLOR.

F. ABT.

1. I'm but a stran-ger here, Heav'n is my home, Earth is a des-ert drear,
2. What though the tem-pest rage, Heav'n is my home, Short is my pil-grim-age,

Heav'n is my home, Dan-ger and sor-row stand, Round me on
Heav'n is my home, And time's wide win-t'ry blast, Soon will be

ev - 'ry hand, Heav'n is my Fa - ther - land, Heav'n is my home.
o - ver past, I shall reach home at last, Heav'n is my home.

# ANGELS, EVER BRIGHT AND FAIR.

HANDEL.

*ad lib.    tempo.*

take me  to your care !    Take,    O take me to  your care !

Speed to your own courts my flight, Clad in robes of virgin

white, Clad  in robes of vir - gin white,  Clad  in robes of  vir - gin white.    Take me,

Angels, Ever Bright and Fair.

# SOFTLY NOW THE LIGHT OF DAY.

WEBER.

1. Soft - ly now the light of day Fades up -
2. Thou whose all - per - vad - ing eye Naught es -

on my sight a - way; Free from care,
capes, with - out, with - in, Par - don each

from la - bor free, Lord, I would com - mune with Thee.
in - fir - mi-ty, O - pen fault, and se - cret sin.

HARMONY

# ALL HAIL THE POWER OF JESUS' NAME.

HOLDEN.

1. All hail the power of Je - sus' name! Let an - gels
2. Crown Him, ye mar - tyrs of our God, Who from His

pros - trate fall; Bring forth the roy - al di - a - dem, And
al - tar call; Ex - tol the Stem of Jes - se's rod, And

crown Him Lord of all, Bring forth the roy - al
crown Him Lord of all, Ex - tol the Stem of

di - a - dem, And crown Him Lord............... of all.
Jes - se's rod, And crown Him Lord............... of all.

# FLEE AS A BIRD.

MRS. M. S. B. DANA.

Moderato.

1. Flee as a bird to your moun - tain, Thou who art wea - ry of
2. He will pro-tect thee for - ev - - - er, Wipe ev - 'ry fall - ing

sin ;............. Go to the clear - flow - ing foun - - tain,
tear ;........... He will for - sake thee, O nev - - - er,

Where you may wash and be clean ; Fly, for th' aven - ger is near thee ;
Shel - tered so ten - der - ly there ; Haste, then, the hours are fly - - ing,

Call and the Sav - iour will hear thee, He on His bo - som will
Spend not the mo - ments in sigh - - ing, Cease from your sor - row and

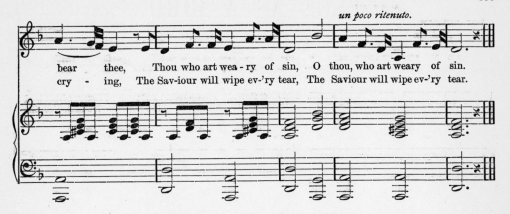

# ABIDE WITH ME.

MONK.

Flee as a Bird.

# THE HOUR OF PRAYER.

MRS. HEMANS.

HEROLD.

1. Child, amidst the flow'rs at play,   While the red light fades a-way;   Moth-er, with thine
2. Traveller, in the stranger's land,   Far from thine own household band;   Mourner, haunt-ed
3. Warrior, that from bat-tle won   Breathest now at set of sun;   Wo-man, o'er the

earn-est eye,   Ev-er following si-lent-ly;   Fa-ther, by   the breeze of eve,
by the tone   Of a voice from this world gone;   Cap-tive in   whose nar-row cell
low-ly slain   Weeping on this bur-ial plain;   Ye that tri-umph, ye that sigh,

Called thy har-vest-work to leave—   Pray, ere yet   the dark hours be,   Lift the heart and bend the
Sunshine hath not   leave to dwell;   Sail-or on   the dark'ning sea,   Lift the heart and bend the
Kindred by one   ho-ly tie,   Heav'n's first star   a-like ye see,   Lift the heart and bend the

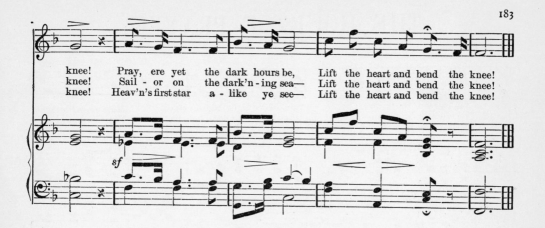

knee! Pray, ere yet the dark hours be, Lift the heart and bend the knee!
knee! Sail - or on the dark'n - ing sea— Lift the heart and bend the knee!
knee! Heav'n's first star a - like ye see— Lift the heart and bend the knee!

# JERUSALEM THE GOLDEN.

EWING.

1. Je - ru - sa - lem the gold - en, With milk and hon-ey blest, Be-neath thy con-tem -

- pla - tion Sink heart and voice to rest. I know not—oh, I know not, What

joys a-wait me there, What ra-dian-cy of glo - ry, What bliss beyond com-pare.

The Hour of Prayer.

# ONWARD, CHRISTIAN SOLDIERS.

ARTHUR SULLIVAN.

1. On-ward, Christian sol - diers, March-ing as to war, With the cross of
2. At the sign of tri - umph, Sa-tan's host doth flee; On, then, Christian

Je - sus Go-ing on be - fore. Christ, the roy - al Mas - ter,
sol - diers, On to vic-to - ry. Hell's foun-da-tions quiv - er

Leads a - gainst the foe; For-ward in - to bat - tle See, his ban - ners
At the shout of praise; Brothers, lift your voi - ces, Loud your an - thems

go. On - ward, Chris - tian sol - diers, March - ing as to
raise. On - ward, Chris - tian sol - diers, March - ing as to

war, With the cross of Je - sus Go - ing on be - fore.
war, With the cross of Je - sus Go - ing on be - fore.

# HARK! HARK, MY SOUL.

H. SMART.

1. Hark! hark, my soul! an - gel - ic songs are swell - ing O'er earth's green fields, and
2. On - ward we go, for still we hear them sing - ing, "Come, wea - ry souls, for

o - cean's wave-beat shore; How sweet the truth those bles - sed strains are tell - ing
Je - sus bids you come;" And thro' the dark, its ech - oes sweet - ly ring - ing

Of that new life when sin shall be no more. An - gels of Je - sus,
The mus - ic of the Gos - pel leads us home. An - gels of Je - sus,

An - gel of light, Sing - ing to wel - come the pil - grims of the night. A - men.

# LEAD, KINDLY LIGHT.

REV. J. B. DYKES.

1. Lead, kind-ly Light, a-mid the encircling gloom, Lead thou me on;
2. I was not ev - er thus, nor pray'd that thou Shouldst lead me on;

The night is dark, and I am far from home, Lead thou me on.
I loved to choose and see my path; but now Lead thou me on.

Keep Thou my feet; I do not ask to see
I loved the gar - rish day; and spite of fears,

The dis - tant scene; one step e - nough for me.
Pride ruled my will; re - mem-ber not past years. A - men.

CHORISTER GIRLS

# ADESTE FIDELES.

JOHN READING.

1. Oh, come, all ye faith - ful, Joy - ful and tri - umph - ant; Oh,
2. God of God, Light of Light,
3. Sing, choirs of an - gels, Sing in ex - ul - ta - tion,
4. Yea, Lord, we greet thee, Born this hap - py morn - ing;

come ye, oh, come ye, to Beth - le - hem; Come, and be - hold him,
Lo! he ab - hors not the Vir - gin's womb; Ve - ry God, Be -
Sing, all ye cit - i - zens of heav'n a - bove, Glo - ry to God
Je - sus, to thee be glo - ry giv'n; Word of the Fa - ther,

Born the King of an - gels; Oh, come, let us a - dore him, Oh,
got - ten not cre - a - ted; Oh, come, let us a - dore him, Oh,
In the high - est; Oh, come, let us a - dore him, Oh,
'Now in flesh ap - pear - ing; Oh, come, let us a - dore him, Oh.

come, let us a - dore him, Oh, come, let us a - dore him, Christ the Lord.

# CHRISTMAS SONG.

J. S. DWIGHT.

ADOLPHE ADAM.

Andante maestoso.

1. O ho - ly night! the stars are brightly shin - ing; It is the night of the dear Saviour's birth!
2. Led by the light of Faith se-rene - ly beam - ing; With glowing hearts by His cra - dle we stand:
3. Tru - ly He taught us to love one an - oth - er; His law is Love, and His gos - pel is Peace;

Long lay the world in sin and sor- row pin - ing, 'Till He ap -
So, led by light of a star sweetly gleam - ing, Here came the
Chains shall He break for the slave is our broth - er, And in His

Christmas Song.

Christmas Song,

CHORISTER BOYS

# STAR-SPANGLED BANNER.

With Spirit.

1. { Oh! say can you see, by the dawns ear-ly light, What so proud-ly we hail'd at the
   { Whose stripes and bright stars, thro' the per-il-ous fight, O'er the ram-parts we watch'd, were so
2. { On the shore dim-ly seen, thro the mist of the deep, Where the foes haughty host in dread
   { What is that which the breeze, o'er the tow-er-ing steep, As it fit-ful-ly blows, half con-

D. C.

twi-ligt's last gleam-ing, }
gal-lant-ly stream-ing; } And the rock-et's red glare, the bombs burst-ing in air, Gave
si-lence re-pos-es, }
ceals, half dis-clos-es? } Now it catch-es the gleam of the morn-ing's first beam, In full

proof thro' the night that our flag was still there. Oh! say, does that star-span-gled
glo-ry re-flect-ed, now shines in the stream: 'Tis the star-span-gled ban-ner—

ban-ner yet wave O'er the land of the free and the home of the brave.
Oh! long may it wave O'er the land of the free and the home of the brave.

3
And where is that band who so vauntingly swore,
'Mid the havoc of war and the battle's confusion,
A home and a country they'd leave us no more?
Their blood has wash'd out their foul footsteps
    pollution,
No refuge could save the hireling and slave,
From the terror of fight, or the gloom of the grave,
And the star-spangled banner in triumph doth wave
O'er the land of the free and the home of the brave.

4
Oh! thus be it ever, when freemen shall stand
Between their loved home and the war's desolation;
Blest with vict'ry and peace, may the heav'n-rescued
    land               [us a nation.
Praise the Power that hath made and preserved
Then conquer we must, when our cause it is just,
And this be our motto, "In God is our trust,"
And the star-spangled banner in triumph shall wave
O'er the land of the free and the home of the brave.

# SALLY IN OUR ALLEY.

Music by HENRY CAREY.

*Andante.*

1. Of all the girls that are so smart, There's none like pret-ty Sal-ly; She is the
2. Of all the days that's in the week, I dear-ly love but one day, And that's the

dar-ling of my heart, And she lives in our al-ley, There's ne'er a lady in the land That's half so sweet as
day that comes between, A Sat-ur-day and Monday For then I'm drest all in my best, To walk abroad with

*mez.*

Sal-ly: She is the dar-ling of my heart, And she lives in our...... al-ley.
Sal-ly: She is the dar-ling of my heart, And she lives in our...... al-ley.

# HOW CAN I LEAVE THEE?

VOLKS SONG.

1. How can I leave thee! How can I from thee part! Thou hast a-

lone my heart, Dear one, be - lieve. Thou hast this soul of mine,

'Tis but a part of thine, Love have I none be-sides but thee a - lone.

# ANNIE LAURIE.

FINLAY DUNN.

1. Max-well-ton braes are bon-nie, Where ear-ly fa's the dew; And it's there that An-nie
2. Her brow is like the snowdrift, Her throat is like the swan; Her face it is the
3. Like dew on the gowan ly-ing, Is the fa' o' her fai-ry feet; And like winds in sum-mer

*p colla voce.*

Lau-rie, Gie'd me her prom-ise true, Gie'd me her prom-ise true, Which
fair-est That e'er the sun shone on, That e'er the sun shone on; And
sigh-ing: Her voice is low and sweet, Her voice is low and sweet; And

ne'er for-got will be; And for bon-nie An-nie Lau-rie, I'd lay me doune and dee.
dark blue is her e'e: And for bon-nie An-nie Lau-rie, I'd lay me doune and dee.
she is a' the world to me; And for bon-nie An-nie Lau-rie, I'd lay me doune and dee.

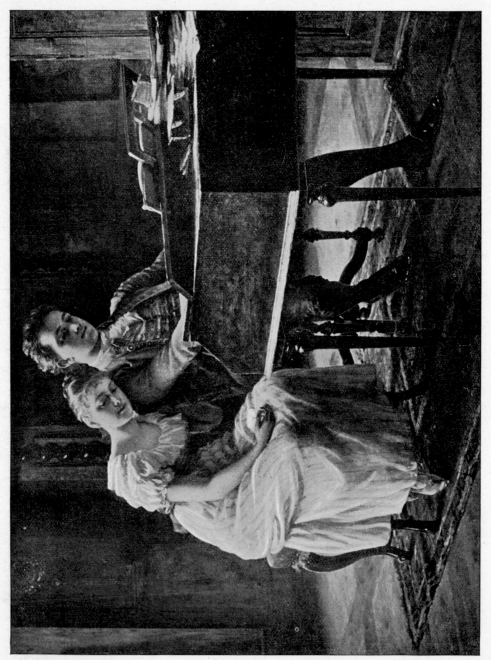

OLD SONGS

# THE OPEN WINDOW.

H, W. LONGFELLOW.

ALFRED SCOTT GATTY.

*Andante con molto espressione.*

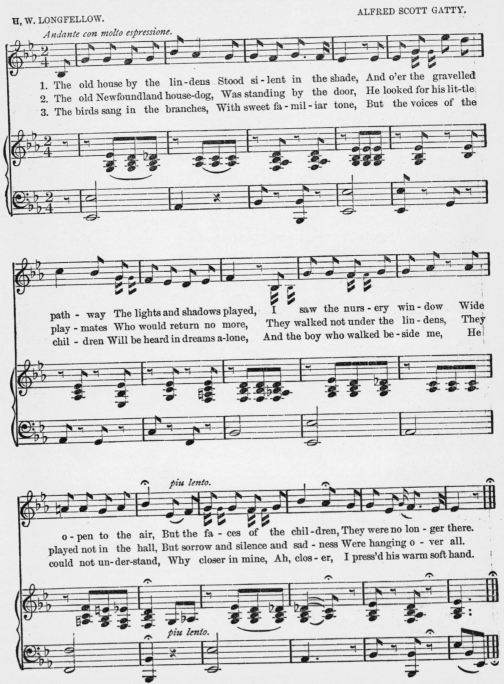

1. The old house by the lin-dens Stood si-lent in the shade, And o'er the gravelled
2. The old Newfoundland house-dog, Was standing by the door, He looked for his lit-tle
3. The birds sang in the branches, With sweet fa-mil-iar tone, But the voices of the

path-way The lights and shadows played, I saw the nurs-ery win-dow Wide
play-mates Who would return no more, They walked not under the lin-dens, They
chil-dren Will be heard in dreams a-lone, And the boy who walked be-side me, He

*piu lento.*

o-pen to the air, But the fa-ces of the chil-dren, They were no lon-ger there.
played not in the hall, But sorrow and silence and sad-ness Were hanging o-ver all.
could not un-der-stand, Why closer in mine, Ah, clos-er, I press'd his warm soft hand.

# LOVE'S OLD, SWEET SONG.

Words by G. C. BINGHAM.

MOLLOY.

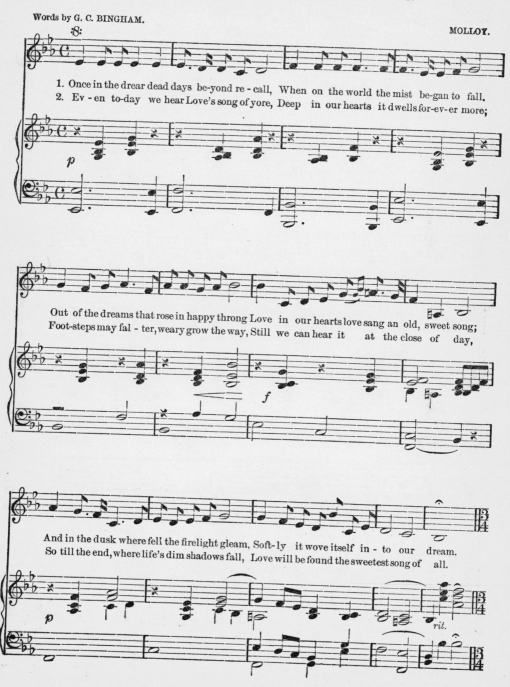

1. Once in the drear dead days be-yond re - call, When on the world the mist be-gan to fall.
2. Ev - en to-day we hear Love's song of yore, Deep in our hearts it dwells for-ev-er more;

Out of the dreams that rose in happy throng Love in our hearts love sang an old, sweet song;
Foot-steps may fal - ter, weary grow the way, Still we can hear it at the close of day,

And in the dusk where fell the firelight gleam, Soft-ly it wove itself in - to our dream.
So till the end, where life's dim shadows fall, Love will be found the sweetest song of all.

Love's Old, Sweet Song.

# A MOTHER'S SONG.

DR. BLATHERWICK.

VIRGINIA GABRIEL.

1. Sleep, ba - by, sleep, your father's a-way, Sleep, ba - by, sleep, and mother will pray,
2. Sleep, ba - by, sleep, your father's a-way, Sleep, ba - by, sleep, and mother will pray,

Pray for poor fa - ther who sails on the sea, Pray while I'm rock-ing his
Pray all the night thro' the sea's sul - len roar, Pray while I'm watching and

babe on my knee; May breez-es blow gen - tly wher - e'er he may be, And
weep - ing so sore; But there's father's voice com-ing up from the shore, And

blow him home safe-ly to  ba - by and me;  Safe - ly,  safe - ly to
ba - by and moth-er are  weep-ing no more;  Ba - by and mother are

ba - by and me,...............................  to  ba - by and me.
weeping no more,...............................  are weep - ing no more.

# 'TIS ALL THAT I CAN SAY.

TOM HOOD.                                                                    HOPE TEMPLE.

*Allegro con anima.*            *f amoroso.*

1. I love thee,   I love thee,   'tis
2. I love thee,   I love thee,   is

A Mother's Song.

'Tis All That I Can Say.

# BIRDIE IN THE CRADLE.

FRANZ APT.

1. In the tall boughs on the tree - top, there's a nest so snug and warm; In it
2. And the wind blows thro' the branch-es, rocks the cra - dle to and fro; Hap-py

lies a lit - tle bir - die, safe in sun - shine, safe in storm; In it
bir - die! chirp - ing, chirp - ing, dan - ger bir - die can - not know; Hap-py

lies a lit - tle bir - die, safe in sun - shine, safe in storm.
bir - die! chirp - ing, chirp - ing, dan - ger bir - die can - not know.

# COMIN' THRO' THE RYE.

1. Gin a bod-y meet a bod-y com-in' thro' the rye; Gin a bod-y kiss a bod-y
2. Gin a bod-y meet a bod-y com-in' frae the town; Gin a bod-y meet a bod-y
3. Amang the train there is a swain, I dear - ly love mysel, But what's his name or where's his hame

Need a bod - y cry! Il - ka las - sie has her lad-die, Nane they say ha'e
Need a bod - y frown! Il - ka las - sie has her lad-die, Nane they say ha'e
I dinna choose to tell. Il - ka las - sie has her lad-die, Nane they say ha'e

I, Yet a' the lads they smile at me When com-in' thro' the rye!
I, Yet a' the lads they smile at me When com-in' thro' the rye!
I, Yet a' the lads they smile at me When com-in' thro' the rye!

# REMEMBER OR FORGET.

HAMILTON AIDÈ.

1. I sat be-side the streamlet, I watch'd the water flow, As we to-geth-er watch'd it One
2. The nightingales made musical June's palace pav'd with gold, I watch'd the rose you gave me Its

lit-tle year a-go; The soft rain pattered on the leaves, The April grass was wet, Ah! fol-ly to re-
warm red heart unfold; But sight of rose and song of bird, Were fraught with wild regret, 'Tis madnass to re-

mem-ber 'Tis wis-er to for-get, Ah! fol-ly to re-mem-ber, 'Tis wis-er to for-get.
mem-ber 'Twere wisdom to for-get, 'Tis madness to re-mem-ber, 'Twere wisdom to for-get.

# HOME, SWEET HOME.

1. 'Mid pleas - ures and pal - a - ces, though we may roam, Be it ev - er so hum - ble, there's no place like home! A charm from the skies seems to hal - low us

2. An ex - ile from home, splendor daz - zles in vain; Oh, give me my low - ly thatch'd cot - tage a - gain; The birds sing - ing gai - ly, that come at my

Home, Sweet Home.

# THE HARP THAT ONCE THRO' TARA'S HALLS.

THOMAS MOORE.

*Andante.*

1. The harp that once thro' Ta - ra's halls The soul of mu - sic shed, Now hangs as mute on
2. No more to chiefs and la - dies bright The harp of Ta - ra swells: The chord, a - lone that

Ta-ra's walls As if that soul were fled; So sleeps the pride of for-mer days, So glo-ry's thrill is
breaks at night, Its tale of ru - in tells; Thus free-dom now so seldom wakes, The on-ly throb she

o'er,   And hearts that once beat high for praise Now feel that pulse no more.
gives   Is when some heart in - dig - nant breaks To show that still she lives.

# BOOK IV.

---

## A CLUSTER OF FINE ART.

ART WINS THE HEART

*Thumann.*

AURORA

*Guido*

## SISTINE MADONNA
*Raphael.*

LAST SUPPER

*Leonardo da Vinci*

DESCENT FROM THE CROSS.

*Rubens.*

THE DUCHESS OF DEVONSHIRE
*Gainsborough.*

**MADAME RECAMIER**

*Louis David Jacques*

CHRIST DESCENDING FROM THE PRAETORIUM

*Doré*

SHADOW OF THE CROSS
*Holman Hunt.*

CHRIST BEFORE PILATE

*Munkacsy*

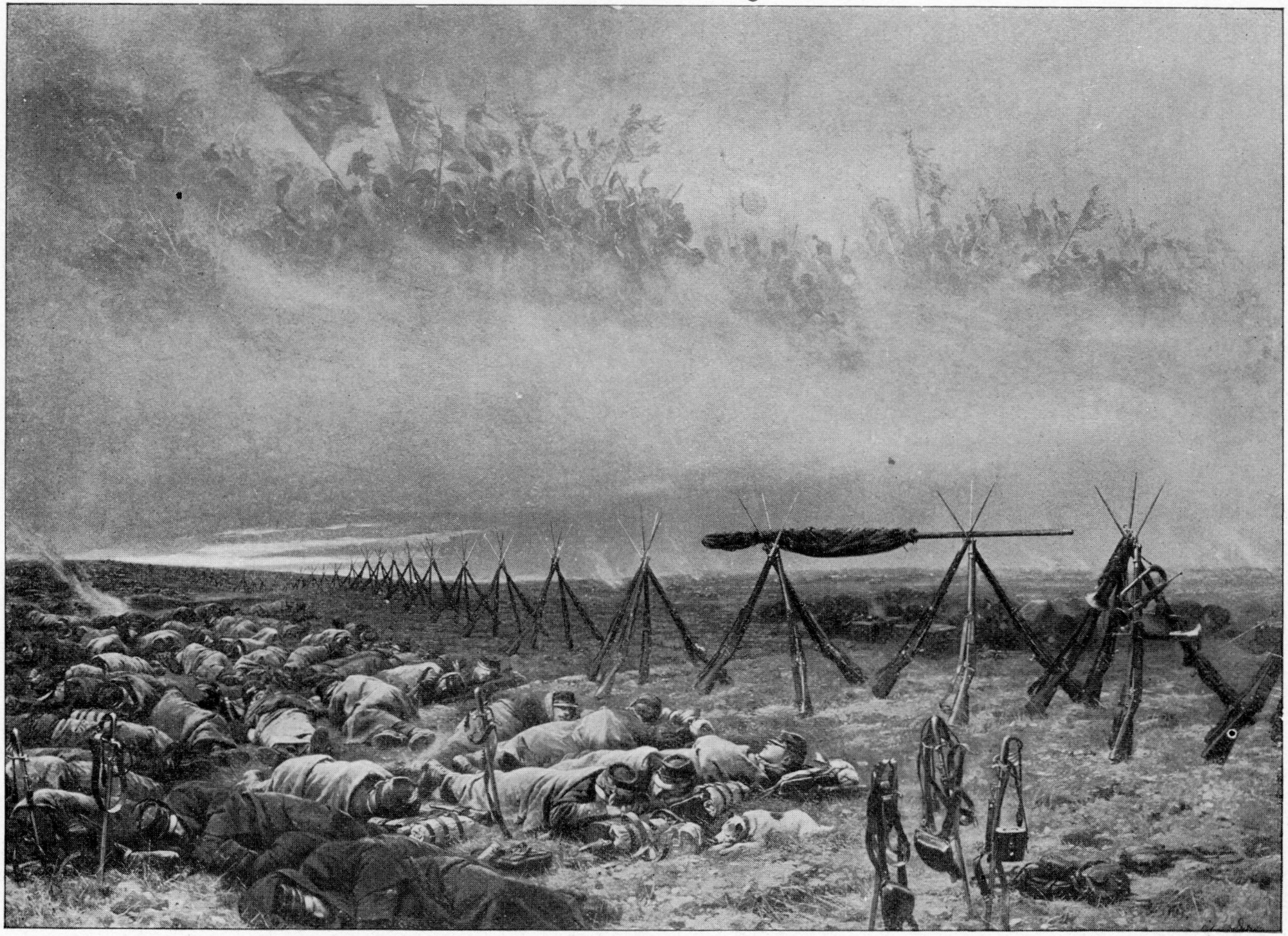

THE SOLDIER'S DREAM

*Detaille*

THE HORSE FAIR

*Rosa Bonheur*

A FISHERMAN'S LOVE

*Kray.*

THE FATES

*Thumann.*

CHRIST BLESSING LITTLE CHILDREN

*Kirchback*

DIANA OR CHRIST

*Long*

WOMEN AND CHILDREN FIRST.

*Hemy.*

FAMILY OF VENDERS

*Tanoux*

VICTIMS OF THE SEA

*Breton*

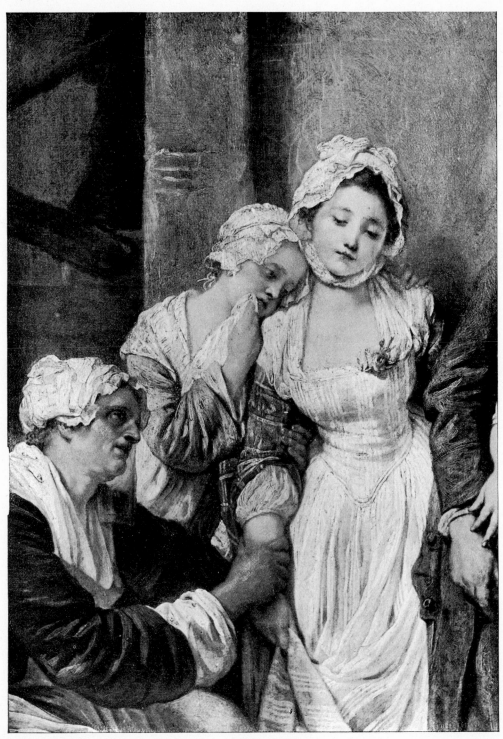

THE PEACEMAKER
*Greive.*

A PROPOSAL

*DeBlaas*

**BUTTERFLIES**

*Gampenrieder.*

## GALLANT HEROES

*Devoir.*

KITCHEN IN A MONASTERY

*Greutzner*

NAPOLEON

*Meissonier*

# BOOK V.

———

## GEMS OF POETRY.

A SPRING MORNING

# Book V.

# Gems of Poetry.

## THE TROJAN WAR.

NOW had the Grecians snatch'd a short
    repast,
And buckled on their shining arms in haste,
Troy rous'd as soon; for on that dreadful day
The fate of fathers, wives, and infants lay.
The gates unfolding pour forth all their train;
Squadrons on squadrons cloud the dusty plain;
Men, steeds, and chariots shake the trembling
    ground;
The tumult thickens, and the skies resound.
And now with shouts the shocking armies clos'd;
To lances lances, shields to shields oppos'd;
Host against host their shadowy legions drew;
The sounding darts in iron tempests flew;
Victors and vanquish'd join promiscuous cries;
Triumphant shouts and dying groans arise;
With streaming blood the slipp'ry fields are
    dy'd,
And slaughter'd heroes swell the dreadful tide.
Long as the morning beams increasing bright,
O'er heav'n's clear azure spread the sacred
    light,
Promiscuous death the fate of war confounds,
Each adverse battle gor'd with equal wounds.
But when the sun the height of heav'n ascends,
The sire of gods his golden scales suspends
With equal hand; in these explores the fate
Of Greece and Troy, and pois'd the mighty
    weight.
Press'd with its load the Grecian balance lies
Low sunk on earth; the Trojan strikes the
    skies.
Then Jove from Ida's top his horror spreads;
The clouds burst dreadful o'er the Grecian heads;
Thick lightnings flash; the mutt'ring thunder
    rolls,
Their strength he withers, and unmans their
    souls.
Before his wrath the trembling hosts retire,
The god in terrors, and the skies on fire.

          HOMER (*The Iliad.*)

## HECTOR AND ANDROMACHE.

TOO daring prince! Ah, whither dost thou
    run?
Ah, too forgetful of thy wife and son!
And think'st thou not how wretched we shall be,
A widow I, a helpless orphan he?
For sure such courage length of life denies,
And thou must fall, thy virtue's sacrifice.
Greece in her single heroes strove in vain;
Now hosts oppose thee, and thou must be slain!
Oh, grant me, gods! ere Hector meets his doom,
All I can ask of heav'n, an early tomb!
So shall my days in one sad tenor run,
And end with sorrows, as they first begun.
No parent now remains my griefs to share,
No father's aid, no mother's tender care.
Yet while my Hector still survives, I see
My father, mother, brethren, all in thee.
Alas! my parents, brothers, kindred, all,
Once more will perish, if my Hector fall.
Thy wife, thy infant, in thy danger share;
Oh, prove a husband's and a parent's care.
That quarter most the skillful Greeks annoy,
Where yon wild fig-trees join the wall of Troy.
Thou from this tow'r defend th' important post,
There Agamemnon points his dreadful host;
That pass Tydides, Ajax, strives to gain,
And there the vengeful Spartan fires his train.
Thrice our bold foes the fierce attack have giv'n,
Or led by hopes, or dictated from heav'n.
Let others in the field their arms employ;
But stay my Hector here, and guard his Troy."
    The chief replied, "That post shall be my care;
Nor that alone, but all the works of war.
How would the sons of Troy, in arms renown'd,
And Troy's proud dames, whose garments sweep
    the ground,
Attaint the lustre of my former name,
Should Hector basely quit the field of fame?
My early youth was bred to warlike pains;
My soul impels me to the martial plains.
Still foremost let me stand to guard the throne,

To save my father's honors and my own.
Yet come it will! the day decreed by fates!
(How my heart trembles,while my tongue relates!)
The day when thou, imperial Troy! must bend!
Must see thy warriors fall, thy glories end.
And yet no presage dire so wounds my mind,
My mother's death, the ruin of my kind;
Not Priam's hoary hairs defiled with gore,
Not all my brothers gasping on the shore,
As thine, Andromache!—thy griefs I dread!
I see thee trembling, weeping, captive led,
In Argive looms our battles to design,
And woes, of which so large a part was thine:
There while you groan beneath the load of life,
They cry, "Behold the mighty Hector's wife!"
Some haughty Greek, who lives thy tears to see,
Embitters all thy woes by naming me.
The thoughts of glory past, and present shame,
A thousand griefs shall waken at the name!
May I lie cold before that dreadful day,
Press'd with a load of monumental clay!
Thy Hector, wrapt in everlasting sleep,
Shall neither hear thee sigh, nor see thee weep."

Thus having spoke, th' illustrious chief of Troy
Stretch'd his fond arms to clasp the lovely boy.
The babe clung, crying to his nurse's breast
Scar'd with the dazzling helm and nodding crest.
With secret pleasure each fond parent smil'd,
And Hector hastened to relieve his child;
The glitt'ring terrors from his brows unbound,
And plac'd the beaming helmet on the ground.
Then kiss'd the child, and lifting high in air,
Thus to the gods preferr'd a parent's prayer.

" O Thou, whose glory fills th' ethereal throne,
And all ye deathless Pow'rs! protect my son!
Grant him, like me, to purchase just renown,
To guard the Trojans, to defend the crown,
Against his country's foes the war to wage,
And rise the Hector of the future age!
So when triumphant from successful toils
Of heroes slain, he bears the reeking spoils,
Whole hosts may hail him with deserv'd acclaim,
And say,' This chief transcends his father's fame.'
While pleas'd amidst the gen'ral shouts of Troy,
His mother's conscious heart o'erflows with joy."

He spoke, and fondly gazing on her charms,
Restored the pleasing burden to her arms;
Soft on her fragrant breast the babe she laid,
Hush'd to repose, and with a smile survey'd.
The troubled pleasure soon chastis'd with fear,
She mingled with the smile a falling tear.

HOMER (*The Iliad.*)

## AENEAS'S ACCOUNT OF THE SACK OF TROY.

ALL were attentive to the godlike man,
When from his lofty couch he thus began:
Great queen! what you command me to relate
Renews the sad remembrance of our fate;
An empire from its old foundations rent,
And ev'ry wo the Trojans underwent;
A pop'lous city made a desert place;
All that I saw, and part of which I was;
Not ev'n the hardest of our foes could hear,
Nor stern Ulysses tell without a tear.

'Twas now the dead of night, when sleep repairs
Our bodies worn with toils, our minds with cares,
When Hector's ghost before my sight appears;
Shrouded in blood he stood, and bath'd in tears.
Such as when by the fierce Pelides slain,
Thessalian coursers dragged him o'er the plain.
Swoll'n were his feet, as when the thongs were thrust
Through the pierced limbs; his body black with dust.
Unlike that Hector who returned from toils
Of war triumphant in Æacian spoils;
Or him, who made the fainting Greeks retire,
Hurling amidst their fleets the Phrygian fire.
His hair and beard were clotted stiff with gore;
The ghastly wounds he for his country bore,
Now stream'd afresh.
I wept to see the visionary man,
And whilst my trance continued, thus began:
O light of Trojans, and support of Troy,
Thy father's champion, and thy country's joy!
O long expected by thy friends! from whence
Art thou so late return'd to our defence?
Alas! what wounds are these?  What new disgrace
Deforms the manly honors of thy face?

The spectre, groaning from his inmost breast,
This warning in these mournful words express'd;
Haste, goddess-born! Escape, by timely flight,
The flames and horrors of this fatal night.
The foes already have possess'd our wall;
Troy nods from high, and totters to her fall.
Enough is paid to Priam's royal name,
Enough to country, and to deathless fame.
If by a mortal arm my father's throne
Could have been sav'd, this arm the feat had done.

Troy now commends to thee her future state,
And gives her gods companions of thy fate.
Under their umbrage hope for happier walls,
And follow where thy various fortune calls.
  He said, and brought from forth the sacred
    choir,
The gods, and relics of th' immortal fire.
Now peals of shouts come thundering from afar,
Cries, threats, and loud lament, and mingled war.
The noise approaches, though our palace stood
Aloof from streets, embosom'd close with wood;
Louder and louder still, I hear th' alarms
Of human cries distinct, and clashing arms.
Fear broke my slumbers.
  I mount the terrace; thence the town survey,
And listen what the swelling sounds convey.
Then Hector's faith was manifestly clear'd;
And Grecian fraud in open light appear'd.
The palace of Deiphobus ascends
In smoky flames, and catches on his friends.
Ucalegon burns next; the seas are bright
With splendors not their own, and shine with
    sparkling light.
New clamors and new clangors now arise,
The trumpet's voice, with agonizing cries.
With frenzy seiz'd I run to meet th' alarms,
Resolv'd on death, resolv'd to die in arms.
But first to gather friends, with whom t' oppose,
If fortune favor'd, and repel the foes,
By courage rous'd, by love of country fir'd,
With sense of honor and revenge inspir'd.
  Pantheus, Apollo's priest, a sacred name,
Had 'scap'd the Grecian's swords, and pass'd the
    flame.
With relics loaded to my doors he fled,
And by the hand his tender grandson led.
  What hope, O Pantheus? Whither can we
    run?
Where make a stand? Or what may yet be
    done?
Scarce had I spoke, when Pantheus, with a
    groan,
Troy—is no more! Her glories now are gone.
The fatal day, th' appointed hour is come,
When wrathful Jove's irrevocable doom
Transfers the Trojan state to Grecian hands:
Our city's wrapt in flames; the foe commands.
To sev'ral posts their parties they divide;
Some block the narrow streets; some scour the
    wide.
The bold they kill; th' unwary they surprise;
Who fights meets death, and death finds him
    who flies.
                    VIRGIL (*The Æneid*).

## AMONG THE LOST.

"THROUGH me you pass into the city
    of woe:
Through me you pass into eternal pain:
Through me among the people lost for aye.
Justice the founder of my fabric moved:
To rear me was the task of power divine,
Supremest wisdom, and primeval love.
Before me things create were none, save things
Eternal, and eternal I endure.
All hope abandon, ye who enter here."
  Such characters, in color dim, I mark'd
Over a portal's lofty arch inscribed.
Whereat I thus: "Master, these words import
Hard meaning." He as one prepared replied:
"Here thou must all distrust behind thee leave;
Here be vile fear extinguish'd. We are come
Where I have told thee we shall see the souls
To misery doom'd, who intellectual good
Have lost." And when his hand he had stretch'd
    forth
To mine, with pleasant looks, whence I was
    cheer'd,
Into that secret place he led me on.
  Here sighs, with lamentations and loud moans,
Resounded through the air pierced by no star,
That e'en I wept at entering. Various tongues,
Horrible languages, outcries of woe,
Accents of anger, voices deep and hoarse.
With hands together smote that swell'd the
    sounds,
Made up a tumult, that forever whirls
Round through that air with solid darkness
    stain'd,
Like to the sand that in the whirlwind flies.
  I then, with error yet encompassed, cried:
"O master! what is this I hear? what race
Are these, who seem so overcome with woe?"
  He thus to me: "This miserable fate
Suffer the wretched souls of those, who lived
Without or praise or blame, with that ill band
Of angels mix'd, who nor rebellious proved,
Nor yet were true to God, but for themselves
Were only! From his bounds Heaven drove
    them forth
Not to impair his luster; nor the depth
Of Hell receives them, lest the accursed tribe
Should glory thence with exultation vain."
  I then: "Master! what doth aggrieve them
    thus,
That they lament so loud?" He straight replied:

"That will I tell thee briefly.  These of death
No hope may entertain : and their blind life
So meanly passes, that all other lots
They envy.  Fame of them the world hath none,
Nor suffers ; mercy and justice scorn them both.
Speak not of them, but look, and pass them by."
    And I, who straightway look'd, beheld a flag,
Which whirling ran around so rapidly,
That it no pause obtain'd : and following came
Such a long train of spirits, I should ne'er
Have thought that death so many had despoil'd.
    When some of these I recognized, I saw
And knew the shade of him, who to base fear
Yielding, abjured his high estate.  Forthwith
I understood, for certain, this the tribe
Of those ill spirits both to God displeasing
And to his foes.  These wretches, who ne'er
        lived,
Went on in nakedness, and sorely stung
By wasps and hornets, which bedew'd their
        cheeks
With blood, that, mix'd with tears, dropp'd to
    their feet,
And by disgustful worms were gather'd there.
    Then looking further onward, I beheld
A throng upon the shore of a great stream :
Whereat I thus: " Sir ! grant me now to know
Whom here we view, and whence impell'd they
        seem
So eager to pass o'er, as I discern
Through the blear light?"  He thus to me in few :
" This shalt thou know, soon as our steps arrive
Beside the woeful tide of Acheron."
    Then with eyes downward cast and fill'd with
        shame,
Fearing my words offensive to his ear,
Till we had reach'd the river, I from speech
Abstain'd.  And lo ! toward us in a bark
Comes on an old man, hoary white with eld,
Crying, " Woe to you, wicked spirits ! hope not
Ever to see the sky again.  I come
To take you to the other shore across,
Into eternal darkness, there to dwell
In fierce heat and in ice.  And thou, who there
Standest, live spirit ! get thee hence, and leave
These who are dead."  But soon as he beheld
I left them not, " By other way," said he,
" By other haven shalt thou come to shore,
Not by this passage ; thee a nimbler boat
Must carry."  Then to him thus spake my guide:
" Charon ! thyself torment not : so 't is will'd,

Where will and power are one : ask thou no
    more.''
    Straightway in silence fell the shaggy cheeks
Of him, the boatman o'er the livid lake,
Around whose eyes glared wheeling flames.
        Meanwhile
Those spirits, faint and naked, color changed,
And gnash'd their teeth, soon as the cruel words
They heard.  God and their parents they blas-
        phemed,
The human kind, the place, the time, and seed,
That did engender them and give them birth.
    Then all together sorely wailing drew
To the curst strand, that every man must pass
Who fears not God.  Charon, demoniac form,
With eyes of burning coal, collects them all,
Beckoning, and each, that lingers, with his oar,
Strikes.  As fall off the light autumnal leaves,
One still another following, till the bough
Strews all its honors on the earth beneath ;
E'en in like manner, Adam's evil brood
Cast themselves, one by one, down from the
        shore,
Each at a beck, as falcon at his call.
    Thus go they over through the umber'd wave ;
And ever they on the opposing bank
Be landed, on this side another throng
Still gathers.  " Son," thus spake the courteous
        guide,
" Those who die subject to the wrath of God
All here together come from every clime,
And to o'erpass the river are not loth :
For so heaven's justice goads them on, that fear
Is turn'd into desire.  Hence ne'er hath pass'd
Good spirit.  If of thee Charon complain,
Now mayst thou know the import of his words."
    This said, the glomy region trembling shook
So terribly, that yet with clammy dews
Fear chills my brow.  The sad earth gave a blast,
That, lightening, shot forth a vermilion flame,
Which all my senses conquer'd quite, and I
Down dropp'd, as one with sudden slumber
        seized.

.    .    .    .    .    .    .

From the first circle I descended thus
Down to the second, which, a lesser space
Embracing, so much more of grief contains,
Provoking bitter moans.  There Minos stands,
Grinning with ghastly feature : he, of all
Who enter, strict examining the crimes,
Gives sentence, and dismisses them beneath,

IN LOVE

According as he foldeth him around:
For when before him comes the ill-fated soul,
It all confesses; and that judge severe
Of sins, considering what place in hell
Suits the transgression, with his tail so oft
Himself encircles, as degrees beneath
He dooms it to descend. Before him stand
Alway a numerous throng; and in his turn
Each one to judgment passing, speaks, and hears
His fate, thence downward to his dwelling hurl'd.

"O thou! who to this residence of woe
Approachest!" when he saw me coming, cried
Minos, relinquishing his dread employ,
"Look how thou enter here; beware in whom
Thou place thy trust; let not the entrance broad
Deceive thee to thy harm." To him my guide:
"Wherefore exclaimest? Hinder not his way
By destiny appointed; so 'tis will'd,
Where will and power are one. Ask thou no
    more."
    Now 'gin the rueful wailings to be heard.
Now am I come where many a plaining voice
Smites on mine ear. Into a place I came
Where light was silent all. Bellowing there
    groan'd
A noise, as of a sea in tempest torn
By warring winds. The stormy blast of hell
With restless fury drives the spirits on,
Whirl'd round and dash'd amain with sore annoy.
When they arrive before the ruinous sweep,
There shrieks are heard, there lamentations,
    moans,
And blasphemies 'gainst the good Power in
    heaven.
    I understood, that to this torment sad
The carnal sinners are condemn'd, in whom
Reason by lust is sway'd, As in large troops
And multitudinous, when winter reigns,
The starlings on their wings are borne abroad;
So bears the tyrannous gust those evil souls.
On this side and on that, above, below,
It drives them: hope of rest to solace them
Is none, nor e'en of milder pang. As cranes,
Chanting their dolorous notes, traverse the sky,
Stretch'd out in long array; so I beheld
Spirits, who came loud wailing, hurried on
By their dire doom. Then I: "Instructor! who
Are these, by the black air so scourged?" "The
    first
'Mong those, of whom thou question'st," he
    replied,

"O'er many tongues was empress. She in vice
Of luxury was so shameless, that she made
Liking be lawful by promulged decree,
To clear the blame she had herself incurr'd.
This is Semiramis, of whom 'tis writ,
That she succeeded Ninus her espoused;
And held the land, which now the Soldan rules.
The next in amorous fury slew herself,
And to Sicheus' ashes broke her faith:
Then follows Cleopatra, lustful queen."
    There mark'd I Helen, for whose sake so long
The time was fraught with evil; there the great
Achilles, who with love fought to the end.
Paris I saw, and Tristan; and beside,
A thousand more he show'd me, and by name
Pointed them out, whom love bereaved of life.
    When I had heard my sage instructor name
Those dames and knights of antique days, o'er-
    power'd
By pity, well-nigh in amaze my mind
Was lost; and I began: "Bard! willingly
I would address those two together coming,
Which seem so light before the wind." He thus:
"Note thou, when nearer they to us approach.
Then by that love which carries them along,
Entreat; and they will come." Soon as the wind
Sway'd them toward us, I thus framed my
    speech:
"O wearied spirits! come, and hold discourse
With us, if by none else restrain'd." As doves
By fond desire invited, on wide wings
And firm, to their sweet nest returning home,
Cleave the air, wafted by their will along;
Thus issued; from that troop where Dido ranks,
They, through the ill air speeding: with such
My cry prevail'd, by strong affection urged.
    "O gracious creature and benign! who go'st
Visiting, through this element obscure,
Us, who the world with bloody stain imbrued:
If, for a friend, the King of all, we own'd.
Our prayer to him should for thy peace arise,
Since thou hast pity on our evil plight.
Of whatsoever to hear or to discourse
It pleases thee, that will we hear, of that
Freely with thee discourse, while e'er the wind,
As now, is mute. The land, that gave me birth,
Is situate on the coast, where Po descends
To rest in ocean with his sequent streams.
    "Love, that in gentle heart is quickly learnt,
Entangled him by that fair form, from me
Ta'en in such cruel sort, as grieves me still:

Love, that denial takes from none beloved,
Caught me with pleasing him so passing well,
That, as thou seest, he yet deserts me not.
Love brought us to one death: Caina waits
The soul, who split our life." Such were their
    words;
At hearing which, downward I bent my looks.
And held them there so long, that the bard cried:
"What art thou pondering?" I in answer thus:
"Alas! by what sweet thoughts, what fond
    desire,
Must they at length to that ill pass have
    reach'd!"
    Then turning, I to them my speech address'd,
And thus began: "Francesca! your sad fate
Even to tears my grief and pity moves.
But tell me; in the time of your sweet sighs,
By what, and how Love granted, that ye knew
Your yet uncertain wishes?" She replied:
"No greater grief than to remember days
Of joy, when misery is at hand   That kens
Thy learn'd instructor. Yet so eagerly
If thou art bent to know the primal root,
From whence our love gat being, I will do
As one, who weeps and tells his tale.  One day,
For our delight we read of Lancelot,
How him love thrall'd.  Alone we were, and no
Suspicion near us.  Oft-times by that reading
Our eyes were drawn together, and the hue
Fled from our alter'd cheek.  But at one point
Alone we fell.  When of that smile we read,
The wished smile so rapturously kiss'd
By one so deep in love, then he, who ne'er
From me shall separate, at once my lips
All trembling kiss'd.  The book and writer both
Were love's purveyors.  In its leaves that day
We read no more." While thus one spirit spake,
The other wail'd so sorely, that heart-struck
I, through compassion fainting, seem'd not far
From death, and like a corse fell to the ground
            DANTE (*The Inferno.*)

## THE DAISY.

OF all the floures in the mede,
    Than love I most these floures white
      and rede,
Soch that men callen daisies in our town;
To hem I have so great affection,
As I said erst, whan comen is the May,
That is me bedde there daweth me no day

That I nam up and walking in the mede;
To sene this flour agenst the sunne sprede,
Whan it upriseth early by the morow,
That blissful sight softeneth all my sorow,
So glad am I whan that I have the presence
Of it, to done it all reverence;
And ever I love it, and ever ylike newe,
And ever shall, till that mine herte die:
All swere I not, of this I will not lie.
            CHAUCER.

## UNA AND THE LION.

NOUGHT is there under heaven's wide
    hallowness
    That moves more dear compassion of
      mind,
Than beauty brought t' unworthy wretched-
    ness
Through envy's snares, or fortune's freaks
    unkind.
I, whether lately through her brightness blind,
Or through allegiance and fast fealty,
Which I do owe unto all womankind,
Feel my heart pierced with so great agony,
When such I see, that all for pity I could die.

And now it is empassioned so deep,
For fairest Una's sake, of whom I sing,
That my frail eyes these lines with tears do
    steep,
To think how she through guileful handeling,
Though true as touch, though daughter of a
    king,
Though fair as ever living wight was fair,
Though nor in word nor deed ill meriting,
Is from her Knight divorced in despair,
And her due loves derived to that vile Witch's
    share.

Yet she, most faithful Lady all this while,
Forsaken, woeful, solitary maid,
Far from all people's press, as in exile,
In wilderness and wasteful deserts stray'd
To seek her Knight; who, subtilly betray'd
Through that late vision which th' enchanter
    wrought,
Had her abandon'd; she, of nought affray'd,
Through woods and wasteness wide him daily
    sought;
Yet wished tidings none of him unto her brought.

One day, nigh weary of the irksome way,
From her unhasty beast she did alight;

And on the grass her dainty limbs did lay
In secret shadow, far from all men's sight
From her fair head her fillet she undight,
And laid her stole aside ; her angel's face,
As the great eye of heaven, shined bright,
And made a sunshine in the shady place :
Did never mortal eye behold such heavenly grace.

It fortuned out of the thickest wood
A ramping lion rushed suddenly,
Hunting full greedy after savage blood :
Soon as the royal Virgin he did spy,
With gaping mouth at her ran greedily,
To have at once devour'd her tender corse ;
But to the prey whenas he drew more nigh,
His bloody rage assuaged with remorse,
And, with the sight amazed, forgot his furious
    force.

Instead thereof, he kiss'd her weary feet,
And lick'd her lily hands with fawning tongue,
As he her wronged innocence did weet.
O, how can beauty master the most strong,
And simple truth subdue avenging wrong !
Whose yielded pride and proud submission,
Still dreading death, when she had marked
    long,
Her heart 'gan melt in great compassion ;
And drizzling tears did shed for pure affection.

"The lion, lord of every beast in field,"
Quoth she, "his princely puissance doth abate,
And mighty proud to humble weak does yield,
Forgetful of the hungry rage which late
Him prick'd, in pity of my sad estate :—
But he, my lion, and my noble lord,
How does he find in cruel heart to hate
Her that him loved, and ever most adored
As the god of my life? why hath he me ab-
    horr'd ?"

Redounding tears did choke th' end of her
    plaint,
Which softly echo'd from the neighbor wood ;
And, sad to see her sorrowful constraint,
The kingly beast upon her gazing stood ;
With pity calm'd, down fell his angry mood.
At last, in close heart shutting up her pain,
Arose the Virgin born of heavenly brood,
And to her snowy palfrey got again,
To seek her stray'd Champion if she might attain.

The lion would not leave her desolate,
But with her went along, as a strong guard

Of her chaste person, and a faithful mate
Of her sad troubles and misfortunes hard :
Still, when she slept, he kept both watch and
    ward ;
And, when she waked, he waited diligent,
With humble service to her will prepared :
From her fair eyes he took commandment,
And ever by her looks conceived her intent.

EDMUND SPENCER.

## PARADISE LOST.

 thou that, with surpassing glory crown'd,
    Look'st from thy sole dominion, like
    the god
Of this new world ; at whose sight all the stars
Hide their diminished heads ; to thee l call,
But with no friendly voice, and add thy name,
O Sun, to tell thee how I hate thy beams,
That bring to my remembrance from what state
I fell ; how glorious once above thy sphere ;
Till pride and worse ambition threw me down,
Warring in heaven against heaven's matchless
    King :
Ah, wherefore ? He deserv'd no such return
From me, whom he created what I was
In that bright eminence, and with his good
Upbraided none : nor was his service hard.
What could be less than to afford him praise,
The easiest recompense, and pay him thanks?
How due ! yet all his good proved ill in me,
And wrought but malice : lifted up so high,
I disdained subjection ; thought one step higher
Would set me high'st, and in a moment quit
The debt immense of endless gratitude,
So burdensome still paying, still to owe.
Forgetful what from him I still receiv'd,
And understood not, that a grateful mind
By owing, owes not, but still pays : at once
Indebted, and discharged ; what burden then?
Oh, had his pow'rful destiny ordain'd
Me some inferior angel, I had stood
Then happy ; no unbounded hope had rais'd
Ambition. Yet why not? some other pow'r
As great might have aspir'd, and me, though
    mean,
Drawn to his part. But other pow'rs as great
Fell not, but stand unshaken, from within,
Or from without, to all temptations arm'd.
Hadst thou the same free-will, and pow'r to
    stand?

Thou hadst: whom hast thou, then, or what
    t'accuse,
But heaven's free love dealt equally to all?
Be then his love accurs'd! since love or hate,
To me alike it deals eternal woe.
Nay, curs'd be thou; since against his, thy will
Chose freely what it now so justly rues.
Me miserable! which way shall I fly
Infinite wrath, and infinite despair?
Which way I fly is hell; myself am hell;
And in the lowest deep, a lower deep
Still threat'ning to devour me, opens wide,
To which the hell I suffer, seems a heav'n—
Oh, then, at last, relent. Is there no place
Left for repentance? None for pardon left?
None left, but by submission; and that word
Disdain forbids me, and my dread of shame
Among the spirits beneath, whom I seduc'd
With other promises, and other vaunts
Than to submit; boasting I could subdue
Th' Omnipotent. Ah, me! they little know
How dearly I abide that boast so vain;
Under what torments inwardly I groan,
While they adore me on the throne of hell,
With diadem and scepter high advanc'd,
The lower still I fall, only supreme
In misery; such joy ambition finds.
But say I could repent, and could obtain,
By act of grace, my former state; how soon
Would height recall high thoughts, how soon
    unsay
What feign'd submission swore! Ease would
    recant
Vows made in pain, as violent and void.
For never can true reconcilement grow
Where wounds of deadly hate have pierc'd so
    deep:
Which would but lead me to a worse relapse,
And heavier fall: so should I purchase dear
Short intermission bought with double smart.
This knows my Punisher, therefore as far
From granting he, as I from begging peace:
All hope excluded thus, behold instead
Of us outcast, exil'd, his new delight,
Mankind created, and for them this world.
So farewell, hope; and with hope farewell fear;
Farewell, remorse; all good to me is lost;
Evil, be thou my good; by thee at least
Divided empire with heaven's King I hold;
By thee, and more than half, perhaps, shall reign,
As man, ere long, and this new world shall know.
              MILTON.

## SONNETS.

WHEN, in disgrace with fortune and men's
    eyes,
I all alone beweep my outcast state,
And trouble deaf Heaven with my bootless cries,
And look upon myself, and curse my fate;
Wishing me like to one more rich in hope,
Featured like him, like him with friends possest,
Desiring this man's art, and that man's scope,
With what I most enjoy contented least;
Yet in these thoughts myself almost despising;
Haply I think on thee, and then my state,
Like to the lark at break of day arising
From sullen earth, sings hymns at Heaven's
    gate:
For thy sweet love remember'd such wealth
    brings,
That then I scorn to change my state with kings.

WHEN to the sessions of sweet silent though
I summon up remembrance of things past,
I sigh the lack of many a thing I sought,
And with old woes new wail my dear time's
    waste:
Then can I drown an eye, unused to flow,
For precious friends hid in death's dateless night,
And weep afresh love's long-since-cancell'd woe,
And moan th' expense of many a vanish'd sight.
Then can I grieve at grievances foregone,
And heavily from woe to woe tell o'er
The sad account of fore-bemoaned moan,
Which I now pay as if not paid before;
But if the while I think on thee, dear friend,
All losses are restored, and sorrows end.

FULL many a glorious morning have I seen
Flatter the mountain tops with sovereign eye,
Kissing with golden face the meadows green,
Gilding pale streams with heavenly alchemy;
Anon permit the basest clouds to ride
With ugly rack on his celestial face,
And from the forlorn world his visage hide,
Stealing unseen to West with this disgrace.
Even so my sun one early morn did shine,
With all-triumphant splendor on my brow;
But, out, alack! he was but one hour mine;
The region cloud hath mask'd him from me
    now.
Yet him for this my love no whit disdaineth;
Suns of the world may stain, when heaven's Sun
    staineth.

LET me not to the marriage of true minds
Admit impediments: love is not love,
Which alters when it alteration finds,
Or bends with the remover to remove:
O, no! it is an ever-fixed mark,
That looks on tempests, and is never shaken;
It is the star to every wandering bark,
Whose worth's unknown, although his height
    be taken.
Love's not Time's fool, though rosy lips and
    cheeks
Within his bending sickle's compass come;
Love alters not with his brief hours and weeks,
But bears it out even to the edge of doom.
If this be error, and upon me proved,
I never writ, nor no man ever loved.

                  SHAKESPEARE.

## ALEXANDER'S FEAST.

'TWAS at the royal feast for Persia won
    By Philip's warlike son—
      Aloft, in awful state,
The god-like hero sat
    On his imperial throne.
      His valiant peers were plac'd around,
Their brows with roses and with myrtle
    bound:
      So should desert in arms be crown'd.
The lovely Thais, by his side,
Sat like a blooming eastern bride,
In flower of youth and beauty's pride.—
      Happy, happy, happy pair!
      None but the brave,
      None but the brave,
      None but the brave deserves the fair.

Timotheus, plac'd on high
Amid the tuneful choir,
    With flying fingers touched the lyre;
The trembling notes ascend the sky
    And heavenly joys inspire—
    The list'ning crowd admire the lofty
      sound:
A present deity! they shout around!
A present deity! the vaulted roofs re-
    bound—
      With ravish'd ears
      The monarch hears,
      Assumes the god,
      Affects to nod,
And seems to shake the spheres.

The praise of Bacchus, then, the sweet
    musician sung,
    Of Bacchus, ever fair and ever young!
The jolly God in triumph comes!
    Sound the trumpets! beat the drums!
Flush'd with a purple grace,
    He shows his honest face.
Now give the hautboys breath! he comes!
    he comes!
    Bacchus ever fair and young,
    Drinking joys did first ordain;
      Bacchus' blesssings are a treasure;
      Drinking is the soldier's pleasure:
      Rich the treasure;
      Sweet the pleasure;
      Sweet is pleasure after pain.

Sooth'd with the sound, the king grew
    vain;
    Fought all his battles o'er again;
And thrice he routed all his foes, and thrice
    he slew the slain!
    The master saw the madness rise;
    His glowing cheeks, his ardent eyes;
    And, while he heav'n and earth de-
      fied—
    Chang'd his hand and check'd his
      pride.
    He chose a mournful muse,
    Soft pity to infuse:
    He sung Darius, great and good,
    By too severe a fate,
    Fall'n! fall'n! fall'n! fall'n!
    Fall'n from his high estate,
    And weltering in his blood!
Deserted at his utmost need
By those his former bounty fed,
On the bare earth exposed he lies,
With not a friend to close his eyes!
    With downcast look the joyless victor
      sat,
    Revolving, in his alter'd soul,
      The various turns of fate below;
    And, now and then, a sigh he stole,
      And tears began to flow!

The mighty master smil'd, to see
That love was in the next degree;
'Twas but a kindred sound to move;
For pity melts the mind to love.
    Softly sweet, in Lydian measures,
    Soon he sooth'd his soul to pleasures.
War, he sung, is toil and trouble;

Hon·: but an empty bubble;
  Never ending, still beginning,
Fighting still, and still destroying,
  If the world be worth thy winning,
Think, oh, think it worth enjoying!

.    .    .    .    .    .

The many rend the skies with loud
    applause:
So love was crown'd; but music won the
    cause.
Now, strike the golden lyre again!
A louder yet, and yet a louder strain!
Break his bands of sleep asunder,
And rouse him, like a rattling peal of
    thunder!
  Hark! hark! the horrid sound
  Has rais'd up his head,
  As awak'd from the dead;
  And amaz'd he stares around.

Revenge! revenge! Timotheus cries—
  See the furies arise!
  See the snakes that they rear,
  How they hiss in their hair,
  And the sparkles that flash from their
    eyes!
  Behold a ghastly band,
  Each a torch in his hand!
These are Grecian ghosts, that in battle
    were slain,
  And, unburied, remain
  Inglorious on the plain!
  Give the vengeance due
  To the valiant crew!
Behold! how they toss their torches on
    high,
  How they point to the Persian abodes,
  And glitt'ring temples of their hostile
    gods!
The princes applaud with a furious joy;
And the king seiz'd a flambeau, with zeal
    to destroy;
  Thais led the way,
  To light him to his prey;
And, like another Helen, fired another
    Troy!

  Thus, long ago,
  Ere heaving bellows learn'd to blow,
  While organs yet were mute;
  Timotheus, to his breathing flute
    And sounding lyre,

Could swell the soul to rage—or kindle
    soft desire.
  At last, divine Cecilia came,
  Inventress of the vocal frame.
The sweet enthusiast from her sacred
    store,
  Enlarg'd the former narrow bounds,
  And added length to solemn sounds,
With nature's mother wit, and arts un-
    known before.
  Let old Timotheus yield the prize,
  Or both divide the crown:
  He rais'd a mortal to the skies;
  She drew an angel down!

                    JOHN DRYDEN.


### FATE.

HEAV'N from all creatures hides the book
    of Fate,
All but the page prescrib'd, their present state;
From brutes what men, from men what spirits
    know,
Or who could suffer being here below?
The lamb thy riot dooms to bleed to-day,
Had he thy reason, would he skip and play?
Pleas'd to the last, he crops the flow'ry food,
And licks the hand just raised to shed his blood.
O blindness to the future! kindly given,
That each may fill the circle mark'd by Heav'n:
Who sees with equal eye, as God of all,
A hero perish, or a sparrow fall;
Atoms or systems into ruin hurl'd,
And now a bubble burst, and now a world.
  Hope humbly then, with trembling pinions
    soar;
Wait the great teacher, Death; and God adore.
What future bliss, he gives not thee to know,
But gives that Hope to be thy blessing now.
Hope springs eternal in the human breast;
Man never *is*, but always *to be* blest:
The soul, uneasy and confin'd from home,
Rests and expatiates in a life to come.
  Lo, the poor Indian! whose untutor'd mind
Sees God in clouds, and hears him in the wind;
His soul proud Science never taught to stray
Far as the solar walk, or milky way;
Yet simple Nature to his hope has given,
Behind the cloud-topp'd hill, an humbler heav'n:
Some safer world in depth of woods embrac'd,
Some happier island in the wat'ry waste,

Where slaves once more their native land behold,
No fiends torment, nor Christians thirst for gold.
To be content his natural desire,
He asks no angel's wing, no seraph's fire:
But thinks, admitted to that equal sky,
His faithful dog shall bear him company.

Go, wiser thou! and in thy scale of sense,
Weigh thy opinion against Providence;
Call imperfection what thou fanciest such.
Say, here he gives too little—there too much:
Destroy all creatures for thy sport or gust,
Yet cry, if man's unhappy, God's unjust;
If man alone engross not Heaven's high care,
Alone made perfect here, immortal there:
Snatch from his hand the balance and the rod,
Rejudge his justice, be the god of GOD.
In pride, in reasoning pride, our error lies;
All quit their sphere, and rush into the skies.
Pride still is aiming at the blest abodes,
Men would be angels, angels would be gods.
Aspiring to be gods, if angels fell,
Aspiring to be angels, men rebel: ·
And who but wishes to invert the laws
Of ORDER, sins against th' Eternal Cause.
                                POPE.

## CHARLES THE TWELFTH.

ON what foundation stands the warrior's
        pride!
How just his hopes, let Swedish Charles decide!
A frame of adamant, a soul of fire,
No dangers fright him and no labors tire;
O'er love, o'er fear extends his wide domain,
Unconquered lord of pleasure and of pain;
No joys to him pacific sceptres yield,
War sounds the trump, he rushes to the field,
Behold surrounding kings their powers combine
And one capitulate, and one resign;
Peace courts his hand, but spreads her charms in
        vain:
" Think nothing gained," he cries, " till naught
        remain;
On Moscow's wall till Gothic standards fly,
And all be mine beneath the Polar sky."
The march begins in military state,
And nations on his eye suspended wait.
Stern Famine guards the solitary coast,
And Winter barricades the realms of Frost;
He comes—nor want nor cold his course delay;—
Hide, blushing Glory, hide Pultowa's day!

The vanquished hero leaves his broken bands,
And shows his miseries in distant lands;
Condemned a needy supplicant to wait,
While ladies interpose, and slaves debate.
But did not Chance at length her error mend?
Did no subverted empire mark his end?
Did rival monarchs give the fatal wound?
Or hostile millions press him to the ground?
His fall was destined to a barren strand,
A petty fortress, and a dubious hand;
He left the name, at which the world grew pale,
To point a moral, or adorn a tale!
                        SAMUEL JOHNSON.

## ELEGY IN A COUNTRY CHURCHYARD.

THE curfew tolls the knell of parting day;
    The lowing herd winds slowly o'er the lea;
The ploughman homeward plods his weary way,
    And leaves the world to darkness—and to me.

Now fades the glimmering landscape on the
        sight,
    And all the air a solemn stillness holds;
Save where the beetle wheels his droning flight,
    And drowsy tinklings lull the distant folds;

Save that, from yonder ivy-mantled tow'r,
    The moping owl does to the moon complain
Of such, as wandering near her secret bow'r,
    Molest her ancient, solitary reign.

Beneath these rugged elms, that yew-tree's
        shade,
    Where heaves the turf in many a mould'ring
        heap,
Each in his narrow cell for ever laid,
    The rude forefathers of the hamlet sleep.

The breezy call of incense-breathing morn,
    The swallow twitt ring from her straw-built
        shed,
The cock's shrill clarion, or the echoing horn,
    No more shall rouse them from their lowly bed.

For them no more the blazing hearth shall burn,
    Or busy housewife ply her evening care;
No children run to lisp their sire's return,
    Or climb his knees the envied kiss to share.

Oft did the harvest to their sickle yield;
    Their furrow oft the stubborn glebe has broke.
How jocund did they drive their team afield!
    How bow'd the woods beneath their sturdy
        stroke!

Let not Ambition mock their useful toil,
   Their homely joys, and destiny obscure;
Nor Grandeur hear with a disdainful smile,
   The short and simple annals of the poor.
The boast of heraldry, the pomp of pow'r,
   And all that beauty, all that wealth, e'er gave,
Await, alike, the inevitable hour:
   The paths of glory lead—but to the grave.

Nor you, ye proud, impute to these the fault,
   If mem'ry o'er their tomb no trophies raise,
Where, through the long-drawn aisle and fretted
     vault,
   The pealing anthem swells the note of praise:

Can storied urn or animated bust
   Back to its mansion call the fleeting breath?
Can honor's voice provoke the silent dust,
   Or flatt'ry soothe the dull cold ear of death?

Perhaps in this neglected spot is laid
   Some heart once pregnant with celestial fire;
Hands, that the rod of empire might have
     sway'd,
   Or wak'd to ecstasy the living lyre;

But Knowledge to their eyes her ample page,
   Rich with the spoils of time, did ne'er unroll;
Chill penury repress'd their noble rage.
   And froze the genial current of the soul.

Full many a gem of purest ray serene
   The dark unfathom'd caves of ocean bear;
Full many a flower is born to blush unseen,
   And waste its sweetness on the desert air.

Some village Hampden, that with dauntless
     breast
   The little tyrant of his fields withstood;
Some mute inglorious Milton here may rest;
   Some Cromwell, guiltless of his country's
     blood.

Th' applause of list'ning senates to command,
   The threats of pain and ruin to despise,
To scatter plenty o'er a smiling land,
   And read their history in a nation's eyes,

Their lot forbade: nor circumscrib'd alone
   Their growing virtues, but their crimes con-
     fined;
Forbade to wade through slaughter to a throne,
   And shut the gates of mercy on mankind;

The struggling pangs of conscious truth to hide:
   To quench the blushes of ingenuous shame;
Or heap the shrine of luxury and pride,
   With incense kindled at the muse's flame.

Far from the madding crowd's ignoble strife,
   (Their sober wishes never learn'd to stray,)
Along the cool sequester'd vale of life
   They kept the noiseless tenor of their way.

Yet even these bones from insult to protect,
   Some frail memorial still erected nigh,
With uncouth rhymes and shapeless sculpture
     deck'd,
   Implores the passing tribute of a sigh.

Their name, their years, spell'd by th' unlettered
     muse,
   The place of fame and elegy supply;
And many a holy text around she strews,
   That teach the rustic moralist to die.

For who, to dumb forgetfulness a prey,
   This pleasing anxious being e'er resign'd,
Left the warm precincts of the cheerful day,
   Nor cast one longing ling'ring look behind?

On some fond breast the parting soul relies,
   Some pious drops the closing eye requires;
Ev'n from the tomb the voice of Nature cries,
   Ev'n in our ashes live their wonted fires.

For thee, who, mindful of th' unhonor'd dead,
   Dost in these lines their artless tale relate;
If chance, by lonely contemplation led,
   Some kindred spirit shall inquire thy fate,

Haply some hoary-headed swain may say—
   "Oft have we seen him at the peep of dawn,
Brushing, with hasty steps, the dews away,
   To meet the sun upon the upland lawn.

"There, at the foot of yonder nodding beech,
   That wreathes its old fantastic roots so high,
His listless length at noontide would he stretch,
   And pore upon the brook that babbles by.

"Hard by yon wood, now smiling as in scorn,
   Mutt'ring his wayward fancies, he would rove;
Now drooping, woeful, wan, like one forlorn,
   Or craz'd with care, or crossed in hopeless
     love.

"One morn I miss'd him on th' accustom'd hill,
   Along the heath, and near his favorite tree;
Another came, nor yet beside the rill,
   Nor up the lawn, nor at the wood was he.

"The next, with dirges due, in sad array,
   Slow through the churchyard path we saw
     him borne —
Approach, and read (for thou canst read) the lay,
   Grav'd on the stone beneath yon aged thorn."

GOSSIP AT THE WELL

THE EPITAPH.

Here rests his head upon the lap of earth,
    A youth to fortune and to fame unknown ;
Fair Science frown'd not on his humble birth,
    And Melancholy mark'd him for her own.

Large was his bounty, and his soul sincere,
    Heav'n did a recompense as largely send :
He gave to mis'ry all he had—a tear ;
    He gain'd from heav'n ('twas all he wish'd) a
        friend.

No farther seek his merits to disclose,
    Or draw his frailties from their dread abode ;
(There they, alike, in trembling hope repose,)
    The bosom of his Father and his God.
                    THOMAS GRAY.


## LOCHINVAR.

 YOUNG LOCHINVAR is come out of
    the West,—
Through all the wide Border his steed was the
    best :
And save his good broadsword he weapons had
    none,—
He rode all unarmed and he rode all alone.
So faithful in love, and so dauntless in war,
There never was knight like the young Loch-
    invar.

He stayed not for brake, and he stopped not for
    stone,
He swam the Eske river where ford there was
    none ;
But ere he alighted at Netherby gate,
The bride had consented, the gallant came late :
For a laggard in love, and a dastard in war,
Was to wed the fair Ellen of brave Lochinvar.

So boldly he entered the Netherby hall,
'Mong bride's-men, and kinsmen, and brothers,
    and all.
Then spoke the bride's father, his hand on his
    sword
(For the poor craven bridegrooom said never a
    word),
"O, come ye in peace here, or come ye in war,
Or to dance at our bridal, young Lord Loch-
    invar?"

I long wooed your daughter,—my suit you
    denied ;—
Love swells like the Solway, but ebbs like its
    tide,
And now am I come, with this lost love of mine,
To lead but one measure, drink one cup of wine.
There are maidens in Scotland more lovely by far,
That would gladly be bride to the young Loch-
    invar."

The bride kissed the goblet ; the knight took it up,
He quaffed off the wine, and he threw down the
    cup.
She looked down to blush, and she looked up to
    sigh,
With a smile on her lips, and a tear in her eye.
He took her soft hand, ere her mother could bar,—
" Now tread we a measure !" said young Loch-
    invar.

So stately his form, and so lovely her face,
That never a hall such a galliard did grace ;
While her mother did fret, and her father did
    fume,
And the bridegroom stood dangling his bonnet
    and plume
And the bridemaidens whispered, " 'Twere better,
    by far,
To have matched our fair cousin with young
    Lochinvar."

One touch to her hand, and one word in her ear,
When they reached the hall door, and the charger
    stood near,
So light to the croupe the fair lady he swung,
So light to the saddle before her he sprung !
" She is won ! we are gone, over bank, bush, and
    scaur,
They'll have fleet steeds that follow," quoth
    young Lochinvar.

There was mounting 'mong Græmes of the Ne-
    therby clan ;
Forsters, Fenwicks, and Musgraves, they rode,
    and they ran ;
There was racing and chasing on Cannobie Lee,
But the lost bride of Netherby ne'er did they see.
So daring in love, so dauntless in war,
Have ye e'er heard of gallant like young Loch-
    invar?
                    SCOTT.

## HIGHLAND MARY.

E banks, and braes, and streams around
    The castle o' Montgomery.
Green be your woods, and fair your flowers,
    Your waters never drumlie!
There simmer first unfauld her robes,
    And there the langest tarry;
For there I took the last farweel
    O' my sweet Highland Mary.

How sweetly bloomed the gay green birk,
    How rich the hawthorn's blossom,
As underneath their fragrant shade
    I clasped her to my bosom!
The golden hours, on angel wings,
    Flew o'er me and my dearie;
For dear to me as life and light
    Was my sweet Highland Mary.

Wi' mony a vow, and locked embrace,
    Our parting was fu' tender;
And, pledging aft to meet again,
    We tore oursels asunder;
But oh! fell death's untimely frost,
    That nipt my flower sae early!
Now green's the sod, and cauld's the clay,
    That wraps my Highland Mary.
O pale, pale now, those rosy lips
    I aft hae kissed sae fondly!
And closed for aye the sparkling glance
    That dwelt on me sae kindly!
And mouldering now in silent dust
    The heart that lo'ed me dearly!
But still within my bosom's core
    Shall live my Highland Mary.
                    BURNS.

## GIVE ME BACK MY YOUTH AGAIN.

HEN give me back that time of pleasures,
    While yet in joyous growth I sang,—
When, like a fount, the crowding measures
Uninterrupted gushed and sprang!
Then bright mist veiled the world before me,
In opening buds a marvel woke,
As I the thousand blossoms broke
Which every valley richly bore me?
I nothing had, and yet enough for youth—
Joy in Illusion, ardent thirst for Truth.
Give unrestrained the old emotion,
The bliss that touched the verge of pain,
  The strength of Hate, Love's deep devotion,—
O, give me back my youth again!
                    GOETHE.

## THE GLOVE.

EFORE his lion-garden gate,
    The wild-beast combat to await,
King Francis sate:
Around him were his nobles placed,
The balcony above was graced
By ladies of the court, in gorgeous state:
And as with his finger a sign he made,
The iron grating was open laid,
And with stately step and mien
A lion to enter was seen.
With fearful look
His mane he shook,
And yawning wide,
Staring around him on every side;
And stretched his giant limbs of strength,
And laid himself down at his fearful length

And the king a second signal made,—
And instant was opened wide
A second gate, on the other side,
From which, with fiery bound,
A tiger sprung.
Wildly the wild one yelled,
When the lion he beheld;
And bristling at the look,
With his tail his sides he strook,
And rolled his rabid tongue.
And, with glittering eye,
Crept round the lion slow and shy
Then, horribly howling,
And grimly growling,
Down by his side himself he laid.

And the king another signal made;
The open grating vomited then
Two leopards forth from their dreadful den,—
They rush on the tiger, with signs of rage.
Eager the deadly fight to wage,
Who, fierce, with paws uplifted stood.
And the lion sprang up with an awful roar,
Then were still the fearful four:
And the monsters on the ground
Crouched in a circle round,
Greedy to taste of blood.

Now, from the balcony above,
A snowy hand let fall a glove:
Midway between the beasts of prey,
Lion and tiger,—there it lay,
The winsome lady's glove!

And the Lady Kunigund, in bantering mood,
Spoke to Knight Delorges, who by her stood;—
"If the flame which but now to me you swore
Burns as strong as it did before,
Go pick up my glove, Sir Knight."
And he, with action quick as sight,
In the horrible place did stand:
And with dauntless mien,
From the beasts between
Took up the glove, with fearless hand;
And as ladies and nobles the bold deed saw,
Their breath they held, through fear and awe.
The glove he brings back, composed and light.
His praise was announced by voice and look,
And Kunigund rose to receive the knight
With a smile that promised the deed to requite;
But straight in her face he flung the glove,—
"I neither desire your thanks nor love;"
And from that same hour the lady forsook.
SCHILLER.

## THE SKYLARK.

BIRD of the wilderness,
  Blithesome and cumberless,
Sweet be thy matin o'er mooreland and lea!
  Emblem of happiness,
  Blest be thy dwelling-place—
Oh, to abide in the desert with thee!
  Wild is thy lay and loud
  Far in the downy cloud,
Love gives it energy, love gave it birth.
  Where, on thy dewy wing,
  Where art thou journeying?
Thy lay is in heaven, thy love is on earth.

  O'er fell and fountain sheen,
  O'er moor and mountain green,
O'er the red streamer that heralds the day,
  Over the cloudlet dim,
  Over the rainbow's rim,
Musical cherub, soar, singing, away!
  Then, when the gloaming comes,
  Low in the heather blooms,
Sweet will thy welcome and bed of love be!
  Emblem of happiness,
  Blest is thy dwelling-place—
Oh, to abide in the desert with thee!
HOGG.

## VISIONS OF THE HEART.

SHE was a Phantom of delight
  When first she gleam'd upon my sight;
A lovely apparition, sent
To be a moment's ornament:
Her eyes as stars of twilight fair;
Like twilight's, too, her dusky hair;
But all things else about her drawn
From May-time and the cheerful dawn;
A dancing shape, an image gay,
To haunt, to startle and waylay.

I saw her upon nearer view,
A Spirit, yet a Woman too!
Her household motions light and free,
And steps of virgin liberty;
A countenance in which did meet
Sweet records, promises as sweet;
A creature not too bright or good
For human nature's daily food;
For transient sorrows, simple wiles,
Praise, blame, love, kisses, tears and
  smiles.

And now I see with eyes serene
The very pulse of the machine;
A being breathing thoughful breath,
A traveller between life and death;
The reason firm, the temperate will,
Endurance, foresight, strength and skill;
A perfect woman, nobly plann'd
To warn, to comfort, and command;
And yet a Spirit still, and bright
With something of angelic light.
WORDSWORTH.

## APOSTROPHE TO THE OCEAN.

THERE is a pleasure in the pathless woods;
  There is a rapture on the lonely shore;
There is society where none intrudes,
By the deep sea, and music in its roar:
I love not Man the less, but Nature more,
From these our interviews, in which I steal
From all I may be, or have been before,
To mingle with the Universe, and feel
What I can ne'er express, yet cannot all conceal.

Roll on, thou deep and dark blue ocean—roll!
Ten thousand fleets sweep over thee in vain;
Man marks the earth with ruin—his control
Stops with the shore;—upon the watery plain

The wrecks are all thy deed, nor doth remain
A shadow of man's ravage, save his own,
When, for a moment, like a drop of rain,
He sinks into thy depths with bubbling groan,
Without a grave, unknell'd, uncoffin'd and un-
    known.

His steps are not upon thy paths,—thy fields
Are not a spoil for him,—thou dost arise
And shake him from thee; the vile strength he
    wields
For earth's destruction thou dost all despise,
Spurning him from thy bosom to the skies,
And send'st him, shivering, in thy playful
    spray,
And howling, to his gods, where haply lies
His petty hope in some near port or bay,
And dashest him again to earth:—there let him lay.
The armaments which thunder-strike the walls
Of rock-built cities, bidding nations quake,
And monarchs tremble in their capitals,—
The oak leviathans, whose huge ribs make
Their clay creator the vain title take
Of lord of thee, and arbiter of war;
These are thy toys, and as the snowy flake,
They melt into thy yeast of waves, which mar
Alike the Armada's pride, or spoils of Trafalgar.

Thy shores are empires, changed in all save
    thee—
Assyria, Greece, Rome, Carthage, what are
    they?
Thy waters wasted them while they were free,
And many a tyrant since; their shores obey
The stranger, slave, or savage; their decay
Has dried up realms to deserts:—not so thou,
Unchangeable save to thy wild waves' play—
Time writes no wrinkle on thine azure brow
Such as creation's dawn beheld, thou rollest now.

Thou glorious mirror, where the Almighty's
    form
Glasses itself in tempests; in all time,
Calm or convuls'd—in breeze, or gale, or
    storm,
Icing the pole, or in the torrid clime
Dark-heaving;—boundless, endless, and sub-
    lime—
The image of Eternity—the throne
Of the Invisible; even from out thy slime
The monsters of the deep are made; each zone
Obeys thee; thou goest forth, dread, fathomless,
    alone.

And I have loved thee, Ocean! and my joy
Of youthful sport was on thy breast to be
Borne, like thy bubbles, onward: from a boy
I wanton'd with thy breakers—they to me
Were a delight; and if the freshening sea
Made them a terror—'twas a pleasing fear
For I was as it were a child of thee,
And trusted to thy billows far and near,
And laid my hand upon thy mane—as I do here.
        BYRON, (*Childe Harold.*)

## THE BIRD, LET LOOSE IN EASTERN SKIES.

THE bird, let loose in eastern skies,
    When hastening fondly home,
Ne'er stoops to earth her wing, nor flies
    Where idle warblers roam;
But high she shoots through air and light,
    Above all low delay,
Where nothing earthly bounds her flight,
    Nor shadow dims her way.

So grant me, God! from every care
    And stain of passion free,
Aloft, through virtue's purer air,
    To hold my course to thee!
No sin to cloud,—no lure to stay
    My soul, as home she springs;—
Thy sunshine on her joyful way,
    Thy freedom on her wings!
        MOORE.

## THE BATTLE OF HOHENLINDEN.

ON LINDEN, when the sun was low,
    All bloodless lay th' untrodden snow;
And dark as winter was the flow
    Of Iser, rolling rapidly.

But Linden showed another sight,
When the drum beat at dead of night,
Commanding fires of death to light
    The darkness of her scenery!

By torch and trumpet fast arrayed,
Each horseman drew his battle-blade;
And furious every charger neighed,
    To join the dreadful revelry.

Then shook the hills with thunder riven;
Then rushed the steed to battle driven;
And, louder than the bolts of heaven,
    Far flashed the red artillery.

SUNNY ITALY

But redder yet those fires shall glow
On Linden's hills of stained snow;
And bloodier yet shall be the flow
    Of Iser, rolling rapidly.

'Tis morn—but scarce yon level sun
Can pierce the war-cloud rolling dun,
Where furious Frank and fiery Hun
    Shout 'mid their sulphurous canopy.

The combat deepens: On, ye brave!
Who rush to glory or the grave!
Wave, Munich, all thy banners wave,
    And charge with all thy chivalry!

Few, few shall part where many meet!
The snow shall be their winding-sheet;
And every turf beneath their feet
    Shall be a soldier's sepulchre!
        THOMAS CAMPBELL.

## HYMN TO MOUNT BLANC.

AST thou a charm to stay the morning star
    In his steep course? So long he seems
      to pause
On thy bald awful head, O sovereign Blanc!
The Arve and the Arveiron at thy base
Rave ceaselessly; but thou, most awful form,
Risest from forth thy silent sea of pines,
How silently! Around thee and above
Deep is the air and dark, substantial, black,
An ebon mass: methinks thou piercest it,
As with a wedge! But, when I look again,
It is thine own calm home, thy crystal shrine,
Thy habitation from eternity.
O dread and silent mount! I gazed upon thee,
Till thou, still present to the bodily sense,
Didst vanish from my thought: entranced in
    prayer,
I worshipp'd the Invisible alone.
    Yet, like some sweet beguiling melody,
So sweet, we know not we are listening to it,
Thou, the meanwhile, wast blending with my
    thought,
Yea, with my life and life's own secret joy;
Till the dilating soul—enrapt, transfused,
Into the mighty vision passing—there,
As in her natural form, swell'd vast to heaven!
    Awake, my soul! not only passive praise
Thou owest; not alone these swelling tears,
Mute thanks, and secret ecstasy. Awake,
Voice of sweet song! Awake, my heart, awake!

15

Green vales and icy cliffs, all join my hymn.
    Thou first and chief, sole sovereign of the
      vale!
O, struggling with the darkness all the night,
And visited all night by troops of stars,
Or when they climb the sky or when they sink;
Companion of the morning-star at dawn,
Thyself Earth's rosy star, and of the dawn
Co-herald; wake, O, wake, and utter praise!
Who sank thy sunless pillars deep in earth?
Who fill'd thy countenance with rosy light?
Who made thee parent of perpetual streams?
    And you, ye five wild torrents fiercely glad!
Who call'd you forth from night and utter death,
From dark and icy caverns call'd you forth,
Down those precipitous, black, jagged rocks,
For ever shatter'd and the same for ever?
Who gave you your invulnerable life,
Your strength, your speed, your fury, and your
    joy,
Unceasing thunder and eternal foam?
And who commanded, (and the silence came,)
Here let the billows stiffen, and have rest?
    Ye ice-falls! ye that from the mountain's
      brow
Adown enormous ravines slope amain—
Torrents, methinks, that heard a mighty voice,
And stopp'd at once amid their maddest plunge!
Motionless torrents! silent cataracts!
Who made you glorious as the gates of Heaven
Beneath the keen full Moon? Who bade the Sun
Clothe you with rainbows? Who, with living
    flowers
Of loveliest blue, spread garlands at your feet?—
God! let the torrents, like a shout of nations
Answer! and let the ice-plains echo, God!
God! sing ye meadow-streams with gladsome
    voice!
Ye pine-groves, with your soft and soul-like
    sounds!
And they too have a voice, yon piles of snow,
And in their perilous fall shall thunder, God!
    Ye living flowers that skirt th' eternal frost;
Ye wild goats sporting around the eagle's nest;
Ye eagles, playmates of the mountain-storm;
Ye lightnings, the dread arrows of the clouds;
Ye signs and wonders of the element—
Utter forth God, and fill the hills with praise!
    Thou too, hoar Mount, with thy sky-pointing
      peaks,
Oft from whose feet the avalanche, unheard,

Shoots downward, glittering through the pure
    serene
Into the depth of clouds, that veil thy breast—
Thou too again, stupendous Mountain! thou
That, as I raise my head, awhile bow'd low
In adoration, upward from thy base
Slow travelling with dim eyes suffused with tears,
Solemnly seemest like a vapory cloud,
To rise before me—rise, O, ever rise,
Rise like a cloud of incense from the Earth!
Thou kingly Spirit throned among the hills,
Thou dread ambassador from Earth to Heaven,
Great hierarch! tell thou the silent sky,
And tell the stars, and tell yon rising Sun,
Earth, with her thousand voices, praises God.
                COLERIDGE.

## TO A NIGHTINGALE.

Y heart aches, and a drowsy numbness
    pains
    My sense, as though of hemlock I had
    drunk,
Or emptied some dull opiate to the drains
One minute past, and Lethe-wards had sunk;
'Tis not through envy of thy happy lot,
But being too happy in thy happiness—
That thou, light-winged Dryad of the trees,
    In some melodious plot
Of beechen green, and shadows numberless,
Singest of Summer in full throated ease.

I cannot see what flowers are at my feet,
Nor what soft incense hangs upon the boughs;
But, in embalmed darkness, guess each sweet
Wherewith the seasonable month endows
The grass, the thicket, and the fruit tree wild;
White hawthorn, and the pastoral eglantine;
Fast-fading violets cover'd up in leaves;
    And mid-May's eldest child,
The coming musk-rose, full of dewy wine,
The murmurous haunt of flies on summer eves.

Darkling I listen; and for many a time
I have been half in love with easeful Death;
Call'd him soft names in many a mused rhyme,
To take into the air my quiet breath:
Now more than ever it seems rich to die,
To cease upon the midnight with no pain,
While thou art pouring forth thy soul abroad
    In such an ecstasy!
Still wouldst thou sing, and I have ears in
    vain—
To thy high requiem become a sod.

Thou wast not born for death, immortal Bird!
No hungry generations tread thee down;
The voice I hear this passing night was heard
In ancient days by emperor and clown:
Perhaps the self-same song that found a path
Through the sad heart of Ruth, when, sick for
    home,
She stood in tears amid the alien corn;
        The same that oft-times hath
Charm'd magic casements, opening on the foam
Of perilous seas, in fairy lands forlorn.

Forlorn! the very word is like a bell
To toll me back from thee to my sole self.
Adieu! The fancy cannot cheat so well
As she is famed to do, deceiving elf.
Adieu, adieu! thy plaintive anthem fades
Past the near meadows, over the still stream,
Up the hill-side; and now 'tis buried deep
    In the next valley-glades:
Was it a vision, or a waking dream?
Fled is that music:—do I wake, or sleep?
            JOHN KEATS.

## TO A SKYLARK.

AIL to thee, blithe spirit!
    Bird thou never wert,
That from heaven, or near it,
    Pourest thy full heart
In profuse strains of unpremeditated art.

Higher still and higher
    From the earth thou springest
Like a cloud of fire,
    The blue deep thou wingest,
And singing still dost soar, and soaring, ever
    singest.

In the golden lightning
    Of the sunken sun,
O'er which clouds are brightening,
    Thou dost float and run,
Like an unbodied joy whose race is just begun.

The pale, purple even
    Melts around thy flight,
Like a star of heaven.
    In the broad daylight
Thou art unseen, but yet I hear thy shrill delight.

Keen as are thy arrows,
    Of that silver sphere,
Whose intense lamp narrows
    In the white dawn clear.
Until we hardly see, we feel that it is there.

Waking or asleep
  Thou of death must deem
Things more true and deep
  Than we mortals dream,
Or how could thy notes flow in such a crystal
    stream?

We look before and after
  And pine for what is not;
Our sincerest laughter
  With some pain is fraught;
Our sweetest songs are those that tell of saddest
    thought.

Yet if we could scorn
  Hate and pride and fear;
If we were things born
  Not to shed a tear,
I know not how thy joy we ever should come
    near.

Better than all measures
  Of delightful sound,
Better than all treasures
  That in books are found,
Thy skill to poet were, thou scorner of the
    ground.

Teach me half the gladness
  That thy brain must know,
Such harmonious madness
  From my lips would flow,
The world should listen then, as I am listening
    now.

              SHELLEY.

## BURIAL OF SIR JOHN MOORE.

NOT a drum was heard, not a funeral note,
  As his corse to the rampart we hurried;
Not a soldier discharged his farewell shot
  O'er the grave where our hero we buried.

We buried him darkly at dead of night,
  The sods with our bayonets turning;
By the struggling moonbeam's misty light,
  And the lantern dimly burning.

No useless coffin inclosed his breast,
  Nor in sheet nor in shroud we wound him;
But he lay like a warrior taking his rest,
  With his martial cloak around him.

Few and short were the prayers we said,
  And we spoke not a word of sorrow;
But we steadfastly gazed on the face of the
    dead,
  And we bitterly thought of the morrow.

We thought, as we hollow'd his narrow bed
  And smooth'd down his lonely pillow,
That the foe and the stranger would tread
    o'er his head,
  And we far away on the billow!

Lightly they'll talk of the spirit that's gone,
  And o'er his cold ashes upbraid him;
But little he'll reck, if they let him sleep on
  In the grave where a Briton has laid him.

But half of our heavy task was done
  When the clock toll'd the hour for retiring;
And we heard the distant and random gun
  That the foe was sullenly firing.

Slowly and sadly we laid him down,
  From the field of his fame fresh and gory;
We carved not a line, we raised not a stone,
  But we left him alone with his glory.
          CHARLES WOLFE.

## SLAVERY.

OH! for a lodge in some vast wilderness,
  Some boundless contiguity of shade,
  Where rumor of oppression and deceit,
Of unsuccessful or successful war,
Might never reach me more! My ear is pain'd,
My soul is sick with every day's report
Of wrong and outrage with which earth is fill'd.
There is no flesh in man's obdurate heart—
It does not feel for man.  That natural bond
Of brotherhood is sever'd as the flax
That falls asunder at the touch of fire.
He finds his fellow guilty—of a skin
Not color'd like his own; and, having power
To enforce the wrong, for such a worthy cause,
Dooms and devotes him as his lawful prey.
Lands intersected by a narrow frith
Abhor each other.  Mountains interpos'd
Make enemies of nations who had else,
Like kindred drops been mingled into one.
Thus man devotes his brother and destroys;
And, worse than all, and most to be deplor'd,
As human nature's broadest, foulest blot,
Chains him, and tasks him, and exacts his sweat
With stripes, that Mercy, with a bleeding heart,

Weeps, when she sees inflicted on a beast.
Then what is man?  And what man seeing this,
And having human feelings, does not blush
And hang his head, to think himself a man?
I would not have a slave to till my ground,
To carry me, to fan me while I sleep,
And tremble when I wake, for all the wealth
That sinews bought and sold have ever earn'd.
No: dear as freedom is, and in my heart's
Just estimation, prized above all price,
I had much rather be myself the slave,
And wear the bonds than fasten them on him.
We have no slaves at home—then why abroad?
And they themselves, once ferried o'er the wave
That parts us, are emancipate and loos'd.
Slaves cannot breathe in England; if their lungs
Receive our air, that moment they are free;
They touch our country, and their shackles fall!
That's noble, and bespeaks a nation proud
And jealous of the blessing.  Spread it then,
And let it circulate through every vein
Of all your empire; that, where Britain's power
Is felt, mankind may feel her mercy too.
                    COWPER, (*The Task.*)

### THE SONG OF THE SHIRT.

WITH fingers weary and worn,
    With eyelids heavy and red,
A woman sat in unwomanly rags,
    Plying her needle and thread—
        Stitch! stitch! stitch!
In poverty, hunger, and dirt,
    And still with a voice of dolorous pitch
She sang the "Song of the Shirt!"

"Work! work! work!
While the cock is crowing aloof!
    And work—work—work,
Till the stars shine through the roof!
It's O! to be a slave
    Along with the barbarous Turk,
Where woman has never a soul to save,
    If this is Christian work!

"Work—work—work
Till the brain begins to swim!
    Work—work—work
Till the eyes are heavy and dim!
Seam, and gusset, and band,
    Band, and gusset, and seam,
Till over the buttons I fall asleep,
    And sew them on in a dream!

"O, men, with sisters dear!
    O, men, with mothers and wives!
It is not linen you're wearing out,
    But human creatures' lives!
        Stitch—stitch—stitch,
    In poverty, hunger, and dirt,
Sewing at once, with a double thread,
    A shroud as well as a shirt.

"But why do I talk of death?
    That phantom of grisly bone,
I hardly fear his terrible shape,
    It seems so like my own—
It seems so like my own,
    Because of the fasts I keep;
O, God! that bread should be so dear,
    And flesh and blood so cheap!

"Work—work—work!
    My labor never flags;
And what are its wages?  A bed of straw,
    A crust of bread—and rags.
That shattered roof—and this naked floor—
    A table—a broken chair—
And a wall so blank, my shadow I thank
    For sometimes falling there!

"Work—work—work!
    From weary chime to chime!
Work—work—work,
    As prisoners work for crime!
Band, and gusset, and seam,
    Seam, and gusset, and band,
Till the heart is sick, and the brain benumbed
    As well as the weary hand.

"Work—work—work,
In the dull December light,
    And work—work—work,
When the weather is warm and bright—
While underneath the eaves
    The brooding swallows cling,
As if to show me their sunny backs,
    And twit me with the spring.

"O! but to breathe the breath
    Of the cowslip and primrose sweet—
With the sky above my head,
    And the grass beneath my feet,
For only one short hour
    To feel as I used to feel,
Before I knew the woes of want,
    And the walk that costs a meal!

RETURN OF THE FISHERMEN

"O! but for one short hour!
  A respite however brief!
No blessed leisure for love or hope,
  But only time for grief!
A little weeping would ease my heart,
  But in their briny bed
My tears must stop, for every drop
  Hinders needle and thread!"

With fingers weary and worn,
  With eyelids heavy and red,
A woman sat in unwomanly rags,
  Plying her needle and thread—
    Stitch! stitch! stitch!
In poverty, hunger, and dirt,
And still with a voice of dolorous pitch,—
  Would that its tone could reach the rich!—
  She sang this "Song of the Shirt!"
                          HOOD.

## THE OLD FAMILIAR FACES.

I HAVE had playmates, I have had companions,
In my days of childhood, in my joyful school-days:
All, all are gone, the old familiar faces.

I have been laughing, I have been carousing,
Drinking late, sitting late, with my bosom cronies;
All, all are gone, the old familiar faces.

I loved a love once, fairest among women:
Closed are her doors on me, I must not see her:
All, all are gone, the old familiar faces.

I have a friend, a kinder friend has no man:
Like an ingrate I left my friend abruptly;
Left him, to muse on the old familiar faces,

Ghost-like I paced 'round the haunts of my childhood:
Earth seemed a desert I was bound to traverse,
Seeking to find the old familiar faces.

Friend of my bosom, thou more than a brother,
Why wert not thou born in my father's dwelling?
So might we talk of the old familiar faces,—

How some they have died, and some they have left me,
And some are taken from me; all are departed;
All, all are gone, the old familiar faces.
                          LAMB.

## ODE ON THE PASSIONS.

WHEN Music, heavenly maid! was young,
  While yet in early Greece she sung,
The Passions oft, to hear her shell,
Throng'd around her magic cell;
Exulting, trembling, raging, fainting,
Possess'd beyond the Muse's painting,
By turns they felt the glowing mind
Disturb'd, delighted, rais'd, refin'd;
Till once, 'tis said, when all were fir'd,
Fill'd with fury, rapt, inspir'd,
From the supporting myrtles round
They snatch'd her instruments of sound;
And as they oft had heard apart
Sweet lessons of her forceful art,
Each (for madness ruled the hour)
Would prove his own expressive pow'r.

First Fear his hand, its skill to try,
Amid the chords, bewilder'd laid—
And back recoil'd, he knew not why
E'en at the sound himself had made.

Next Anger rush'd, his eyes on fire;
In lightnings own'd his secret stings;
In one rude clash he struck the lyre,
And swept with hurried hand the strings.

With woeful measures wan Despair—
Low sullen sounds his grief beguil'd;
A solemn, strange, and mingled air:
'Twas sad by fits, by starts 'twas wild.

But thou, O Hope! with eyes so fair,
What was thy delighted measure?
Still it whisper d promis'd pleasure,
And bade the lovely scenes at distance hail!
  Still would her touch the strain prolong;
  And from the rocks, the woods, the vale,
She call'd on Echo still through all the song;
  And where her sweetest theme she chose,
A soft responsive voice was heard at every close;
And Hope enchant'd smil'd, and wav'd her
    golden hair:

And longer had she sung—but with a frown
  Revenge impatient rose:
He threw his blood-stain'd sword in thunder
    down,
    And, with a withering look,
  The war-denouncing trumpet took,
  And blew a blast so loud and dread,
Were ne'er prophetic sounds so full of woe;

And ever and anon he beat
The doubling drum with furious heat;
And though sometimes, each dreary pause
between,
Dejected pity at his side
Her soul-subduing voice applied,
Yet still he kept his wild unalter'd mien,
While each strain'd ball of sight seem'd bursting
from his head.

Thy numbers, Jealousy, to nought were
fix'd;
Sad proof of thy distressful state;
Of diff'ring themes the veering song was
mix'd,
And now it courted love, now raving call'd on
Hate.

With eyes uprais'd, as one inspir'd'
Pale Melancholy sat retir'd,
And from her wild sequester'd seat,
In notes by distance made more sweet,
Pour'd through the mellow horn her pensive
soul;
And dashing soft from rocks around,
Bubbling runnels joined the sound;
Through glades and glooms the mingled mea-
sure stole:
Or o'er some haunted stream with fond
delay,
Round a holy calm diffusing.
Love of peace and lonely musing,
In hollow murmurs died away.

But, O! how alter'd was its sprightlier tone,
When Cheerfulness, a nymph of healthiest hue,
Her bow across her shoulder flung,
Her buskins gemm'd with morning dew,
Blew an inspiring air, that dale and thicket rung.
The hunter's call, to Fawn and Dryad
known;
The oak-crown'd sisters, and their chaste-
eyed queen,
Satyrs and sylvan boys, were seen
Peeping from forth their alleys green;
Brown Exercise rejoic'd to hear,
And Sport leap'd up, and seized his b
spear.

Last came Joy's ecstatic trial:
He, with viny crown advancing,
First to the lively pipe his hand address'd;
But soon he saw the brisk, awakening viol,

Whose sweet entrancing voice he lov'd the
best.
They would have thought, who heard the
strain,
They saw, in Tempe's vale, her native maids,
Amidst the festal sounding shades,
To some unwearied minstrel dancing:
While, as his flying fingers kiss'd the strings,
Love fram'd with Mirth a gay fantastic round,
Loose were her tresses seen, her zone unbound,
And he, amidst his frolic play,
As if he would the charming air repay,
Shook thousand odors from his dewy wings.

O Music! sphere-descended maid,
Friend of pleasure, wisdom's aid,
Why, Goddess! why, to us denied,
Lay'st thou thy ancient lyre aside?
As in that lov'd Athenian bow'r,
You learn'd an all-commanding pow'r;
Thy mimic soul, O nymph endear'd!
Can well recall what then it heard.
Where is thy native simple heart,
Devote to virtue, fancy, art?
Arise, as in that elder time,
Warm, energetic, chaste, sublime
Thy wonders in that godlike age
Fill thy recording Sister's page—
'Tis said, and I believe the tale,
Thy humblest reed could more prevail.
Had more of strength, diviner rage,
Than all which charms this laggard age;
Even all at once together found,
Cecilia's mingled world of sound.
O bid our vain endeavors cease,
Revive the just designs of Greece;
Return in all thy simple state,
Confirm the tale her sons relate!
                                        COLLINS.


## ADIEU.

ET time and chance combine, combine,
    Let time and chance combine:
    The _____ from heaven above,
    That love of yours was mine,
                My dear.
    That love of yours was mine.

The past is fled and gone, and gone,
    The past is fled and gone;
If naught but pain to me remain,

I'll fare in memory on,
My dear,
I'll fare in memory on.

The saddest tears must fall, must fall,
The saddest tears must fall;
In weal or woe, in this world below,
I love you ever and all,
My dear,
I love you ever and all.

A long road full of pain, of pain,
A long road full of pain,
One soul, one heart, sworn ne'er to part,—
We ne'er can meet again,
My dear,
We ne'er can meet again.

Hard fate will not allow, allow,
Hard fate will not allow;
We blessed were as the angels are,—
Adieu forever now,
My dear,
Adieu forever now.

CARLYLE.

## TO A WATERFOWL.

WHITHER, 'midst falling dew,
While glow the heavens with the last
steps of day,
Far, through their rosy depths, dost thou pursue
Thy solitary way?

Vainly the fowler's eye
Might mark thy distant flight to do thee wrong,
As, darkly limn'd upon the crimson sky,
Thy figure floats along.

Seek'st thou the plashy brink
Of weedy lake, or marge of river wide,
Or where the rocking billows rise and sink
On the chafed ocean side?

There is a Power whose care
Teaches thy way along that pathless coast,—
The desert and illimitable air,—
Lone wandering, but not lost.

All day thy wings have fann'd,
At that far height, the cold, thin atmosphere,
Yet stoop not, weary, to the welcome land,
Though the dark night is near.

And soon that toil shall end;
Soon shalt thou find a summer home, and rest,
And scream among thy fellows; reeds shall bend,
Soon, o'er thy shelter'd nest.

Thou'rt gone; the abyss of heaven
Hath swallow'd up thy form; yet on my heart
Deeply hath sunk the lesson thou hast given,
And shall not soon depart.

He who, from zone to zone,
Guides through the boundless sky thy certain
flight,
In the long way that I must tread alone,
Will lead my steps aright.

BRYANT.

## THE RAVEN.

ONCE upon a midnight dreary, while I
ponder'd, weak and weary,
Over many a quaint and curious volume of forgotten lore,—
While I nodded, nearly napping, suddenly there
came a tapping,
As of some one gently rapping, rapping at my
chamber-door,—
"'Tis some visitor," I mutter'd, "tapping at my
chamber-door,—
Only this, and nothing more."

Ah! distinctly I remember, it was in the bleak
December,
And each separate dying ember wrought its ghost
upon the floor.
Eagerly I wish'd the morrow;—vainly I sought
to borrow
From my books surcease of sorrow,—sorrow for
the lost Lenore,—
For the rare and radiant maiden whom the angels
name Lenore,—
Nameless here for evermore.

And the silken sad uncertain rustling of each purple curtain
Thrill'd me,—fill'd me with fantastic terrors never
felt before;
So that now, to still the beating of my heart, I
stood repeating
"'Tis some visitor entreating entrance at my
chamber-door;
Some late visitor entreating entrance at my
chamber-door:
This it is and nothing more."

Presently my soul grew stronger: hesitating
    then no longer,
"Sir," said I, "or madam, truly your forgive-
    ness I implore;
But the fact is I was napping, and so gently you
    came rapping,
And so faintly you came tapping, tapping at my
    chamber-door,
That I scarce was sure I heard you,"—here I
    open'd wide the door,—
      Darkness there, and nothing more.

Deep into that darkness peering, long I stood
    there wondering, fearing,
Doubting, dreaming dreams no mortal ever dared
    to dream before;
But the silence was unbroken, and the stillness
    gave no token,
And the only word there spoken was the whis-
    per'd word, " Lenore !"
This I whisper'd, and an echo murmur'd back
    the word, " Lenore !"
      Merely this, and nothing more.

Back into the chamber turning, all my soul with-
    in me burning,
Soon again I heard a tapping something louder
    than before.
"Surely," said I, —" surely that is something at
    my window-lattice;
Let me see, then, what thereat is, and this mys-
    tery explore,—
Let my heart be still a moment, and this mys-
    tery explore.
      'Tis the wind, and nothing more.

Open here I flung the shutter, when, with many
    a flirt and flutter,
In there stepp'd a stately Raven of the saintly
    days of yore.
Not the least obeisance made he; not a minute
    stopp'd or stay'd he;
But, with mien of lord or lady, perch'd above my
    chamber-door,—
Perch'd upon a bust of Pallas, just above my
    chamber-door,—
      Perch'd, and sat, and nothing more.

Then this ebony bird beguiling my sad fancy
    into smiling,
By the grave and stern decorum of the counte-
    nance it wore,

" Though thy crest be shorn and shaven, thou,"
    I said, " art sure no craven,
Ghastly, grim, and ancient Raven, wandering
    from the nightly shore,—
Tell me what thy lordly name is on the night's
    Plutonian shore !"
      Quoth the Raven, " Never more.'

Much I marvell'd this ungainly fowl to hear dis-
    course so plainly,
Though its answer little meaning—little rele-
    vancy—bore;
For we cannot help agreeing that no living
    human being
Ever yet was bless'd with seeing bird above his
    chamber-door,—
Bird or beast upon the sculptured bust above his
    chamber-door,—
      With such name as " Nevermore."

But the Raven, sitting lonely on that placid bust,
    spoke only
That one word, as if his soul in that one word he
    did outpour.
Nothing further then he utter'd;—not a feather
    then he flutter'd;—
Till I scarcely more than mutter'd, " Other
    friends have flown before—
On the morrow *he* will leave me, as my hopes
    have flown before."
      Then the bird said, " Never more."

Startled at the stillness broken by reply so aptly
    spoken,
"Doubtless," said I, " what it utters is its only
    stock and store,
Caught from some unhappy master, whom un-
    merciful disaster
Follow'd fast and follow'd faster, till his songs
    one burden bore,—
Till the dirges of his hope that melancholy
    burden bore,
      Of · Never—never more.' "

But the Raven still beguiling all my sad soul
    into smiling,
Straight I wheel'd a cushioned seat in front of
    bird and bust and door;
Then upon the velvet sinking, I betook myself
    to linking
Fancy unto fancy, thinking what this ominous
    bird of yore,—

What this grim, ungainly, ghastly, gaunt, and
 ominous bird of yore
  Meant in croaking, " Never more."

This I sat engaged in guessing, but no syllable
 expressing
To the fowl whose fiery eyes now burned into
 my bosom's core ;
This and more I sat divining, with my head at
 ease reclining
On the cushion's velvet lining that the lamp-
 light gloated o'er,
But whose velvet violet lining with the lamp-
 light gloating o'er
  *She* shall press, ah, never more!

Then, methought, the air grew denser, perfumed
 from an unseen censer
Swung by seraphim, whose footfalls tinkled on
 the tufted floor,
" Wretch ! " I cried, " thy god hath lent thee—
 by these angels he hath sent thee
Respite— respite and nepenthe from thy memories
 of Lenore!
Quaff, O quaff this kind nepenthe, and forget
 this lost Lenore !"
  Quoth the Raven, " Never more! "

" Prophet ! " said I, " thing of evil!—prophet
 still, if bird or devil !—
Whether tempter sent, or whether tempest toss'd
 thee here ashore,
Desolate, yet all undaunted, on this desert land
 enchanted —
On this home by horror haunted,—tell me truly,
 I implore,—
Is there—*is* there balm in Gilead?—tell me—tell
 me, I implore ! "
  Quoth the Raven, " Never more."

" Prophet ! " said I, " thing of evil ! "—prophet
 still, if bird or devil !
By that heaven that bends above us—by that
 God we both adore,
Tell this soul, with sorrow laden, if within the
 distant Aiden
It shall clasp a sainted maiden, whom the angels
 name Lenore,—
Clasp a rare and radiant maiden, whom the an-
 gels name Lenore !"
  Quoth the Raven, " Never more."

" Be that word our sign of parting, bird or
 fiend ! " I shrieked, upstarting—
" Get thee back into the tempest and the night's
 Plutonian shore !
Leave no black plume as a token of that lie thy
 soul hath spoken !
Leave my loneliness unbroken !—quit the bust
 above my door!
Take thy beak from out my heart, and take thy
 form from off my door !"
  Quoth the Raven, " Never more."

And the Raven, never flitting, still is sitting, still
 is sitting,
On the pallid bust of Pallas, just above my
 chamber-door ;
And his eyes have all the seeming of a demon's
 that is dreaming.
And the lamp-light, o'er him streaming, throws
 his shadow on the floor ;
And my soul from out that shadow that lies
 floating on the floor
  Shall be lifted—never more!
      POE.

## A PSALM OF LIFE.

What the heart of the young man said to the Psalmist.

TELL me not, in mournful numbers,
  Life is but an empty dream !
For the soul is dead that slumbers,
  And things are not what they seem.

Life is real !  Life is earnest !
  And the grave is not its goal ;
" Dust thou art, to dust returnest "
  Was not spoken of the soul.

Not enjoyment, and not sorrow,
  Is our destined end or way ;
But to act, that each to-morrow
  Find us farther than to-day.

Art is long, and Time is fleeting,
  And our hearts, though stout and brave,
Still, like muffled drums, are beating
  Funeral marches to the grave.

In the world's broad field of battle,
  In the bivouac of Life,
Be not like dumb,  driven cattle !
  Be a hero in the strife !

. Trust no Future, howe'er pleasant!
   Let the dead Past bury its dead!
Act—act in the living Present!
   Heart within, and God o'erhead!

Lives of great men all remind us
   We can make our lives sublime,
And, departing, leave behind us
   Footprints on the sands of time.

Footprints, that perhaps another,
   Sailing o'er life's solemn main,
A forlorn and shipwreck'd brother,
   Seeing, shall take heart again.

Let us, then, be up and doing.
   With a heart for any fate;
Still achieving, still pursuing,
   Learn to labor and to wait.

                LONGFELLOW.

## DAY IS DYING.

**D**AY is dying! Float, O song,
   Down the westward river,
Requiem chanting to the Day—
   Day, the mighty Giver.

Pierced by shafts of Time he bleeds,
   Melted rubies sending
Through the river and the sky,
   Earth and heaven blending;

All the long-drawn earthy banks
   Up to cloud-land lifting;
Slow between them drifts the swan,
   'Twixt two heavens drifting.

Wings half open, like a flower
   Inly deeply flushing,
Neck and breast as virgin's pure,—
   Virgin proudly blushing.

Day is dying! Float O swan,
   Down the ruby river;
Follow, song, in requiem
   To the mighty Giver.

             GEORGE ELIOT.

## LEAD, KINDLY LIGHT.

**L**EAD, Kindly Light, amid the encircling
       gloom,
   Lead Thou me on!
The night is dark, and I am far from home;
   Lead Thou me on!
Keep Thou my feet, I do not ask to see
The distant scene; one step enough for me.

I was not ever thus, nor prayed that Thou
   Shouldst lead me on;
I loved to see and choose my path; but now
   Lead Thou me on!
I loved the garish day, and, spite of fears,
Pride ruled my will. Remember not past years!

So long Thy power hath blest me, sure it still
   Will lead me on
O'er moor and fen, o'er crag and torrent, till
   The night is gone,
And with the morn those angel faces smile
Which I have loved long since, and lost awhile!
               NEWMAN.

## THE BLESSED DAMOZEL.

**T**HE blessed damozel leaned out
   From the gold bar of heaven:
Her eyes were deeper than the depth
   Of waters stilled at even;
She had three lilies in her hand,
   And the stars in her hair were seven.

Her robe, ungirt from clasp to hem,
   No wrought flowers did adorn,
But a white rose of Mary's gift,
   For service meetly worn:
Her hair that lay along her back
   Was yellow like ripe corn.

Her seemed she scarce had been a day
   One of God's choristers;
The wonder was not yet quite gone
   From that still look of hers;
Albeit, to them she left, her day
   Had counted as ten years.

(To one, it is ten years of years.
   . . . Yet now, and in this place,
Surely she leaned o'er me—her hair
   Fell all about my face. . . . .
Nothing: the autumn fall of leaves.
   The whole year sets apace.)

It was the rampart of God's house
　　That she was standing on ;
By God built over the sheer depth
　　The which is space begun ;
So high that looking downward thence
　　She scarce could see the sun.

It lies in heaven, across the flood
　　Of ether, as a bridge.
Beneath, the tides of day and night
　　With flame and darkness ridge
The void, as low as where this earth
　　Spins like a fretful midge.

Around her, lovers, newly met
　　'Mid deathless love's acclaims,
Spoke evermore among themselves
　　Their heart-remembered names ;
And the souls mounting up to God
　　Went by her like thin flames.

And still she bowed herself and stooped
　　Out of the circling charm ;
Until her bosom must have made
　　The bar·she leaned on warm,
And the lilies lay as if asleep
　　Along her bended arm.

From the fixed place of Heaven she saw
　　Time like a pulse shake fierce
Through all the worlds.  Her gaze still strove
　　Within the gulf to pierce
Its path ; and now she spoke as when
　　The stars sang in their spheres.

The sun was gone now ; the curled moon
　　Was like a little feather
Fluttering far down the gulf ; and now
　　She spoke through the still weather.
Her voice was like the voice the stars
　　Had when they sang together.

(Ah sweet!  Even now, in that bird's song,
　　Strove not her accents there,
Fain to be hearkened?  When those bells
　　Possessed the mid-day air,
Strove not his steps to reach my side
　　Down all the echoing stair?)

" I wish that he were come to me,
　　For he will come," she said.
" Have I not prayed in Heaven?—on earth,
　　Lord, Lord, has he not pray'd?
Are not two prayers a perfect strength?
　　And shall l feel afraid?

" When round his head the aureole clings,
　　And he is clothed in white,
I'll take his hand and go with him
　　To the deep wells of light ;
As unto a stream we will step down,
　　And bathe there in God's sight.

" We two will stand beside that shrine.
　　Occult, withheld, untrod,
Whose lamps are stirred continually
　　With prayer sent up to God ;
And see our old prayers, granted, melt
　　Each like a little cloud.

" We two will lie i' the shadow of
　　That living mystic tree
Within whose secret growth the Dove
　　Is sometimes felt to be,
While every leaf that His plumes touch
　　Saith His Name audibly.

"And I myself will teach to him,
　　I myself, lying so,
The songs I sing here ; which his voice
　　Shall pause in, hushed and slow,
And find some knowledge at each pause,
　　Or some new thing to know."

(Alas !  We two, we two, thou say'st !
　　Yea, one wast thou with me
That once of old.  But shall God lift
　　To endless unity
The soul whose likeness with thy soul
　　Was but its love for thee?)

" We two," she said, " will seek the groves
　　Where the Lady Mary is,
With her five handmaidens whose names
　　Are five sweet symphonies,
Cecily, Gertrude, Magdalen,
　　Margaret and Rosalys.

" Circlewise sit they, with bound locks
　　And foreheads garlanded ;
Into the fine cloth white like flame
　　Weaving the golden thread,
To fashion the birth-robes for them
　　Who are just born, being dead.

" He shall fear, haply, and be dumb :
　　When will I lay my cheek
To his, and tell about our love
　　Not once abashed or weak :
And the dear Mother will approve
　　My pride, and let me speak.

" Herself shall bring us, hand in hand,
    To Him round whom all souls
Kneel, the clear-ranged unnumbered heads
    Bowed with their aureoles :
And angels meeting us shall sing
    To their citherns and citoles.

" There will I ask of Christ the Lord
    Thus much for him and me :—
Only to live as once on earth
    With Love,—only to be,
As then awhile, forever now
    Together, I and he."

She gazed and listened and then said,
    Less sad of speech than mild,—
"All this is when he comes." She ceased.
    The light thrilled towards her, fill'd
With angels in strong level flight.
    Her eyes prayed, and she smil'd.

(I saw her smile.) But soon their path
    Was vague in distant spheres
And then she cast her arms along
    The golden barriers,
And laid her face between her hands,
    And wept. (I heard her tears.)
                               ROSSETTI.


## MARCO BOZZARIS.

AT midnight, in his guarded tent,
    The Turk was dreaming of the hour
When Greece, her knee in suppliance bent,
    Should tremble at his power :
In dreams through camp and court he bore
The trophies of a conqueror ;
    In dreams his song of triumph heard ;
Then wore his monarch's signet ring ;
Then pressed that monarch's throne,—a king,—
As wild his thoughts, and gay of wing
    As Eden's garden bird.

An hour passed on,—the Turk awoke ;
    That bright dream was his last ;
He woke to hear his sentries shriek,—
" To arms ! they come ! the Greek ! the Greek !"
He woke, to die midst flame and smoke,
And shout, and groan, and sabre-stroke,

And death-shots falling thick and fast
As lightnings from a mountain cloud ;
And heard, with voice as trumpet loud,
    Bozzaris cheer his band :—
" Strike—till the last armed foe expires !
Strike—for your altars and your fires !
Strike for the green graves of your sires,
    God, and your native land !"

They fought, like brave men, long and well ;
    They piled the ground with Moslem slain ;
They conquered ; but Bozzaris fell,
    Bleeding at every vein.
His few surviving comrades saw
His smile, when rang their proud hurrah,
    And the red field was won ;
Then saw in death his eyelids close,
Calmly as to a night's repose,
    Like flowers at set of sun.

Come to the bridal chamber, Death !
    Come to the mother's when she feels
For the first time her first-born's breath ;
    Come when the blessed seals
That close the pestilence are broke
And crowded cities wail its stroke ;
Come in Consumption's ghastly form,
The earthquake shock, the ocean storm ;
Come when the heart beats high and warm,
    With banquet song, and dance, and wine,—
And thou art terrible : the tear,
The groan, the knell, the pall, the bier,
And all we know, or dream, or fear,
    Of agony, are thine.

But to the hero, when his sword
    Has won the battle for the free,
Thy voice sounds like a prophet's word,
    And in its hollow tones are heard
    The thanks of millions yet to be.
Bozzaris ! with the storied brave
    Greece nurtured in her glory's time,
Rest thee : there is no prouder grave,
    Even in thine own proud clime.
    We tell thy doom without a sigh,
For thou art Freedom's now, and Fame's—
One of the few, the immortal names,
    That were not born to die !
                               HALLECK.

IGNORANCE

## THE AMERICAN FLAG.

WHEN Freedom, from her mountain
    height,
  Unfurled her standard to the air,
She tore the azure robe of night,
  And set the stars of glory there.
She mingled with its gorgeous dyes
The milky baldric of the skies,
And striped its pure celestial white,
With streakings of the morning light.
Then, from his mansion in the sun,
She called her eagle bearer down,
And gave into his mighty hand
The symbol of her chosen land.

Majestic monarch of the cloud,
  Who rear'st aloft thy regal form,
To hear the tempest trumpings loud,
  And see the lightning lances driven,
When strive the warriors of the storm,
  And rolls the thunder-drum of Heaven,—
Child of the Sun! to thee 'tis given
  To guard the banner of the free;
To hover in the sulphur smoke,
To ward away the battle stroke;
And bid its blendings shine afar,
Like rainbows on the cloud of war,
  The harbinger of victory!

Flag of the brave! thy folds shall fly,
The sign of hope and triumph high,
When speaks the signal trumpet tone,
And the long line comes gleaming on,—
Ere yet the life-blood, warm and wet,
Has dimmed the glistening bayonet,—
Each soldier's eye shall brightly turn
To where thy sky-born glories burn;
And, as his springing steps advance,
Catch war and vengeance from the glance.
And when the cannon-mouthings loud,
Heave in wild wreaths the battle shroud,
And gory sabres rise and fall
Like shoots of flame on midnight's pall,
Then shall thy meteor glances glow,
  And cowering foes shall fall beneath
Each gallant arm that strikes below
  That lovely messenger of death.

Flag of the seas! on ocean's wave
Thy stars shall glitter o'er the brave
When Death, careering on the gale,
Sweeps darkly round the bellied sail,
And frighted waves rush wildly back,
Before the broadside's reeling rack,
Each dying wanderer of the sea
Shall look at once to Heaven and thee;
And smile to see thy splendors fly,
In triumph, o'er his closing eye.

Flag of the free heart's hope and home,
  By angel's hands to valor given!
Thy stars have lit the welkin dome,
  And all thy hues were born in Heaven.
Forever float that standard sheet!
  Where breathes the foe but falls before us,
With Feeedom's soil beneath our feet,
  And Freedom's banner streaming o'er us!
                    DRAKE.

## GOOD-BYE, PROUD WORLD.

GOOD-BYE, proud world! I'm going
    home:
  Thou'rt not my friend. and I'm not thine.
Long through thy weary crowds I roam;
  A river-ark on the ocean's brine,
Long I've been toss'd like the driven foam;
But now, proud world! I'm going home.

Good-bye to Flattery's fawning face;
To Grandeur, with his wise grimace;
To upstart Wealth's averted eye;
To Supple Office, low and high;
To crowded halls, to court and street;
To frozen hearts and hasting feet;
To those who go, and those who come;
Good-bye, proud world! I'm going home.

I am going to my own hearth-stone,
Bosom'd in yon green hills alone—
A secret nook in a pleasant land,
Whose groves the frolic fairies plann'd;
Where arches green, the livelong day,
Echo the blackbird's roundelay,
And vulgar feet have never trod
A spot that is sacred to thought and God.

Oh, when I am safe in my sylvan home,
I tread on the pride of Greece and Rome;
And when I am stretch'd beneath the pines,
Where the evening star so holy shines,
I laugh at the lore and the pride of man,
At the sophist schools, and the learned clan;
For what are they all in their high conceit,
When man in the bush with God may meet!
                    EMERSON.

## THE END OF THE PLAY.

THE play is done,—the curtain drops,
  Slow falling to the prompter's bell ;
A moment yet the actor stops,
  And looks around, to say farewell.
It is an irksome word and task ;
  And, when he's laughed and said his say,
He shows, as he removes the mask,
  A face that's anything but gay.

One word, ere yet the evening ends,
  Let's close it with a parting rhyme ;
And pledge a hand to all young friends,
  As fits the merry Christmas time ;
On life's wide scene you too have parts
  That Fate ere long shall bid you play ;
Good night ! with honest, gentle hearts
  A kindly greeting go alway !

Good night ! I'd say the griefs, the joys,
  Just hinted in this mimic page,
The triumphs and defeats of boys, ·
  Are but repeated in our age ;
I'd say your woes were not less keen,
  Your hopes more vain, than those of men,
Your pangs or pleasures of fifteen
  At forty-five played o'er again.

I'd say we suffer and we strive
  Not less nor more as men than boys,
With grizzled beards at forty-five,
  As erst at twelve in corduroys.
And if, in time of sacred youth,
  We learn at home to love and pray,
Pray Heaven that early love and truth
  May never wholly pass away.

And in the world, as in the school,
  I'd say how fate may change and shift,
The prize be sometimes with the fool,
  The race not always to the swift :
The strong may yield, the good may fall,
  The great man be a vulgar clown,
The knave be lifted over all,
  The kind cast pitilessly down.

  ·     ·     ·     ·     ·     ·

Come wealth or want, come good or ill,
  Let young and old accept their part,
And bow before the Awful Will,
  And bear it with an honest heart.

Who misses, or who wins the prize ?
  Go, lose or conquer as you can ;
But if you fail, or if you rise,
  Be each, pray God, a gentleman.

A gentleman, or old or young !
  (Bear kindly with my humble lays,)
The sacred chorus first was sung
  Upon the first of Christmas days,
The shepherds heard it overhead—
  The joyful angels raised it then ;
Glory to Heaven on high, it said,
  And peace on earth to gentlemen !

My song, save this, is little worth ;
  I lay the weary pen aside,
And wish you health and love and mirth,
  As fits the solemn Christmas-tide ;
As fits the holy Christmas birth,
  Be this, good friends, our carol still :
Be peace on earth, be peace on earth,
  To men of gentle will.

                    THACKERAY.

## THE BATTLE OF IVRY.

NOW glory to the Lord of Hosts, from
    whom all glories are !
And glory to our sovereign Liege, King Henry of
    Navarre !
Now let there be the merry sound of music and
    the dance,
Through thy corn-fields green, and sunny vales,
    O pleasant land of France !
And thou, Rochelle, our own Rochelle, proud city
    of the waters,
Again let rapture light the eyes of all thy mourn-
    ing daughters ;
As thou wert constant in our ills, be joyous in
    our joy,
For cold and stiff and still are they who wrought
    thy walls annoy.
Hnrrah ! hurrah ! a single field hath turned the
    chance of war !
Hurrah ! hurrah ! for Ivry and King Henry of
    Navarre !

Oh ! how our hearts were beating, when, at the
    dawn of day,
We saw the army of the League drawn out in
    long array ;

With all its priest-led citizens, and all its rebel peers,

And Appenzel's stout infantry and Egmont's Flemish spears !

There rode the brood of false Lorraine, the curses of our land !

And dark Mayenne was in the midst, a truncheon in his hand ;

And, as we looked on them, we thought of Seine's empurpled flood,

And good Coligni's hoary hair all dabbled with his blood ;

And we cried unto the living God, who rules the fate of war,

To fight for His own holy Name, and Henry of Navarre.

The King has come to marshal us, in all his armor drest,

And he has bound a snow-white plume upon his gallant crest !

He looked upon his People, and a tear was in his eye ;

He looked upon the traitors, and his glance was stern and high.

Right graciously he smiled on us, as rolled from wing to wing,

Down all our line, in deafening shout, " God save our lord the King !"

"And if my standard-bearer fall,—as fall full well he may,

For never saw I promise yet of such a bloody fray,—

Press where you see my white plume shine, amid the ranks of war,

And be your oriflamme, to-day, the helmet of Navarre."

Hurrah ! the foes are moving ! Hark to the mingled din

Of fife, and steed, and trump, and drum, and roaring culverin !

The fiery Duke is pricking fast across Saint Andre's plain,

With all the hireling chivalry of Guelders and Almayne.

Now, by the lips of those ye love, fair gentlemen of France,

Charge for the golden lilies now, upon them with the lance !

A thousand spurs are striking deep, a thousand spears in rest,

A thousand knights are pressing close behind the snow-white crest.

And in they burst, and on they rushed, while, like a guiding star,

Amidst the thickest carnage blazed the helmet of Navarre.

Now, God be praised, the day is ours ! Mayenne hath turned his rein,

D'Aumale hath cried for quarter—the Flemish Count is slain ;

Their ranks are breaking like thin clouds before a Biscay gale ;

The field is heaped with bleeding steeds, and flags, and cloven mail,

And then we thought on vengeance, and all along our van

" Remember St. Bartholomew !" was passed from man to man ;

But outspake gentle Henry, then,—" No Frenchman is my foe ;

Down, down with every foreigner ! but let your brethren go."

O ! was there ever such a knight, in friendship or in war,

As our sovereign lord, King Henry, the soldier of Navarre !

Ho ! maidens of Vienna ! Ho ! matrons of Lucerne !

Weep, weep and rend your hair for those who never shall return !

Ho ! Philip, send for charity thy Mexican pistoles,

That Antwerp monks may sing a mass for thy poor spearmen's souls.

Ho ! gallant nobles of the League, look that your arms be bright !

Ho ! burghers of St. Genevieve, keep watch and ward to-night !

For our God hath crushed the tyrant, our God hath raised the slave,

And mocked the counsel of the wise, and the valor of the brave.

Then glory to His holy name, from whom all glories are !

And glory to our sovereign lord, King Henry of Navarre.

MACAULAY.

## THE THREE FISHERS.

THREE fishers went sailing out into the
          west,
Out into the west as the sun went down;
Each thought on the woman who loved him the
          best,
And the children stood watching them out of
          the town:
For men must work, and women must weep,
And there's little to earn, and many to keep,
          Though the harbor bar be moaning.

Three wives sat up in the lighthouse tower,
And they trimmed the lamps as the sun went
          down;
They looked at the squall, and they looked at
          the shower,
And the night-rack came rolling up ragged and
          brown.
But men must work, and women must weep,
Though storms be sudden, and waters deep,
          And the harbor bar be moaning.

Three corpses lay out on the shining sands,
In the morning gleam as the tide went down,
And the women are weeping and wringing their
          hands
For those who will never come home to the
          town:
For men must work, and women must weep,
And the sooner it's over, the sooner to sleep,
          And good bye to the bar and it's moaning.
                              KINGSLEY.

## THE BROOKSIDE.

I WANDERED by the brookside,
     I wandered by the mill;
I could not hear the brook flow,—
     The noisy wheel was still;
There was no burr of grasshopper,
     No chirp of any bird,
But the beating of my own heart
     Was all the sound I heard.

I sat beneath the elm-tree,
     I watched the long, long shade,
And as it grew still longer,
     I did not feel afraid;
For I listened for a footfall,
     I listened for a word—
But the beating of my own heart
     Was all the sound I heard.

He came not—no, he came not—
     The night came on alone—
The little stars sat one by one
     Each on his golden throne:
The evening wind passed by my cheek,
     The leaves above were stirred—
But the beating of my own heart
     Was all the sound I heard.

Fast, silent tears were flowing,
     When something stood behind:
A hand was on my shoulder—
     I knew its touch was kind:
It drew me nearer—nearer—
     We did not speak one word,
For the beating of our own hearts
     Was all the sound I heard.
                              MILNES.

## THE CHAMBERED NAUTILUS.

THIS is the ship of pearl, which, poets feign,
     Sails the unshadow'd main,—
The venturous bark that flings
On the sweet summer wind its purpled wings
In gulfs enchanted, where the siren sings,
     And coral reefs lie bare,
Where the cold sea-maids rise to sun their
     streaming hair.

Its webs of living gauze no more unfurl;
     Wreck'd is the ship of pearl!
     And every chamber'd cell,
Where its dim dreaming life was wont to dwell,
As the frail tenant shaped his growing shell,
     Before thee lies reveal'd—
Its Iris'd ceiling rent, its sunless crypt unseal'd!

Year after year beheld the silent toil
     That spread his lustrous coil;
     Still, as the spiral grew,
He left the past year's dwelling for the new,
Stole with soft step its shining archway through,
     Built up its idle door,
Stretch'd in his last-found home, and knew the
     old no more.

Thanks for the heavenly message brought by
     thee,
     Child of the wandering sea,
     Cast from her lap, forlorn!
From thy dead lips a clearer note is born
Than ever Triton blew from wreathed horn!

PAYING THE REAPERS

While on mine ear it rings,
Through the deep caves of thought I hear a voice
    that sings :—

Build thee more stately mansions, O my soul,
    As the swift seasons roll !
    Leave thy low-vaulted past !
Let each new temple, nobler than the last,
Shut thee from heaven with a dome more vast,
    Till thou at length art free,
Leaving thine outgrown shell by life's unrest-
    ing sea !
               HOLMES.

## EVELYN HOPE.

BEAUTIFUL Evelyn Hope is dead !
    Sit and watch by her side an hour.
That is her book-shelf, this her bed ;
    She plucked that piece of geranium-flower,
Beginning to die, too, in the glass.
    Little has yet been changed, I think ;
The shutters are shut,—no light may pass
    Save two long rays through the hinge's chink.

Sixteen years old when she died !
    Perhaps she had scarcely heard my name,—
It was not her time to love ; beside,
    Her life had many a hope and aim,
Duties enough and little cares ;
    And now was quiet, now astir,—
Till God's hand beckoned unawares,
    And the sweet white brow is all of her.

Is it too late, then, Evelyn Hope?
    What ! your soul was pure and true :
The good stars met in your horoscope,
    Made you of spirit, fire, and dew ;
And just because I was thrice as old,
    And our paths in the world diverged so wide,
Each was naught to each, must I be told?
    We were fellow-mortals,—naught beside?

No, indeed ! for God above
    Is great to grant as mighty to make,
And creates the love to reward the love ;
    I claim you still, for my own love's sake !
Delayed, it may be, for more lives yet,
    Through worlds I shall traverse, not a few ;
Much is to learn and much to forget
    Ere the time be come for taking you.

But the time will come,—at last it will,—
    When, Evelyn Hope, what is meant, I shall say,
In the lower earth,—in the years long still,—
    That body and soul are so pure and gay?
Why your hair was amber I shall divine,
    And your mouth of your own geranium's red,—
And what you would do with me, in fine,
    In the new life come in the old one's stead.

I have lived, I shall say, so much since then,
    Given up myself so many times,
Gained me the gains of various men,
    Ransacked the ages, spoiled the climes ;
Yet one thing,—one,—in my soul's full scope,
    Either I missed or itself missed me,
And I want and find you, Evelyn Hope !
    What is the issue? let us see !

I loved you, Evelyn, all the while :
    My heart seemed full as it could hold,—
There was place and to spare for the frank young
    smile,
    And the red young mouth, and the hair's
    young gold.
So hush ! I will give you this leaf to keep :
    See, I shut it inside the sweet, cold hand.
There, that is our secret ! go to sleep ;
    You will wake, and remember, and understand,
               BROWNING.

## THREE KISSES.

FIRST time he kissed me, he but only
    kissed
The fingers of this hand wherewith I write ;
And ever since it grew more clean and white,—
Slow to world-greetings—quick with its " O,
    list,"
When the angels speak. A ring of amethyst
I could not wear here, plainer to my sight
Than that first kiss. The second passed in
    height
The first, and sought the forehead, and half
    missed,
Half falling on the hair. O beyond meed !
That was the chrism of love, which love's own
    crown,
With sanctifying sweetness, did precede.
The third upon my lips was folded down
In perfect, purple state ; since when, indeed,
I have been proud and said, " My love, my
    own."
             MRS. BROWNING.

16

## FAREWELL.

THE same year calls, and one goes hence
   with another,
And men sit sad that were glad for their sweet
   song's sake;
The same year beckons, and younger with elder
   brother,
   Takes mutely the cup from his hand that we
   all must take:
They pass ere the leaves be past or the snows be
   come,—
   And the birds are loud, but the lips that out-
   sung them are dumb.
Time takes them home that we loved,—fair
   names and famous,—
   To the soft, long sleep, to the broad, sweet
   bosom of death:
But the flower of their souls he shall take not
   away to shame us,
   Nor the lips lack song forever, that now lack
   breath;
For with us shall the music and perfume that die
   not dwell,
Though the dead to our dead bid welcome, and
   we,—farewell!

             SWINBURNE.

## LOCKSLEY HALL.

COMRADES, leave me here a little, while
   as yet 'tis early morn:
Leave me here, and when you want me, sound
   upon the bugle horn.

'Tis the place, and all around it, as of old, the
   curlews call,
Dreary gleams about the moorland flying over
   Locksley Hall;

Locksley Hall, that in the distance overlooks the
   sandy tracts,
And the hollow ocean-ridges roaring into cater-
   acts.

Many a night from yonder ivied casement, ere I
   went to rest,
Did I look on great Orion sloping slowly to the
   West.

Many a night I saw the Pleiads, rising thro' the
   mellow shade,
Glitter like a swarm of fire-flies tangled in a silver braid.

Here about the beach I wander'd, nourishing a
   youth sublime
With the fairy tales of science, and the long result of Time;

When the centuries behind me like a fruitful land
   reposed;
When I clung to all the present for the promise
   that it closed:

When I dipt into the future far as human eye
   could see;
Saw the Vision of the world, and all the wonder
   that would be.—

In the Spring a fuller crimson comes upon the
   robin's breast;
In the Spring the wanton lapwing gets himself
   another crest;

In the Spring a livelier iris changes on the bur-
   nished dove;
In the Spring a young man's fancy lightly turns
   to thoughts of love.

Then her cheek was pale and thinner than should
   be for one so young,
And her eyes on all my motions with a mute observance hung.

And I said, " My cousin Amy, speak, and speak
   the truth to me,
Trust me, cousin, all the current of my being sets
   to thee."

On her pallid cheek and forehead came a color
   and a light,
As I have seen the rosy red flushing in the northern night.

And she turn'd—her bosom shaken with a sudden storm of sighs—
All the spirit deeply dawning in the dark of hazel
   eyes—

Saying, "I have hid my feelings, fearing they
   should do me wrong";
Saying, " Dost thou love me, cousin?" weeping,
   " I have loved thee long."

   .     .     .     .     .     .     .

Many an evening by the waters did we watch
   the stately ships,
And our spirits rush'd together at the touching
   of the lips.

O my cousin, shallow-hearted! O my Amy,
  mine no more!
O the dreary, dreary moorland! O the barren,
  barren shore!

Falser than all fancy fathoms, falser than all
  songs have sung,
Puppet to a father's threat, and servile to a shrew-
  ish tongue!

Is it well to wish thee happy?—having known
  me—to decline
On a range of lower feelings and a narrower
  heart than mine!

Yet it shall be; thou shalt lower to his level day
  by day,
What is fine within thee growing coarse to sympathize with clay.

As the husband is, the wife is: thou art mated
  with a clown,
And the grossness of his nature will have weight
  to drag thee down.

.    .    .    .    .    .    .

Better thou and I were lying, hidden from the
  heart's disgrace,
Roll'd in one another's arms, and silent in a last
  embrace.

Cursed be the social wants that sin against the
  strength of youth!
Cursed be the social lies that warp us from the
  living truth!

Cursed be the sickly forms that err from honest
  Nature's rule!
Cursed be the gold that gilds the straiten'd fore-
  head of the fool!

.    .    .    .    .    .    .

Where is comfort? in division of the records of
  the mind?
Can I part her from herself, and love her, as I
  knew her, kind!

.    .    .    .    .    .    ,

Can I think of her as dead, and love her for the
  love she bore!
No—she never loved me truly: love is love for
  evermore.

Comfort? comfort scorn'd of devils! this is truth
  the poet sings,
That a sorrow's crown of sorrow is remembering
  happier things.

.    .    .    .    .    .    .

Overlive it—lower yet—be happy! wherefore
  should I care?
I myself must mix with action, lest I wither by
  despair.

What is that which I should turn to, lighting
  upon days like these?
Every door is barr'd with gold, and opens but to
  golden keys.

Every gate is throng'd with suitors, all the mar-
  kets overflow.
I have but an angry fancy: what is that which
  I should do?

I had been content to perish, falling on the foe-
  man's ground,
When the ranks are roll'd in vapor, and the winds
  are laid with sound.

But the jingling of the guinea helps the hurt that
  Honor feels,
And the nations do but murmur, snarling at each
  other's heels.

Can I but relive in sadness? I will turn that ear-
  lier page.
Hide me from my deep emotion, O thou won-
  Mother-Age!

Make me feel the wild pulsation that I felt before
  the strife,
When I heard my days before me, and the tumult
  of my life;

Yearning for the large excitement that the coming years would yield,
Eager-hearted as a boy when first he leaves his
  father's field,

And at night along the dusky highway near and
  nearer drawn,
Sees in heaven the light of London flaring like a
  dreary dawn;

And his spirit leaps within him to be gone before
  him then,
Underneath the light he looks at, in among the
  throngs of men;

Men, my brothers, men the workers, ever reap-
  ing something new:
That which they have done but earnest of the
  things that they shall do:

For I dipt into the future, far as human eye could
  see,
Saw the Vision of the world, and all the wonders
  that would be;

Saw the heavens filled with commerce, argosies
of magic sails,
Pilots of the purple twilight, dropping down with
costly bales ;

Heard the heavens fill with shouting, and there
rain'd a ghastly dew
From the nations' airy navies grappling in the
central blue ;

Far along the world-wide whisper of the south-
wind rushing warm,
With the standards of the peoples plunging thro'
the thunder-storm ;

Till the war-drum throbb'd no longer, and the
battle flags were furl'd
In the Parliament of man, the Federation of the
world.

There the common sense of most shall hold a
fretful realm in awe,
And the kindly earth shall slumber, lapt in universal law.

.    .    .    .    .    .    .

Slowly comes a hungry people, as a lion creep-
ing nigher,
Glares at one that nods and winks behind a
slowly dying fire.

Yet I doubt not thro' the ages one increasing purpose runs,
And the thoughts of men are widen'd with the
process of the suns.

What is that to him that reaps not harvest of his
youthful joys,
Tho' the deep heart of existence beat for ever like
a boy's?

Knowledge comes, but wisdom lingers, and I lin-
ger on the shore,
And the individual withers, and the world is
more and more.

Knowledge comes, but wisdom lingers, and he
bears a laden breast,
Full of sad experience, moving toward the stillness of his rest.

.    .    .    .    .    .    .

Weakness to be wroth with weakness ! woman's
pleasure, woman's pain —
Nature made them blinder motions bounded in a
shallower brain :

Woman is the lesser man, and all thy passions,
matched with mine,
Are as moonlight unto sunlight, and as water
unto wine —

Here at least, where nature sickens, nothing.
Ah, for some retreat
Deep in yonder shining Orient, where my life
began to beat ;

Where in wild Mahratta-battle fell my father
evil-starr'd ; —
I was left a trampled orphan, and a selfish uncle's ward.

Or to burst all links of habit — there to wander
far away,
On from island unto island at the gateways of
the day.

Larger constellations burning, yellow moons and
happy skies,
Breadths of tropic shade and palms in cluster,
knots of Paradise.

Never comes the trader, never floats an European
flag,
Slides the bird o'er lustrous woodland, swings
the trailer from the crag ;

Droops the heavy-blossomed bower, hangs the
heavy-fruited tree —
Summer isles of Eden lying in dark-purple
spheres of sea.

There methinks would be enjoyment more than
in this march of mind,
In the steamship, in the railway, in the thoughts
that shake mankind.

.    .    .    .    .    .    .

Fool, again the dream, the fancy ! but I *know* my
words are wild,
But I count the gray barbarian lower than the
Christian child.

*I*, to herd with narrow foreheads, vacant of our
glorious gains,
Like a beast with lower pleasures, like a beast
with lower pains !

Mated with a squalid savage — what to me were
sun or clime?
I the heir of all the ages, in the foremost files of
time —

ARREST IN THE VILLAGE

I that rather held it better men should perish one
    by one,
Than that earth should stand at gaze like Josh-
    ua's moon in Ajalon!

Not in vain the distant beacons. Forward, for-
    ward let us range.
Let the great world spin for ever down the ring-
    ing grooves of change.

Thro' the shadow of the globe we sweep into the
    younger day:
Better fifty years of Europe than a cycle of Ca-
    thay.

.    .    .    .    .    .

Howsoever these things be, a long farewell to
    Locksley Hall!
Now for me the woods may wither, now for me
    the roof-tree fall.

Comes a vapor from the margin, blackening over
    heath and holt,
Cramming all the blast before it, in its breast a
    thunderbolt.

Let it fall on Locksley Hall, with rain or hail or
    fire or snow!
For the mighty wind arises, roaring seaward,
    and I go.

TENNYSON.

## MAUD MULLER.

AUD MULLER, on a summer's day,
    Raked the meadow sweet with hay.

Beneath her torn hat glow'd the wealth
Of simple beauty and rustic health.

Singing, she wrought, and her merry glee
The mock-bird echoed from his tree.

But, when she glanced to the far-off town,
White from its hill-slope looking down,

The sweet song died, and a vague unrest
And a nameless longing fill'd her breast,—

A wish that she hardly dared to own,
For something better than she had known.

The Judge rode slowly down the lane,
Smoothing his horse's chestnut mane,

He drew his bridle in the shade
Of the apple trees, to greet the maid ;

And ask'd a draught from the spring that flow'd
Through the meadow across the road.

She stoop'd where the cool spring bubbled up,
And fill'd for him her small tin cup,

And blush'd as she gave it, looking down
On her feet so bare, and her tatter'd gown.

" Thanks! " said the Judge, " a sweeter draught
From a fairer hand was never quaff'd."

He spoke of the grass and flowers and trees
Of the singing birds and the humming bees,

Then talk'd of the haying, and wonder'd whether
The cloud in the west would bring foul weather.

And Maud forgot her brier-torn gown,
And her graceful ankles bare and brown ;

And listen'd, while a pleased surprise
Look'd from her long-lash'd hazel eyes.

At last, like one who for delay
Seeks a vain excuse, he rode away.

Maud Muller look'd and sigh'd : "Ah me!
That I the Judge's bride might be!

" He would dress me up in silks so fine,
And praise and toast me at his wine.

" My father should wear a broadcloth coat ;
My brother should sail a painted boat.

"I'd dress my mother so grand and gay,
And the baby should have a new toy each day.

"And I'd feed the hungry, and clothe the poor,
And all should bless me who left our door."

The Judge look'd back as he climbed the hill,
And saw Maud Muller standing still.

"A form more fair, a face more sweet,
Ne'er hath it been my lot to meet.

"And her modest answer and graceful air
Show her wise and good as she is fair.

" Would she were mine, and I to-day,
Like her, a harvester of hay :

" No doubtful balance of rights and wrongs,
Nor weary lawyers with endless tongues,

" But low of cattle and song of birds,
And health, and quiet, and loving words."

But he thought of his sisters proud and cold,
And his mother vain of her rank and gold.

So, closing his heart, the Judge rode on,
And Maud was left in the field alone.

But the lawyers smiled that afternoon,
When he humm'd in court an old love-tune.

And the young girl mused beside the well,
Till the rain on the unraked clover fell.

He wedded a wife of richest dower,
Who lived for fashion, as he for power.

Yet oft, in his marble hearth's bright glow
He watch'd a picture come and go:

And sweet Maud Muller's hazel eyes
Look'd out in their innocent surprise.

Oft, when the wine in his glass was red,
He long'd for the wayside well instead,

And clos'd his eyes on his garnish'd rooms,
To dream of meadows and clover-blooms.

And the proud man sigh'd, with a secret pain:
"Ah, that I were free again!

"Free as when I rode that day,
Where the barefoot maiden raked her hay."

She wedded a man unlearn'd and poor,
And many children play'd round her door.

But care, and sorrow, and childbirth pain,
Left their traces on heart and brain.

And oft, when the summer sun shone hot
On the new-mown hay in the meadow lot,

And she heard the little spring brook fall
Over the roadside, through the wall,

In the shade of the apple tree again
She saw a rider draw his rein,

And, gazing down with timid grace,
She felt his pleased eyes read her face.

Sometimes her narrow kitchen walls
Stretch'd away into stately halls;

The weary wheel to a spinnet turn'd,
The tallow candle an astral burn'd,

And for him who sat by the chimney lug,
Dozing and grumbling o'er pipe and mug,

A manly form at her side she saw,
And joy was duty, and love was law.

Then she took up her burden of life again,
Saying only, "It might have been."

Alas for maiden; alas for Judge,
For rich repiner and household drudge!

God pity them both, and pity us all,
Who vainly the dreams of youth recall.

For of all sad words of tongue or pen,
The saddest are these: "It might have been!"

Ah, well! for us all some sweet hope lies
Deeply buried from human eyes;

And, in the hereafter, angels may
Roll the stone from its grave away!

WHITTIER.

## JUNE.

EARTH gets its price for what Earth gives
us;
  The beggar is taxed for a corner to die in;
The priest has his fee who comes and shrieves us;
  We bargain for the graves we lie in;
At the Devil's booth are all things sold,
Each ounce of dross costs its ounce of gold;
  For a cap and bells our lives we pay,
Bubbles we buy with the whole soul's tasking;
  'Tis heaven alone that is given away,
'Tis only God may be had for the asking;
  No price is set on the lavish summer,
  June may be had by the poorest comer.

And what is so rare as a day in June?
  Then, if ever, come perfect days;
Then heaven tries the earth if it be in tune,
  And over it softly her warm ear lays.
Whether we look, or whether we listen,
  We hear life murmur, or see it glisten;
Every clod feels a stir of might,
  An instinct within it that reaches and towers,
And, groping blindly above it for light,
  Climbs to a soul in grass and flowers.

Now is the high-tide of the year,
  And whatever of life hath ebbed away
Comes flooding back, with a ripply cheer.
  Into every bare inlet and creek and bay;
Now the heart is so full that a drop overfills it,
  We are happy now because God wills it;
No matter how barren the past may have been,
  The soul partakes the season's youth,
And the sulphurous rifts of passion and woe
  Lie deep 'neath a silence pure and smooth,
Like burnt-out craters healed with snow.

LOWELL.

## THE BELLS OF SHANDON.

WITH deep affection
    And recollection
I often think of
    Those Shandon bells,
Whose sounds so wild would,
    In the days of childhood,
Fling round my cradle
    Their magic spells.

On this I ponder
    Where'er I wander,
And thus grow fonder,
    Sweet Cork, of thee,—
With thy bells of Shandon,
    That sound so grand on
The pleasant waters
    Of the river Lee.

I've heard bells tolling
    "Old Adrian's Mole" in,
Their thunder rolling
    From the Vatican,
And cymbals glorious
    Swinging uproarious
In the gorgeous turrets
    Of Notre Dame.

But the sounds are sweeter
    Than the dome of Peter
Flings o'er the Tiber,
    Pealing solemnly,—
O, the bells of Shandon
    Sound far more grand on
The pleasant waters
    Of the river Lee.

There's a bell in Moscow,
    While on tower and kiosk O
In St. Sophia
    The Turkman gets,
And loud in air
    Calls men to prayer,
From the tapering summit
    Of tall minarets.

Such empty phantom
    I freely grant them;
But there's an anthem
    More dear to me,—
'Tis the bells of Shandon,
    That sound so grand on
The pleasant waters
    Of the river Lee.
                    FATHER PROUT.

## LONGING FOR HOME.

THERE once was a nest in a hollow,
    Down in the mosses and knot-grass press'd,
Soft and warm and full to the brim;
Vetches leaned over it purple and dim;
    With buttercup buds to follow.

I pray you hear my song of a nest,
    For it is not long;—
You shall never light in a summer quest
    The bushes among—
Shall never light on a prouder sitter,
    A fairer nestful, nor ever know
A softer sound than their tender twitter,
    That wind-like did come and go.

I had a nestful once of my own—
    Ah, happy, happy I!
Right dearly I loved them; but when they were grown
They spread out their wings to fly.
Oh, one after one they flew away,
    Far up to the heavenly blue,
To the better country, the upper day;
    And—I wish I was going too.

I pray you, what is the nest to me,
    My empty nest?
And what is the shore where I stood to see
    My boat sail down to the west?
Can I call that home where I anchor yet,
    Though my good man has sailed?
Can I call that home where my nest was set,
    Now all its hope has failed?
Nay, but the port where my sailor went,
    And the land where my nestlings be;
There is the home where my thoughts are sent,
    The only home for me—
                Ah, me!
                    INGELOW.

## MY MIND TO ME A KINGDOM IS.

MY minde to me a kingdome is;
    Such perfect joy therein I finde
As far exceeds all earthly blisse
    That God or nature hath assignde.
Though much I want, that most would have,
Yet still my mind forbids to crave.

Content I live, this is my stay;
　I seek no more than may suffice;
I presse to beare no haughtie sway;
　Look what I lack my mind supplies.
Loe! thus I triumph like a king,
Content with that my mind doth bring.

I see how plentie surfets oft,
　And hastie clymbers soonest fall:
I see that such as sit aloft
　Mishap doth threaten most of all:
These get with toile, and keep with feare:
Such cares my mind could never beare.

No princely pompe, nor welthie store.
　No force to winne the victorie,
No wylie wit to salve a sore,
　No shape to winne a lover's eye;
To none of these I yeeld as thrall,
For why, my mind despiseth all.

Some have too much, yet still they crave,
　I little have, yet seek no more;
They are but poore, though much they have;
　And I am rich with little store;
They poor, I rich; they beg, I give;
They lacke, I lend; they pine, I live.

I laugh not at another's losse,
　I grudge not at another's gaine;
No worldly wave my mind can tosse,
　I brooke that is another's bane.
I feare no foe, nor fawne on friend,
I loathe not life, nor dread mine end.

I joy not in no earthly blisse;
　I weigh not Crœsus' welth a straw;
For care, I care not what it is;
　I fear not fortune's fatall law.
My mind is such as may not move
For beautie bright or force of love.

I wish but what I have at will;
　I wander not to seek for more;
I like the plaine, I climb no hill;
　In greatest stormes I sitte on shore,
And laugh at them that toile in vaine
To get what must be lost againe.

I kisse not where I wish to kill;
　I feigne not love where most I hate;
I breake no sleep to winne my will;
　I wayte not at the mighties gate;
Scorne no poore, I feare no rich,
I feel no want, nor have too much.

The court, ne cart, I like, ne loathe;
　Extreames are counted worst of all:
The golden meane betwixt them both
　Doth surest sit, and fears no fall:
This is my choyce, for why, I finde
No wealth is like a quiet minde.

My wealth is health and perfect ease,
　My conscience clere my chiefe defence:
I never seek by brybes to please,
　Nor by desert to give offence;
Thus do I live, thus will I die;
Would all did so as well as I.

MARLOW.

## WHAT CONSTITUTES A STATE.

WHAT constitutes a state?
　　　Not high-rais'd battlement and
　　labored mound,
Thick wall or moated gate;
　Not cities proud, with spires and turrets
　　crown'd:
Not bays and broad-arm'd ports,
　Where, laughing at the storm, rich navies ride:
Not starr'd and spangled courts,
　Where low-bred baseness wafts perfume to
　　pride:
No—men, high-minded men,
　With powers as far above dull brutes endu'd,
In forest, brake, or den,
　As beasts excel cold rocks and brambles rude:
Men, who their duties know.
　But know their rights: and, knowing, dare
　　maintain,
Prevent the long-aim'd blow,
　And crush the tyrant, while they rend the
　　chain.
These constitute a state:
　And sovereign law, that state's collected will,
O'er thrones and globes elate,
　Sits empress, crowning good, repressing ill.

JONES.

## TO ALTHEA FROM PRISON.

WHEN love with unconfined wings
　　Hovers within my gates,
And my divine Althea brings
　　To whisper at the grates;
When I lie tangled in her hair
　　And fetter'd to her eye,
The birds that wanton in the air
　　Know no such liberty.

When flowing cups run swiftly round
    With no allaying Thames,
Our careless heads with roses crown'd,
    Our hearts with loyal flames;
When thirsty grief in wine we steep,
    When healths and draughts go free,
Fishes that tipple in the deep
    Know no such liberty,

When, linnet-like, confined, I
    With shriller note shall sing
The sweetness, mercy, majesty,
    And glories of my King;
When I shall voice aloud how good
    He is, how great should be,
Enlarged winds, that curl the flood,
    Know no such liberty.

Stone walls do not a prison make,
    Nor iron bars a cage;
Minds innocent and quiet take
    That for an heritage:
If I have freedom in my love,
    And in my soul am free,
Angels alone, that soar above,
    Enjoy such liberty.
          RICHARD LOVELACE.

## CATO'S SOLILOQUY ON IMMORTALITY.

IT must be so.—Plato, thou reasonest well
    Else whence this pleasing hope, this fond
        desire,
This longing after immortality?
Or whence this secret dread, and inward norror,
Of falling into naught? Why shrinks the soul
Back on herself, and startles at destruction?
'Tis the divinity that stirs within us,
'Tis Heaven itself, that points out an hereafter,
And intimates eternity to man.
    Eternity!—thou pleasing, dreadful thought!
Through what variety of untried being,
Through what new scenes and changes must we
    pass!
The wide, the unbounded prospect lies before me;
But shadows, clouds and darkness, rest upon it.
Here will I hold. If there's a Power above us,—
And that there is, all Nature cries aloud
Through all her works,—He must delight in
    virtue:
And that which He delights in must be happy.
But when? or where? This world was made for
    Cæsar.

I'm weary of conjectures,—this must end 'em.
    Thus am I doubly armed. My death and life,
My bane and antidote, are both before me.
This in a moment brings me to my end;
But this informs me I shall never die.
The soul, secure in her existence, smiles
At the drawn dagger, and defies its point.
The stars shall fade away, the sun himself
Grow dim with age, and Nature sink in years,
But thou shalt flourish in immortal youth,
Unhurt amid the war of elements,
The wreck of matter, and the crush of worlds.
          ADDISON.

## AMERICA.

THE Muse, disgusted at an age and clime
    Barren of every glorious theme,
In distant lands now waits a better time,
    Producing subjects worthy fame.

In happy climes, where from the genial sun,
    And virgin earth, such scenes ensue,
The force of art by nature seems outdone,
    And fancied beauties by the true:

In happy climes, the seat of innocence,
    Where Nature guides, and Virtue rules,—
Where men shall not impose, for truth and sense
    The pedantry of courts and schools;

There shall be sung another golden age,
    The rise of empire and of arts,
The good and great inspiring epic rage,
    The wisest heads and noblest hearts.

Not such as Europe breeds in her decay,—
    Such as she bred when fresh and young,
When heavenly flame did animate her clay,—
    By future poets shall be sung.

Westward the course of empire takes it way,
    The first four acts already past,
A fifth shall close the drama with the day;
    Time's noblest offspring is the last.
          BERKELEY.

## HOME, SWEET HOME.

MID pleasures and palaces though we
    may roam,
Be it ever so humble, there's no place like home!
A charm from the skies seems to hallow us there,
Which, seek through the world, is ne'er met with
    elsewhere.
        Home! home! sweet home!
        There's no place like home!

An exile from home, splendor dazzles in vain :
Oh, give me my lowly thatch'd cottage again ;
The birds singing gayly that came at my call :
Give me these, and the peace of mind, dearer
than all.
　　　Home ! sweet ! sweet home !
　　　There's no place like home !
　　　　　　　J. H. PAYNE.

### THE OLD OAKEN BUCKET.

OW dear to this heart are the scenes of
　　my childhood,
When fond recollection presents them to view !
The orchard, the meadow, the deep-tangled wild
　　wood,
And every loved spot which my infancy knew;
The wide-spreading pond, and the mill which
　　stood by it,
The bridge, and the rock where the cataract fell ;
The cot of my father, the dairy-house nigh it,
And e'en the rude bucket which hung in the
　　well.
The old oaken bucket, the iron-bound bucket,
The moss-cover'd bucket which hung in the well.

That moss-cover'd vessel I hail as a treasure ;
For often, at noon, when return'd from the
　　field,
I found it the source of an exquisite pleasure,
The purest and sweetest that nature can yield.
How ardent I seized it, with hands that were
　　glowing !
And quick to the white-pebbled bottom it fell ;
Then soon, with the emblem of truth overflowing,
And dripping with coolness, it rose from the
　　well ;
The old oaken bucket, the iron-bound bucket,
The moss-cover'd bucket arose from the well.

How sweet from the green mossy brim to receive
　　it,
As, poised on the curb, it inclined to my lips !
Not a full blushing goblet could tempt me to
　　leave it,
Though fill'd with the nectar that Jupiter sips.
And now, far removed from the loved situation,
The tear of regret will intrusively swell,
As fancy reverts to my father's plantation,
And sighs for the bucket which hangs in the
　　well ;
The old oaken bucket, the iron-bound bucket,
The moss-cover'd bucket which hangs in the
　　well.　　　S. WOODWORTH.

### THE STAR-SPANGLED BANNER.

H, say, can you see, by the dawn's early
　　　light,
What so proudly we hail'd, at the twilight's last
　　gleaming?
Whose broad stripes and bright stars, through
　　the perilous fight,
O'er the ramparts we watch'd, were so gallantly
　　streaming ;
And the rockets' red glare, the bombs bursting
　　in air,
Gave proof through the night that our flag was
　　still there :
Oh, say, does that Star-Spangled Banner yet wave
O'er the land of the free and the home of the brave?

On that shore, dimly seen through the mists of
　　the deep,
Where the foe's haughty host in dread silence
　　reposes,
What is that which the breeze, o'er the towering
　　steep,
As it fitfully blows, now conceals, now discloses?
Now it catches the gleam of the morning's first
　　beam,
In full glory reflected now shines in the stream :
'Tis the Star-Spangled Banner ; oh, long may it
　　wave
O'er the land of the free and the home of the brave !

And where are the foes who so vauntingly swore
That the havoc of war, and the battle's confusion,
A home and a country should leave us no more?
Their blood has wash'd out their foul footsteps'
　　pollution ;
No refuge could save the hireling and slave
From the terror of flight, or the gloom of the
　　grave ;
And the Star-Spangled Banner in triumph doth
　　wave
O'er the land of the free and the home of the brave !

Oh, thus be it ever, when freedom shall stand
Between their loved homes and the war's deso-
　　　lation !
Blest with victory and peace, may the heaven-
　　rescued land
Praise the Power that hath made and preserved
　　us a nation !
Then conquer we must, when our cause it is just,
And this be our motto, " In God is our trust ;"
And the Star-Spangled Banner in triumph shall
　　wave
O'er the land of the free and the home of the brave !
　　　　　　　F. S. KEY.

## HAIL, COLUMBIA.

HAIL, Columbia! happy land!
　　Hail, ye heroes! heaven-born band!
Who fought and bled in Freedom's cause,
Who fought and bled in Freedom's cause.
And when the storm of war was gone,
Enjoy'd the peace your valor won.
　　Let independence be our boast,
　　Ever mindful what it cost;
　　Ever grateful for the prize;
　　Let its altar reach the skies.
　　　　Firm—united—let us be,
　　　　Rallying round our liberty;
　　　　As a band of brothers join'd,
　　　　Peace and safety we shall find.

Immortal patriots! rise once more;
Defend your rights, defend your shore;
　　Let no rude foe, with impious hand,
　　Let no rude foe, with impious hand,
Invade the shrine where sacred lies
Of toil and blood the well-earned prize.
　　While offering peace sincere and just,
　　In Heaven we place a manly trust,
　　That truth and justice will prevail,
　　And every scheme of bondage fail,
　　　　Firm—united, etc.

Sound, sound the trump of Fame!
Let WASHINGTON'S great name
　　Ring through the world with loud applause,
　　Ring through the world with loud applause;
Let every clime to Freedom dear
Listen with a joyful ear.
　　With equal skill and godlike power,
　　He governs in the fearful hour
　　Of horrid war; or guides with ease,
　　The happier times of honest peace.
　　　　Firm—united, etc.

Behold the chief who now commands,
Once more to serve his country stands,—
　　The rock on which the storm will beat,
　　The rock on which the storm will beat;
But, arm'd in virtue firm and true,
His hopes are fix'd on Heaven and you.
　　When Hope was sinking in dismay,
　　And glooms obscured Columbia's day
　　His steady mind, from changes free,
　　Resolved on death or liberty.
　　　　Firm—united, etc.
　　　　　　JOSEPH HOPKINSON.

## OLD GRIMES.

OLD GRIMES is dead—that good old
　　man—
　　We ne'er shall see him more:—
He used to wear a long, black coat
　　All button'd down before.

His heart was open as the day,
　　His feelings all were true;—
His hair was some inclined to gray,
　　He wore it in a queue.

Whene'er he heard the voice of pain,
　　His breast with pity burn'd;—
The large, round head upon his cane
　　From ivory was turn'd.

Kind words he ever had for all;
　　He knew no base design:—
His eyes were dark and rather small,
　　His nose was aquiline.

He lived at peace with all mankind,
　　In friendship he was true:—
His coat had pocket-holes behind,
　　His pantaloons were blue.

Unharm'd, the sin which earth pollutes
　　He pass'd securely o'er,—
And never wore a pair of boots
　　For thirty years or more.

But good old Grimes is now at rest,
　　Nor fears misfortune's frown:—
He wore a double-breasted vest,
　　The stripes ran up and down.

He modest merit sought to find,
　　And pay it its desert:—
He had no malice in his mind,
　　No ruffles on his shirt.

His neighbors he did not abuse,
　　Was sociable and gay:—
He wore large buckles on his shoes,
　　And changed them every day.

His knowledge, hid from public gaze,
　　He did not bring to view,—
Nor make a noise, town-meeting days,
　　As many people do.

His worldly goods he never threw
　　In trust to fortune's chances,—
But lived (as all his brothers do)
　　In easy circumstances.

Thus undisturb'd by anxious cares,
His peaceful moments ran ;—
And everybody said he was
A fine old gentleman.

A. G. GREENE.

## ABOU BEN ADHEM.

ABOU BEN ADHEM (may his tribe increase !)
Awoke one night from a deep dream of peace,
And saw within the moonlight of his room,
Making it rich, and like a lily in bloom,
An angel writing in a book of gold.
Exceeding peace had made Ben Adhem bold,
And, to the presence in the room, he said,
"What writest thou?" The vision raised its head,
And, with a look made of all sweet accord,
Answered, "The names of those who love the Lord!"
"And is mine one'" asked Abou.—"Nay, not so,"
Replied the angel. Abou spake more low,
But cheerly still ; and said—"I pray thee, then,
Write me as one that loves his fellow-men."
The angel wrote and vanished. The next night
It came again, with a great wakening light,
And showed the names whom love of God had blest
And lo! Ben Adhem's name led all the rest !

LEIGH HUNT.

## AMERICA TO GREAT BRITAIN.

ALL hail! thou noble land,
    Our fathers' native soil !
Oh, stretch thy mighty hand,
    Gigantic grown by toil,
O'er the vast Atlantic wave to our shore !
For thou with magic might
Canst reach to where the light
Of Phœbus travels bright
    The world o'er.

The Genius of our clime,
    From his pine-embattled steep,
Shalt hail the guest sublime ;
    While the Tritons of the deep
With their conchs the kindred league shall proclaim.

Then let the world combine,—
O'er the main our naval line
Like the milky-way shall shine
    Bright in fame!

Though ages long have pass'd
    Since our fathers left their home,
Their pilot in the blast,
    O'er untravell'd seas to roam,
Yet lives the blood of England in our veins !
And shall we not proclaim
That blood of honest fame
Which no tyranny can tame
    By its chains?

While the language free and bold
    Which the Bard of Avon sung,
In which our Milton told
    How the vault or heaven rung
When Satan, blasted, fell with his host ;—
While this with reverence meet,
Ten thousand echoes greet,
From rock to rock repeat
    Round our coast ;

While the manners, while the arts,
    That mould a nation's soul,
Still cling around our hearts,—
    Between let ocean roll,
Our joint communion breaking with the Sun :
Yet still from either beach
The voice of blood shall reach,
More audible than speech,
    "We are One."

WASHINGTON ALLSTON.

## EPITHALAMIUM.

I SAW two clouds at morning,
    Tinged with the rising sun ;
And in the dawn they floated on,
    And mingled into one:
I thought that morning cloud was blest,
It moved so sweetly to the west.

I saw two summer currents,
    Flow smoothly to their meeting,
And join their course, with silent force,
    In peace each other greeting :
Calm was their course through banks of green,
While dimpling eddies play'd between.

WASHED ASHORE

Such be your gentle motion,
  Till life's last pulse shall beat ;
Like summer's beam, and summer's stream,
  Float on, in joy, to meet
A calmer sea, where storms shall cease—
A purer sky, where all is peace.

J. G. C. BRAINARD.

## IMMORTALITY OF LOVE.

THEY sin who tell us love can die:
  With life all other passions fly,
All others are but vanity :
In Heaven Ambition cannot dwell,
Nor Avarice in the vaults of Hell ;
Earthly these passions of the Earth,
They perish where they have their birth ;
But Love is indestructible.
Its holy flame forever burneth,
From Heaven it came, to Heaven returneth ;
Too oft on Earth a troubled guest,
At times deceived, at times opprest,
It here is tried and purified,
Then hath in Heaven its perfect rest :
It soweth here with toil and care,
But the harvest-time of Love is there.

SOUTHEY.

## THE COMMON LOT.

ONCE, in the flight of ages past,
  There lived a man ; and Who was He ?
Mortal ! howe'er thy lot be cast,
  That Man resembled Thee,
Unknown the region of his birth,
  The land in which he died unknown :
His name has perished from the earth ;
  This truth survives alone :—

That joy and grief, and hope and fear,
  Alternate triumphed in his breast ;
His bliss and woe,—a smile, a tear !—
  Oblivion hides the rest.
The bounding pulse, the languid limb,
  The changing spirit's rise and fall ;
We know that these were felt by him,
  For these are felt by all.

He suffered,—but his pangs are o'er ;
  Enjoyed,—but his delights are fled ;
Had friends,—his friends are now no more
  And foes,—his foes are dead.

He loved,—but whom he loved the grave
  Hath lost in its unconscious womb :
O, she was fair,—but naught could save
  Her beauty from the tomb.

He saw whatever thou hast seen ;
  Encountered all that troubles thee :
He was—whatever thou hast been ;
  He is—what thou shalt be.
The rolling seasons, day and night,
  Sun, moon and stars, the earth and main,
Erewhile his portion, life and light,
  To him exist in vain.

The clouds and sunbeams, o'er his eye
  That once their shades and glory threw
Have left in yonder silent sky
  No vestige where they flew,
The annals of the human race,
  Their ruins, since the world began,
Of him afford no other trace
  Than this,—There lived a man.

MONTGOMERY.

## THERE IS AN HOUR OF PEACEFUL REST.

THERE is an hour of peaceful rest,
  To mourning wanderers given ;
There is a joy for souls distress'd,
A balm for every wounded breast—
  'Tis found above, in heaven.

There is a soft, a downy bed,
  Far from these shades of even ;
A couch for weary mortals spread,
Where they may rest the aching head,
  And find repose in heaven.

There is a home for weary souls,
  By sin and sorrow driven,
When tossed on life's tempestuous shoals,
Where storms arise and ocean rolls,
  And all is drear—'tis heaven.

There Faith lifts up her cheerful eye,
  The heart no longer riven ;
And views the tempest passing by,
The evening shadows quickly fly,
  And all serene in heaven.

There fragrant flowers, immortal, bloom,
  And joys supreme are given :
There rays divine disperse the gloom,—
Beyond the confines of the tomb
  Appears the dawn of heaven.

W. B. TAPPAN.

## THE EXECUTION OF MONTROSE.

COME hither, Evan Cameron; come, stand
    beside my knee,—
I hear the river roaring down towards the wintry
    sea.
There's shouting on the mountain-side, there's
    war within the blast:
Old faces look upon me,—old forms go trooping
    past.
I hear the pibroch wailing amidst the din of fight,
And my dim spirit wakes again, upon the verge
    of night.

'Twas I that led the Highland host through wild
    Lochaber's snows,
What time the plaided clans came down to battle
    with Montrose.
I've told thee how the Southrons fell beneath the
    broad claymore,
And how we smote the Campbell clan by Inver-
    lochy's shore.
I've told thee how we swept Dundee, and tamed
    the Lindsays' pride,
But never have I told thee yet how the Great
    Marquis died.

A traitor sold him to his foes;—O deed of death-
    less shame!
I charge thee, boy, if e'r thou meet with one of
    Assynt's name,
Be it upon the mountain's side, or yet within the
    glen,
Stand he in martial gear alone, or backed by
    armed men,—
Face him, as thou wouldst face the man who
    wronged thy sire's renown;
Remember of what blood thou art, and strike the
    caitiff down.

They brought him to the Watergate, hard bound
    with hempen span
As though they held a lion there, and not a
    'fenceless man.
But when he came, though pale and wan, he
    looked so great and high,
So noble was his manly front, so calm his stead-
    fast eye,
The rabble rout forbore to shout, and each man
    held his breath;
For well they knew the hero's soul was face to
    face with death.
Had I been there, with sword in hand, and fifty
    Camerons by,
That day, through high Dunedin's streets, had
    pealed the slogan-cry.

Not all their troops of trampling horse, nor might
    of mailed men,
Not all the rebels in the South, had borne us
    backwards then!
Once more his foot on Highland heath had trod
    as free as air,
Or I, and all who bore my name, been laid around
    him there!

It might not be. They placed him next within
    the solemn hall,
Where once the Scottish kings were throned
    amidst their nobles all.
But there was dust of vulgar feet on that pol-
    luted floor,
And perjured traitors filled the place where good
    men sat before.
With savage glee came Warriston, to read the
    murderous doom;
And then uprose the great Montrose in the middle
    of the room.

" Now, by my faith as belted knight, and by the
    name I bear,
And by the bright St. Andrew's cross that waves
    above us there,—
Yea, by a greater, mightier oath,—and O, that
    such should be!—
By that dark stream of royal blood that lies 'twixt
    you and me,—
I have not sought in battlefield a wreath of such
    renown,
Nor hoped I on my dying day to win the mar-
    tyr's crown!

" There is a chamber far away where sleep the
    good and brave,
But a better place ye've named for me than by my
    fathers' grave.
For truth and right, 'gainst treason's might, this
    hand hath always striven,
And ye raise it up for a witness still in the eye of
    earth and Heaven
Then nail my head on yonder tower,—give every
    town a limb,—
And God who made shall gather them: I go
    from you to him!"

The morning dawned full darkly; like a bride-
    groom from his room,
Came the hero from his prison to the scaffold and
    the doom.
There was glory on his forehead, there was lustre
    in his eye,
And he never walked to battle more proudly than
    to die;

There was color in his visage, though the cheeks
  of all were wan,
And they marv'lled as they saw him pass, that
  great and goodly man.

Then radiant and serene he stood, and cast his
  cloak away,
For he had ta'en his latest look of earth and sun
  and day.
He mounted up the scaffold, and he turned him
  to the crowd
But they dared not trust the people,—so he might
  not speak aloud

But he looked upon the Heavens, and they were
  clear and blue,
And in the liquid ether the eye of God shone
  through:

A beam of light fell o'er him, like a glory round
  the shriven,
And he climbed the lofty ladder as it were the
  path to heaven.

Then came a flash from out the cloud, and a
  stunning thunder-roll;
And no man dared to look aloft; fear was on
  every soul.

There was another heavy sound,—a hush, and
  then a groan,
And darkness swept across the sky,—the work
  of death was done.          AYTOUN.

## THE BEGGAR'S PETITION.

PITY the sorrows of a poor old man,
  Whose trembling limbs have borne him to
    your door,
Whose days are dwindled to the shortest span,
Oh, give relief! and Heav'n will bless your store.

These tatter'd clothes my poverty bespeak,
These hoary locks proclaim my lengthen'd years;
  And many a furrow in my grief-worn cheek
Has been the channel to a flood of tears.

Yon house, erected on the rising ground,
With tempting aspect drew me from my road;
  For plenty there a residence has found,
And grandeur a magnificent abode.

Hard is the fate of the infirm and poor!
Here as I craved a morsel of their bread,
  A pamper'd menial drove me from the door,
To seek a shelter in a humbler shed.

Oh! take me to your hospitable dome!
Keen blows the wind, and piercing is the cold!
  Short is my passage to the friendly tomb,
For I am poor and miserably old.

Should I reveal the sources of my grief,
If soft humanity e'er touched your breast,
  Your hands would not withhold the kind
    relief,
And tears of pity would not be repress'd.

Heav'n sends misfortunes, why should we re-
  pine?
'Tis Heav'n has brought me to the state you see;
  And your condition may be soon like mine—
The child of sorrow and of misery .

A little farm was my paternal lot,
Then, like the lark, I sprightly hail'd the morn;
  But ah! oppression forc'd me from my cot,
My cattle died, and blighted was my corn.

My daughter, once the comfort of my age,
Lur'd by a villain from her native home,
  Is cast abandon'd on the world's wide stage,
And doom'd in scanty poverty to roam. .

My tender wife, sweet soother of my care!
Struck with sad anguish at the stern decree,
  Fell, ling'ring fell, a victim to despair,
And left the world to wretchedness and me.

Pity the sorrows of a poor old man,
Whose trembling limbs have borne him to your
    door,
  Whose days are dwindled to the shortest span,
Oh! give relief! and Heav'n will bless your
    store!
                                    MOSS.

## VIRTUE.

SWEET day, so cool, so calm, so bright,
  The bridal of the earth and sky,
The dew shall weep thy fall to-night,
  For thou must die.

Sweet rose, whose hue, angry and brave,
Bids the rash gazer wipe his eye,
Thy root is ever in its grave,
  And thou must die.

Sweet Spring, full of sweet days and roses,
A box where sweets compacted lie,
By music shows ye have your closes,
  And all must die.

Only a sweet and virtuous soul,
Like seasoned timber, never gives;
But, though the whole world turn to coal,
  Then chiefly lives.
                          GEORGE HERBERT.

## FLOWERS.

SWEET nurselings of the vernal skies,
    Bathed in soft airs, and fed with dew,
What more than magic in you lies
    To fill the heart's fond view!
In childhood's sports, companions gay;
In sorrow, on Life's downward way,
How soothing! in our last decay
    Memorials prompt and true.

Relics ye are of Eden's bowers,
As pure, as fragrant, and as fair,
As when ye crown'd the sunshine hours
    Of happy wanderers there.
Fall'n all besides,—the world of life,
How is it stain'd with fear and strife!
In Reason's world what storms are rife
    What passions range and glare!

But cheerful and unchanged the while
Your first and perfect form ye show,
The same that won Eve's matron smile
    In the world's opening glow.
The stars of heaven a course are taught
Too high above our human thought;
Ye may be found if ye are sought,
    And, as we gaze, we know.

Ye dwell beside our paths and homes,
Our paths of sin, our homes of sorrow;
And guilty man, where'er he roams,
    Your innocent mirth may borrow.
The birds of air before us fleet,
They cannot brook our shame to meet;
But we may taste your solace sweet,
    And come again to-morrow.

Ye fearless in your nests abide;
Nor may we scorn, too proudly wise,
Your silent lessons, undescried
    By all but lowly eyes:
For ye could draw th' admiring gaze
Of Him who worlds and hearts surveys:
Your order wild, your fragrant maze,
    He taught us how to prize.

Ye felt your Maker's smile that hour,
As when He paused and own'd you good
His blessing on Earth's primal bower,
    Ye felt it all renew'd.
What care ye now, if Winter's storm
Sweep ruthless o'er each silken form?
Christ's blessing at your heart is warm,
    Ye fear no vexing mood.

Alas! of thousand bosoms kind
That daily court you and caress,
How few the happy secret find
    Of your calm loveliness!
"Live for to-day! to-morrow's light
To-morrow's cares shall bring to sight;
Go sleep like closing flowers at night,
    And Heaven thy morn will bless."
                                KEBLE.

## DEATH'S FINAL CONQUEST.

THE glories of our blood and state
        Are shadows, not substantial things;
There is no armor against Fate;
    Death lays his icy hand on Kings!
        Sceptre, Crown,
        Must tumble down,
And in the dust be equal made
With the poor crooked scythe and spade.

Some men with swords may reap the field,
    And plant fresh laurels where they kill;
But their strong nerves at last must yield,—
    They tame but one another still.
        Early or late,
        They stoop to Fate,
And must give up their conquering breath,
When they, pale captives, creep te Death.

The garlands wither on your brow!—
    Then boast no more your mighty deeds:
Upon Death's purple altar now
    See where the victor-victim bleeds!
        All heads must come
        To the cold tomb;
Only the actions of the just
Smell sweet, and blossom in the dust.
                            J. SHIRLEY.

# BOOK VI.

---

## FAMOUS ORATIONS.

PATRICK HENRY ON RESISTANCE TO BRITISH AGGRESSION

# Book VI.

# Famous Orations.

___

### LEONIDAS TO HIS THREE HUNDRED.

___

YE men of Sparta, listen to the hope with which the gods inspire Leonidas! Consider how largely our death may redound to the glory and benefit of our country. Against this barbarian king, who, in his battle array, reckons as many nations as our ranks do soldiers, what could united Greece effect? In this emergency there is need that some unexpected power should interpose itself;—that a valor and devotion, unknown hitherto, even to Sparta, should strike, amaze, confound, this ambitious Despot! From our blood, here freely shed to-day, shall this moral power, this sublime lesson of patriotism, proceed. To Greece it shall teach the secret of her strength; to the Persians, the certainty of their weakness. Before our scarred and bleeding bodies, we shall see the great King grow pale at his own victory, and recoil affrighted. Or, should he succeed in forcing the pass of Thermopylæ, he will tremble to learn, that, in marching upon our cities, he will find ten thousand, after us, equally prepared for death. Ten thousand, do I say? O, the swift contagion of a generous enthusiasm! Our example shall make Greece all fertile in heroes. An avenging cry shall follow the cry of her affliction. Country! Independence! From the Messenian hills to the Hellespont, every heart shall respond; and a hundred thousand heroes, with one sacred accord, shall arm themselves, in emulation of our unanimous death. These rocks shall give back the echo of their oaths. Then shall our little band,—the brave three hundred,—from the world of shades, revisit the scene; behold the haughty Xerxes, a fugitive, re-cross the Hellespont in a frail bark; while Greece, after eclipsing the most glorious of her exploits, shall hallow a new Olympus in the mound that covers our tombs.

Yes, fellow-soldiers, history and posterity shall consecrate our ashes. Wherever courage is honored, through all time, shall Thermopylæ and the Spartan three hundred be remembered. Ours shall be an immortality such as no human glory has yet attained. And when ages shall have swept by, and Sparta's last hour shall have come, then, even in her ruins, shall she be eloquent. Tyrants shall turn away from them, appalled; but the heroes of liberty—the poets, the sages, the historians of all time—shall invoke and bless the memory of the gallant three hundred of Leonidas!

## AESCHINES ON THE CROWN.

WHEN Demosthenes boasts to you, O Athenians, of his Democratic zeal, examine, not his harangues, but his life ; not what he professes to be, but what he really is ;—redoubtable in words, impotent in deeds, plausible in speech, perfidious in action.  As to his courage—has he not himself, before the assembled People, confessed his poltroonery ?  By the laws of Athens, the man who refuses to bear arms, the coward, the deserter of his post in battle, is excluded from all share in the public deliberation—denied admission to our religious rites, and rendered incapable of receiving the honor of a crown.  Yet now it is proposed to crown a man whom your laws expressly disqualify.

Which, think you, was the more worthy citizen,—Themistocles, who commanded your fleet when you vanquished the Persian at Salamis, or Demosthenes the deserter ?—Miltiades, who conquered the Barbarians at Marathon, or this hireling traitor ?—Aristides, surnamed the Just, or Demosthenes, who merits a far different surname ?  By all the gods of Olympus, it is a profanation to mention in the same breath this monster and those great men !  Let him cite, if he can, one among them all to whom a crown was decreed.  And was Athens ungrateful ?  No ! She was magnanimous ;  and those uncrowned citizens were worthy of Athens.  They placed their glory, not in the letter of a decree, but in the remembrance of a country, of which they had merited well,—in the living, imperishable remembrance !

And now a popular orator—the mainspring of our calamities—a deserter from the field of battle, a deserter from the city—claims of us a crown, exacts the honor of a proclamation !  Crown *him ?*  Proclaim *his* worth ?  My countrymen, this would not be to exalt Demosthenes, but to degrade yourselves—to dishonor those brave men who perished for you in battle.  Crown *him ?*  Shall *his* recreancy win what was denied to *their* devotion ?  This would indeed be to insult the memory of the dead, and to paralyze the emulation of the living.

When Demosthenes tells you that, as ambassador, he wrested Byzantium from Philip,—that, as orator, he roused the Acarnanians, and subdued the Thebans,—let not the braggart impose on you.  He flatters himself that the Athenians are simpletons enough to believe him,—as if in him they cherished the very genius of persuasion, instead of a vile calumniator.  But when, at the close of his defence, he shall summon to his aid his accomplices in corruption, imagine then, O Athenians, that you behold, at the foot of this tribune, from which I now address you, the great benefactors of the Republic arrayed against them.  Solon, who environed our liberty with the noblest institutions,—Solon, the philosopher, the mighty legislator,—with that benignity so characteristic, implores you not to pay more regard to the honeyed phrases of Demosthenes than to your own oaths, your own laws.  Aristides, who fixed for Greece the apportionment of her contributions, and whose orphan daughters were dowered by the People, is moved to indignation at this prostitution of justice, and exclaims : " Think on your fathers !  Arthmius of Zelia brought gold from Media into Greece, and, for the act, barely escaped death in banishment ; and now Demosthenes, who has not merely *brought* gold, but who *received* it as the price of treachery, and still retains it,—Demosthenes it is unblushingly proposed to invest with a golden crown ! '' From those who fell at Marathon and at Platæa—from Themistocles— from the very sepulchres of your ancestors—issues the protesting groan of condemnation and rebuke.

## DEMOSTHENES AGAINST PHILIP.

WHEN I compare, Athenians, the speeches of some amongst us with their actions, I am at a loss to reconcile what I see with what I hear. Their protestations are full of zeal against the public enemy ; but their measures are so inconsistent, that all their professions become suspected. By confounding you with a variety of projects, they perplex your resolutions ; and lead you from executing what is in your power, by engaging you in schemes not reducible to practice.

Observe, I beseech you, men of Athens, how different your conduct appears, from the practices of your ancestors. They were friends to truth and plain dealing, and detested flattery and servile compliance. By unanimous consent, they continued arbiters of all Greece, for the space of forty-five years, without interruption : a public fund, of no less than ten thousand talents, was ready for any emergency : they exercised over the kings of Macedon that authority which is due to barbarians ; obtained, both by sea and land, in their own persons, frequent and signal victories ; and by their noble exploits, transmitted to posterity an immortal memory of their virtue, superior to the reach of malice and detraction. It is to them we owe that great number of public edifices, by which the city of Athens exceeds all the rest of the world in beauty and magnificence. It is to them we owe so many stately temples, so richly embellished, but, above all, adorned with the spoils of vanquished enemies. But, visit their own private habitations ; visit the houses of Aristides, Miltiades, or any other of those patriots of antiquity ; you will find nothing, not the least mark or ornament, to distinguish them from their neighbors. They took part in the government, not to enrich themselves, but the public ; they had no scheme or ambition, but for the public : nor knew any interest, but the public. It was by a close and steady application to the general good of their country, by an exemplary piety towards the immortal gods, by a strict faith and religious honesty, betwixt man and man, and a moderation always uniform and of a piece, they established that reputation which remains to this day, and will last to utmost posterity.

Such, O men of Athens ! were your ancestors : so glorious in the eye of the world ; so bountiful and munificent to their country ; so sparing, so modest, so self-denying to themselves. What resemblance can we find, in the present generation, of these great men ? At a time, when your ancient competitors have left you a clear stage ; when the Lacedemonians are disabled ; the Thebans employed in troubles of their own ; when no other state whatever is in a condition to rival or molest you ; in short, when you are at full liberty ; when you have the opportunity and the power to become, once more, the sole arbiters of Greece ; you permit, patiently, whole provinces to be wrested from you ; you lavish the public money in scandalous and obscure uses ; you suffer your allies to perish in time of peace, whom you preserved in time of war ; and, to sum up all, you yourselves, by your mercenary court, and servile resignation to the will and pleasure of designing, insidious leaders, abet, encourage, and strengthen the most dangerous and formidable of your enemies. Yes, Athenians, I repeat it, you yourselves are the contrivers of your own ruin. Lives there a man who has confidence enough to deny it ? Let him rise and assign, if he can, any other cause of the success and prosperity of Philip. "But," you reply, "what Athens may have lost in reputation abroad, she has gained in splendor at home. Was there ever a greater appearance of prosperity ; a greater face of plenty ? Is not the city enlarged ? Are not the streets better paved, houses repaired and beautified ? " Away with such trifles ! shall I be paid with counters ? An old square new vamped up ! a fountain ! an aqueduct ! Are these acquisitions to boast of ? Cast your eyes upon the magistrate, under whose ministry you boast these precious improvements. Behold the despicable creature raised, all at once, from dirt to opulence ; from the lowest obscurity to the highest honors. Have not some of these upstarts built private houses and seats vieing with the most sumptuous of our public palaces ? And how have their fortunes and their power increased, but as the Commonwealth has been ruined and impoverished.

Believe me, Athenians, if, recovering from this lethargy, you would assume the ancient freedom and spirit of your fathers ; if you would be your own soldiers and your own commanders, confiding no longer your affairs in foreign or mercenary hands ; if you would charge yourself with your own defence, employing abroad, for the public, what you waste in unprofitable pleasures at home ; the world might, once more, behold you making a figure worthy of Athenians. "You would have us then (you say) do service in our armies, in our own persons ; and, for so doing, you would have the pensions we receive in time of peace accepted as pay in time of war. Is it thus we are to understand you ? " Yes, Athenians, 'tis my plain meaning. I would make it a standing rule, that no person, great or little, should be the better for the public money, who should grudge to employ it for the public service. Are we in peace ? the public is charged with your subsistence. Are we in war, or under a necessity, as at this time, to enter into a war ? let your gratitude oblige you accept, as pay, in defence of your benefactors, what you receive in peace, as mere bounty. Thus, without any innovation ; without altering or abolishing anything, but pernicious novelties, introduced for the encouragement of sloth and idleness ; by converting only, for the future, the same funds, for the use of the serviceable, which are spent, at present, upon the unprofitable ; you may be well served in your armies ; your troops regularly paid ; justice duly administered ; the public revenues reformed and increased ; and every member of the Commonwealth rendered useful to his country, according to his age and ability, without any further burden to the state.

WASHINGTON

This, O men of Athens ! is what my duty prompted me to represent to you upon this occasion. May the gods inspire you to determine upon such measures, as may be most expedient, for the particular and general good of our country !

## CICERO AGAINST CATILINE.

OW far, O Catiline, wilt thou abuse our patience? How long shalt thou baffle justice in thy mad career? To what extreme wilt thou carry thy audacity? Art thou nothing daunted by the nightly watch, posted to secure the Palatium? Nothing, by the city guards? Nothing, by the rally of all good citizens? Nothing, by the assembling of the Senate in this fortified place? Nothing, by the averted looks of all here present? Seest thou not that all thy plots are exposed?—that thy wretched conspiracy is laid bare to every man's knowledge, here in the Senate?— that we are well aware of thy proceedings of last night; of the night before;—the place of meeting, the company convoked, the measures concerted? Alas, the times! Alas, the public morals! The Senate understands all this. The Consul sees it. Yet the traitor lives! Lives? Ay, truly, and confronts us here in council,— takes part in our deliberations,—and, with his measuring eye, marks out each man of us for slaughter! And we, all this while, strenuous that we are, think we have amply discharged our duty to the State, if we but *shun* this madman's sword and fury!

Long since, O Catiline, ought the Consul to have ordered thee to execution and brought upon thy own head the ruin thou hast been meditating against others! There was that virtue once in Rome, that a wicked citizen was held more execrable than the deadliest foe. We have a law still, Catiline, for thee. Think not that we are powerless, because forbearing. We have a decree,—though it rests among our archives like a sword in its scabbard,—a decree, by which thy life would be made to pay the forfeit of thy crimes. And, should I order thee to be instantly seized and put to death, I make just doubt whether all good men would not think it done rather too late than any man too cruelly. But, for good reasons, I will yet defer the blow long since deserved. *Then* will I doom thee, when no man is found, so lost, so wicked, nay, so like thyself, but shall confess that it was justly dealt. While there is one man that dares defend thee, live! But thou shalt live so beset, so surrounded, so scrutinized, by the vigilant guards that I have placed around thee, that thou shalt not stir a foot against the Republic, without my knowledge. There shall be eyes to detect thy slightest movement, and ears to catch thy wariest whisper, of which thou shalt not dream. The darkness of night shall not cover thy treason—the walls of privacy shall not stifle its voice. Baffled on all sides, thy most secret counsels clear as noon-day, what canst thou now have in view? Proceed, plot, conspire, as thou wilt; there is nothing you can contrive, nothing you can propose, nothing you can attempt, which I shall not know, hear and promptly understand. Thou shalt soon be made aware that I am even more active in providing for the preservation of the State than thou in plotting its destruction!

## ANTONY'S ORATION OVER CAESAR'S BODY.

FRIENDS, Romans, countrymen! lend me your ears; I come to bury Cæsar, not to praise him.  The evil that men do lives after them; the good is oft interred with their bones: so let it be with Cæsar!  The noble Brutus hath told you Cæsar was ambitious: if it were so it was a grievous fault; and grievously hath Cæsar answered it!  Here, under leave of Brutus and the rest, (for Brutus is an honorable man; so are they all—all honorable men;) come I to speak in Cæsar's funeral.

He was my friend, faithful and just to me: but Brutus says he was ambitious; and Brutus is an honorable man.  He hath brought many captives home to Rome, whose ransoms did the general coffers fill: did this in Cæsar seem ambitious?  When that the poor have cried, Cæsar hath wept: ambition should be made of sterner stuff: yet Brutus says he was ambitious; and Brutus is an honorable man.  You all did see, that, on the Lupercal, I thrice presented him a kingly crown, which he did thrice refuse—was this ambition?  Yet Brutus says he was ambitious; and, sure, he is an honorable man.  I speak, not to disprove what Brutus spoke; but here I am to speak what I do know.  You all did love him once; not without cause: what cause withholds you then to mourn for him?  O judgment! thou art fled to brutish beasts, and men have lost their reason.  Bear with me; my heart is in the coffin there with Cæsar; and I must pause till it come back to me.

But yesterday, the word of Cæsar might have stood against the world; now lies he there, and none so poor to do him reverence.  O Masters! if I were disposed to stir your hearts and minds to mutiny and rage, I should do Brutus wrong, and Cassius wrong; who, you all know, are honorable men: I will not do them wrong; I rather choose to wrong the dead, to wrong myself, and you, than I will wrong such honorable men.  But here's a parchment with the seal of Cæsar: I found it in his closet, 'tis his will!  Let but the commons hear this testament, (which, pardon me, I do not mean to read.)  And they would go and kiss dead Cæsar's wounds and dip their napkins in his sacred blood; yea, beg a hair of him for memory, and, dying, mention it within their wills, bequeathing it as a rich legacy unto their issue!

If you have tears prepare to shed them now.  You all do know this mantle! I remember the first time ever Cæsar put it on: 'twas on a summer's evening in his tent, that day he overcame the Nervii:—Look! in this place ran Cassius's dagger through—see what a rent the envious Casca made: through this the well-beloved Brutus stabbed; and, as he plucked his cursed steel away, mark how the blood of Cæsar followed it! as rushing out of doors to be resolved if Brutus so unkindly knocked, or no; for Brutus, as you know, was Cæsar's angel: judge, O ye gods, how dearly Cæsar loved him!  This, this was the unkindest cut of all; for when the noble Cæsar saw him stab, ingratitude, more strong than traitor's arms, quite vanquished him: then burst his mighty heart; and, in his mantle, muffling up his face, even at the base of Pompey's statue (which all the while ran blood)—great Cæsar fell. Oh, what a fall was there, my countrymen! Then I, and you, and all of us fell down; whilst bloody treason flourished over us. Oh, now you weep; and I perceive you feel the dint of pity: these are gracious drops. Kind souls! what, weep you, when you but behold our Cæsar's vesture wounded? Look you here! here is himself—marred, as you see, by traitors!—Good friends! sweet friends! let me not stir you up to such a sudden flood of mutiny: they that have done this deed are honorable; what private griefs they have, alas, I know not, that made them do it; they are wise and honorable, and will, no doubt, with reason answer you. I come not, friends, to steal away your hearts: I am no orator, as Brutus is; but, as you know me all, a plain, blunt man, that love my friend; and that they know full well, that gave me public leave to speak of him: for I have neither wit, nor words, nor worth, action, nor utterance, nor the power of speech, to stir men's blood; I only speak right on. I tell you that which you yourselves do know; show you sweet Cæsar's wounds, poor, poor dumb mouths, and bid them speak for me. But were I Brutus, and Brutus Antony, there were an Antony would ruffle up your spirits, and put a tongue in every wound of Cæsar, that should move the stones of Rome to rise and mutiny!

---

## SPARTACUS TO THE GLADIATORS.

YE call me chief; and ye do well to call *him* chief who for twelve long years has met upon the arena every shape of man or beast the broad empire of Rome could furnish, and who never yet lowered his arm. If there be one among you who can say, that ever, in public fight or private brawl, my actions did belie my tongue, let him stand forth, and say it. If there be three in all your company dare face me on the bloody sands, let them come on. And yet I was not always thus,—a hired butcher, a savage chief of still more savage men! My ancestors came from old Sparta, and settled among the vine-clad rocks and citron groves of Syrasella. My early life ran quiet as the brooks by which I sported; and when, at noon, I gathered the sheep beneath the shade, and played upon the shepherd's flute, there was a friend, the son of a neighbor, to join me in the pastime. We led our flocks to the same pasture, and partook together our rustic meal. One evening, after the sheep were folded, and we were all seated beneath the myrtle which shaded our cottage, my grandsire, an old man, was telling of Marathon, and Leuctra; and how, in ancient times, a little band of Spartans, in a defile of the mountains, had withstood a whole army. I did not then know what war was; but my cheeks burned, I knew not why, and I clasped the knees of that venerable man, until my mother, parting the hair from off my forehead, kissed my throbbing temples, and bade me go to rest, and think no more of those old tales and savage wars. That very night the Romans landed on our coast. I saw the breast that had nourished me trampled by the hoof of the war-horse; the bleeding body of my father flung amidst the blazing rafters of our dwelling!

To-day I killed a man in the arena; and, when I broke his helmet-clasps, behold! he was my friend. He knew me, smiled faintly, gasped, and died;—the same sweet smile upon his lips that I had marked, when, in adventurous boyhood, we scaled the lofty cliff to pluck the first ripe grapes, and bear them home in childish triumph. I told the prætor that the dead man had been my friend, generous and brave; and I begged that I might bear away the body, to burn it on a funeral pile, and mourn over its ashes. Ay! upon my knees, amid the dust and blood of the arena, I begged that poor boon, while all the assembled maids and matrons, and the holy virgins they call Vestals, and the rabble, shouted in derision, deeming it rare sport, forsooth, to see Rome's fiercest gladiator turn pale and tremble at sight of that piece of bleeding clay! And the prætor drew back as I were pollution, and sternly said,—"Let the carrion rot; there are no noble men but Romans!" And so, fellow-*gladiators,* must you, and so must I, die like dogs. O, Rome! Rome! thou hast been a tender nurse to me. Ay! thou hast given, to that poor, gentle, timid shepherd lad, who never knew a harsher tone than a flute-note, muscles of iron and a heart of flint; taught him to drive the sword through plaited mail and links of rugged brass, and warm it in the marrow of his foe;—to gaze into the glaring eye-balls of the fierce Numidian lion, even as a boy upon a laughing girl! And he shall pay thee back, until the yellow Tiber is red as frothing wine, and in its deepest ooze thy life-blood lies curdled!

Ye stand here now like giants, as ye are! The strength of brass is in your toughened sinews; but to-morrow some Roman Adonis, breathing sweet perfume from his curly locks, shall with his lily fingers pat your red brawn, and bet his sestérces upon your blood. Hark! hear ye yon lion roaring in his den? 'Tis three days since he tasted flesh; but to-morrow he shall break his fast upon yours,—and a dainty meal for him ye will be! If ye are *beasts,* then stand here like fat oxen, waiting for the butcher's knife! If ye are *men,*—follow me! Strike down yon guard, gain the mountain passes, and there do bloody work, as did your sires at Old Thermopylæ! Is Sparta dead? Is the old Grecian spirit frozen in your veins, that you do crouch and cower like a belabored hound beneath his master's lash? O, comrades! warriors! Thracians!—if we must fight, let us fight for *ourselves!* If we must slaughter, let us slaughter our *oppressors!* If we must die, let it be under the clear sky, by the bright waters, in noble, honorable battle!

---

## PAUL TO THE ATHENIANS.

YE men of Athens, I perceive that in all things ye are too superstitious.

For as I passed by, and beheld your devotions, I found an altar with this inscription, TO THE UNKNOWN GOD. Whom therefore ye ignorantly worship, him declare I unto you.

God that made the world and all things therein, seeing that he is Lord of heaven and earth, dwelleth not in temples made with hands;

Neither is worshipped with men's hands, as though he needed any thing, seeing he giveth to all life, and breath, and all things ;

And hath made of one blood all nations of men for to dwell on all the face of the earth, and hath determined the times before appointed, and the bounds of their habitation ;

That they should seek the Lord, if haply they might feel after him, and find him, though he be not far from every one of us.

For in him we live, and move, and have our being ; as certain also of your own poets have said, For we are also His offspring.

Forasmuch then as we are the offspring of God, we ought not think that the Godhead is like unto gold, or silver, or stone, graven by art and man's device.

And the times of this ignorance God winked at ; but now commandeth all men everywhere to repent :

Because he hath appointed a day in which he will judge the world in righteousness by *that* man whom he hath ordained ; *whereof* he hath given assurance unto all *men*, in that he hath raised him from the dead.

## PITT'S REPLY TO WALPOLE.

SIR, the atrocious crime of being a young man, which the honorable gentleman has with such spirit and decency charged upon me, I shall neither attempt to palliate nor deny ; but content myself with wishing that I may be one of those whose follies may cease with their youth, and not of that number who are ignorant in spite of experience. Whether youth can be imputed to any man as a reproach, I will not, sir, assume the province of determining ; but, surely age may become justly contemptible, if the opportunities which it brings have passed away without improvement, and vice appears to prevail when the passions have subsided. The wretch who, after having seen the consequences of a thousand errors, continues still to blunder, and whose age has only added obstinacy to stupidity, is surely the object of either abhorrence or contempt, and deserves not that his gray hairs should secure him from insult. Much more, sir, is he to be abhorred, who, as he has advanced in age, has receded from virtue, and becomes more wicked with less temptation ; who prostitutes himself for money which he cannot enjoy, and spends the remains of his life in the ruin of his country. But youth, sir, is not my only crime : I have been accused of acting a theatrical part.—A theatrical part may either imply some peculiarities of gesture, or dissimulation of my real sentiments, and an adoption of the opinions and language of another man.

In the first sense, sir, the charge is too trifling to be confuted, and deserves only to be mentioned to be despised. I am at liberty, like every other man, to use my own language, and though, perhaps, I may have some ambition to please this gentleman, I shall not lay myself under any restraint, or very solicitously copy his diction or his mien, however matured by age or modelled by experience. But if any man shall, by charging me with theatrical behavior, imply that I utter any senti-ments but my own, I shall treat him as a calumniator and a villain ; nor shall any protection shelter him from the treatment he deserves. I shall, on such an occasion, without scruple, trample upon all those forms with which wealth and dignity intrench themselves, nor shall any thing but age restrain my sentiment ;—age, which always brings one privilege, that of being insolent and supercilious without punishment. But with regard, sir, to those whom I have offended, I am of opinion, that, if I *had* acted a borrowed part, I should have avoided their censure : the heat that has offended them is the ardor of conviction, and that zeal for the service of my country, which neither hope nor fear shall influence me to suppress. I will not sit unconcerned while my liberty is invaded, nor look in silence upon public robbery. I will exert my endeavors, at whatever hazard, to repel the aggressor, and drag the thief to justice, whoever may protect him in his villany, and whoever may partake of his plunder.

---

## LORD CHATHAM AGAINST THE AMERICAN WAR.

I CANNOT, my Lords, I will not, join in congratulation on misfortune and disgrace. This, my Lords, is a perilous and tremendous moment. It is not a time for adulation ; the smoothness of flattery cannot save us in this rugged and awful crisis. It is now necessary to instruct the throne in the language of truth. We must, if possible, dispel the delusion and darkness which envelope it, and display, in its full danger and genuine colors, the ruin which is brought to our doors. Can ministers still presume to expect support in their infatuation ? Can parliament be so dead to its dignity and duty, as to give their support to measures thus obtruded and forced upon them ? Measures, my Lords, which have reduced this late flourish-ing empire to scorn and contempt ! "But yesterday and Britain might have stood against the world ; now, none so poor as to do her reverence."—The people, whom we at first despised as rebels, but whom we now acknowledge as enemies, are abetted against us, supplied with every military store, have their interest consulted, and their ambassadors entertained, by our inveterate enemy—and ministers do not, and dare not, interpose, with dignity or effect. The desperate state of our army abroad is in part known. No man more highly esteems and honors the British troops than I do ; I know their virtues and their valor ; I know they can achieve anything but impossibilities ; and I know that the conquest of British America is an impossibility. You cannot, my Lords, you cannot conquer America. What is your present situation there ? We do not know the *worst;* but we know that in three campaigns we have done nothing and suffered much. You may swell every expense, accumulate every assistance, and extend your traffic to the shambles of every German despot : your attempts will be for ever vain and impotent—doubly so, indeed, from this mercenary aid on which you rely, for it irritates, to an incurable resentment, the minds of your adversaries to overrun them with the mercenary sons of rapine and plunder, devoting them and their possessions to the rapacity of hireling cruelty. If I were an American as I am an Englishman, while a foreign troop was landed in my country, I never would lay down my arms—*never, never, never!*

---

## LORD BROUGHAM ON NEGRO SLAVERY.

---

I TRUST that, at length, the time is come, when parliament will no longer bear to be told, that slave-owners are the best law-givers on slavery: no longer suffer our voice to roll across the Atlantic, in empty warnings and fruitless orders. Tell me not of rights—talk not of the property of the planter in his slaves. I deny his right—I acknowledge not the property. The principles, the feelings of our common nature, rise in rebellion against it. Be the appeal made to the understanding or to the heart, the sentence is the same—that rejects it! In vain you tell me of laws that sanction such a claim! There is a law, above all the enactments of human codes—the same, throughout the world—the same, in all times: such as it was, before the daring genius of Columbus pierced the night of ages, and opened to one world the sources of power, wealth, and knowledge ; to another, all utterable woes,—such is it at this day: it is the law written by the finger of God on the heart of man ; and by that law, unchangeable and eternal—while men despise fraud, and loathe rapine, and hate blood—they shall reject, with indignation, the wild and guilty fantasy, that man can hold property in man!

In vain you appeal to treaties—to covenants between nations. The covenants of the Almighty, whether the old covenant or the new, denounce such unholy pretensions. To these laws did they of old refer, who maintained the African trade. Such treaties did they cite—and not untruly ; for, by one shameful compact, you bartered the glories of Blenheim for the traffic in blood. Yet, in despite of law and of treaty, that infernal traffic is now destroyed, and its votaries put to death like other pirates. How came this change to pass ? Not, assuredly, by parliament leading the way : but the country at length awoke ; the indignation of the people was kindled ; it descended in thunder, and smote the traffic, and scattered its guilty profits to the winds. Now, then, let the planters beware—let their assemblies beware—let the government at home beware—let the parliament beware ! The same country is once more awake—awake to the condition of negro slavery ; the same indignation kindles in the bosom of the same people ; the same cloud is gathering, that annihilated the slave trade ; and if it shall descend again, they on whom its crash may fall, will not be destroyed before I have warned them ; but I pray, that their destruction may turn away from us the more terrible judgments of God !

## SHERIDAN AGAINST POLITICAL JOBBING.

IS this a time for selfish intrigues, and the little dirty traffic for lucre and emolu-
ment? Does it suit the honor of a gentleman to ask at such a moment? Does
it become the honesty of a minister to grant? What! in such an hour as this,—at
a moment pregnant with the national fate, when, pressing as the exigency may be,
the hard task of squeezing the money from the pockets of an impoverished people,
from the toil, the drudgery of the shivering poor, must make the most practised
collector's heart ache while he tears it from them,—can it be that people of high
rank, and professing high principles,—that they or their families should seek to
thrive on the spoils of misery, and fatten on the meals wrested from industrious
poverty? O, shame! shame! Is it intended to confirm the pernicious doctrine so
industriously propagated, that all public men are impostors, and that every politician
has his price? Or, even where there is no principle in the bosom, why does not
prudence hint to the mercenary and the vain to abstain a while, at least, and wait
the fitting of the times? Improvident impatience! Nay, even from those who
seem to have no direct object of office or profit, what is the language which their
actions speak?

"The Throne is in danger! we will support the Throne; but let us share the
smiles of royalty!" "The order of nobility is in danger! I will fight for nobility,"
says the Viscount; "but my zeal would be greater if I were made an Earl!"
"Rouse all the Marquis within me," exclaims the Earl, "and the Peerage never
turned forth a more undaunted champion in its cause than I shall prove!" "Stain
my green ribbon blue," cries out the illustrious Knight, "and the fountain of honor
will have a fast and faithful servant!"

What are the people to think of our sincerity? What credit are they to give
to our professions? Is this system to be persevered in? Is there nothing that
whispers to that right honorable gentleman that the crisis is too big, that the times
are too gigantic, to be ruled by the little hackneyed and every-day means of ordinary
corruption? Or, are we to believe that he has within himself a conscious feeling
that disqualifies him from rebuking the ill-timed selfishness of his new allies? Let
him take care that the corruptions of the Government shall not have lost it
the public heart; that the example of selfishness in the *few* has not extinguished
public spirit in the *many*!

## BURKE ON THE IMPEACHMENT OF WARREN HASTINGS.

MY LORDS, I have done; the part of the Commons is concluded. With a trembling solicitude we consign this product of our long, long labors, to your
charge. Take it!—Take it! It is a sacred trust. Never before was a cause of
such magnitude submitted to any human tribunal.

My Lords, at this awful close, in the name of the Commons, and surrounded by
them, I attest the retiring, I attest the advancing generations, between which, as a

JOHN QUINCY ADAMS

link in the great chain of eternal order we stand. We call this nation, we call the world to witness, that the Commons have shrunk from no labor, that we have been guilty of no prevarication, that we have made no compromise with crime, that we have not feared any odium whatsoever, in the long warfare which we have carried on with the crimes, with the vices, with the exorbitant wealth, with the enormous and overpowering influence of Eastern corruption. This war we have waged for twenty-two years, and the conflict has been fought at your Lordships' bar for the last seven years. My Lords, twenty-two years is a great space in the scale of the life of man; it is no inconsiderable space in the history of a great nation.

My Lords, your House yet stands,—it stands as a great edifice; but let me say that it stands in the midst of ruins,—in the midst of the ruins that have been made by the greatest moral earthquake that ever convulsed and shattered this globe of ours. My Lords, it has pleased Providence to place us in such a state, that we appear every moment to be upon the verge of some great mutations. There is one thing, and one thing only, which defies all mutation,—that which existed before the world and will survive the fabric of the world itself: I mean justice,—that justice which, emanating from the Divinity, has a place in the breast of every one of us, given us for our guide with regard to ourselves and with regard to others, and which will stand, after this globe is burned to ashes, our advocate or accuser before the great Judge.

My Lords, the Commons will share in every fate with your Lordships; there is nothing sinister which can happen to you, in which we shall not be involved. And if it should so happen that we shall be subjected to some of those frightful changes which we have seen; if it should happen that your Lordships, stripped of all the decorous distinctions of human society, should, by hands at once base and cruel, be led to those scaffolds and machines of murder upon which great kings and glorious queens have shed their blood, amidst the prelates, amidst the nobles, amidst the magistrates who supported their thrones, may you, in those moments feel that consolation which I am persuaded they felt in the critical moments of their agony!

My Lords, may you stand as unimpeached in honor as in power! May you stand, not as a substitute for virtue, but as an ornament of virtue, as a security for virtue! May you stand long, and long stand the terror of tyrants! May you stand the refuge of afflicted nations! May you stand a sacred temple, for the perpetual residence of an inviolable justice!

---

## MIRABEAU'S EULOGIUM ON FRANKLIN.

FRANKLIN is dead! Restored to the bosom of the Divinity in that genius which gave freedom to America, and rayed forth torrents of light upon Europe. The sage whom two worlds claim—the man whom the History of Empires and the History of Science alike contend for—occupied, it cannot be denied, a lofty rank among his species. Long enough have political Cabinets signalized the death of those who were great in their funeral eulogies only. Long enough has the etiquette of Courts prescribed hypocritical mournings. For their benefactors only should Nations assume the emblems of grief; and the Representatives of Nations should commend only the heroes of humanity to public veneration.

In the fourteen States of the Confederacy, Congress has ordained a mourning of two months for the death of Franklin; and America is at this moment acquitting herself of this tribute of honor to one of the Fathers of her Constitution. Would it not become us, Gentlemen, to unite in this religious act; to participate in this homage, publicly rendered, at once to the rights of man, and to the philosopher who has contributed most largely to their vindication throughout the world? Antiquity would have erected altars to this great and powerful genius, who, to promote the welfare of mankind, comprehending both the Heavens and the Earth in the range of his thought, could at once snatch the bolt from the cloud and the sceptre from tyrants. France, enlightened and free, owes at least the acknowledgement of her remembrance and regret to one of the greatest intellects that ever served the united cause of philosophy and liberty. I propose that it be now decreed that the National Assembly wear mourning, during three days, for Benjamin Franklin.

---

## PATRICK HENRY AGAINST BRITISH AGGRESSION.

MR. PRESIDENT it is natural to man to indulge in the illusions of Hope. We are apt to shut our eyes against a painful truth, and listen to the song of that siren, till she transforms us into beasts. Is this the part of wise men, engaged in a great and arduous struggle for liberty? Are we disposed to be of the number of those who, having eyes, see not, and having ears, hear not, the things which so nearly concern our temporal salvation? For my part, whatever anguish of spirit it may cost, I am willing to know the whole truth,—to know the worst, and to provide for it.

I have but one lamp, by which my feet are guided; and that is the lamp of experience. I know of no way of judging of the future but by the past. And, judging by the past, I wish to know what there has been in the conduct of the British ministry, for the last ten years, to justify those hopes with which gentlemen have been pleased to solace themselves and the House? Is it that insidious smile with which our petition has been lately received? Trust it not, Sir; it will prove a snare to your feet! Suffer not yourselves to be betrayed with a kiss! Ask yourselves how this gracious reception of our petition comports with those warlike preparations which cover our waters and darken our land. Are fleets and armies necessary to a work of love and reconciliation? Have we shown ourselves so unwilling to be reconciled, that force must be called in to win back our love?

Let us not deceive ourselves, Sir. These are the implements of war and subjugation,—the last arguments to which Kings resort. I ask Gentlemen, Sir, what means this martial array, if its purpose be not to force us to submission? Can Gentlemen assign any other possible motive for it? Has Great Britain any enemy in this quarter of the world, to call for all this accumulation of navies and armies? No, Sir, she has none. They are meant for us; they can be meant for no other. They are sent over to bind and rivet upon us those chains which the British ministry have been so long forging. And what have we to oppose to them?—Shall we try argument? Sir, we have been trying that, for the last ten years. Have we anything new to offer upon this subject? Nothing. We have held the subject up in every light of which it is capable; but it has been all in vain.

Shall we resort to entreaty and humble supplication? What terms shall we find which have not already been exhausted. Let us not, I beseech you, Sir, deceive ourselves longer. Sir, we have done everything that could be done, to avert the storm which is now coming on. We have petitioned, we have remonstrated, we have supplicated, we have prostrated ourselves before the Throne, and have implored its interposition to arrest the tyrannical hands of the Ministry and Parliament. Our petitions have been slighted, our remonstrances have produced additional violence and insult, our supplications have been disregarded, and we have been spurned, with contempt, from the foot of the Throne.

In vain, after these things, may we indulge the fond hope of peace and reconciliation. There is no longer any room for hope. If we wish to be free,—if we mean to preserve inviolate those inestimable privileges for which we have been so long contending,—if we mean not basely to abandon the noble struggle in which we have been so long engaged, and which we have pledged ourselves never to abandon until the glorious object of our contest shall be obtained,—we must fight; I repeat it, Sir, we must fight! An appeal to arms, and to the God of Hosts, is all that is left us!

They tell us, Sir, that we are weak,—unable to cope with so formidable an adversary. But when shall we be stronger? Will it be the next week, or the next year? Will it be when we are totally disarmed, and when a British guard shall be stationed in every house? Shall we gather strength by irresolution and inaction? Shall we acquire the means of effectual resistance by lying supinely on our backs, and hugging the delusive phanton of hope, until our enemies shall have bound us hand and foot? Sir, we are not weak, if we make a proper use of those means which the God of nature hath placed in our power.

Three millions of People, armed in the holy cause of liberty, and in such a country as that which we possess, are invincible by any force which our enemy can send against us. Besides, Sir, we shall not fight our battles alone. There is a just God who presides over the destinies of Nations, and who will raise up friends to fight our battles for us. The battle, Sir, is not to the strong alone; it is to the vigilant, the active, the brave. Besides, Sir, we have no election. If we were base enough to desire it, it is now too late to retire from the contest. There is no retreat but in submission and slavery! Our chains are forged! Their clanking may be heard on the plains of Boston! The war is inevitable; and let it come! I repeat it, Sir, let it come!

It is in vain, Sir, to extenuate the matter. Gentlemen may cry. peace, peace! —but there is no peace. The war is actually begun! The next gale that sweeps from the North will bring to our ears the clash of resounding arms ! Our brethren are already in the field ! Why stand we here idle ? What is it that gentlemen wish ? What would they have ? Is life so dear, or peace so sweet, as to be purchased at the price of chains and slavery ? Forbid it, Almighty God ! I know not what course others may take ; but as for me, give me liberty, or give me death !

## FRANKLIN ON GOD IN GOVERNMENT.

IN this situation of this Assembly,—groping, as it were, in the dark, to find political truth, and scarce able to distinguish it when presented to us,—how has it happened, Sir, that we have not hitherto once thought of humbly applying to the Father of Light to i luminate our understanding? In the beginning of the contest with Britain, when we were sensible of danger, we had daily prayers in this room for the divine protection. Our prayers, Sir, were heard,—and they were graciously answered. All of us who were engaged in the struggle must have observed frequent instances of a superintending Providence in our favor. To that kind Providence we owe this happy opportunity of consulting in peace on the means of establishing our future national felicity. And have we now forgotten that powerful Friend? or do we imagine we no longer need His assistance? I have lived, Sir, a long time; and the longer I live, the more convincing proofs I see of this truth,— *that God governs in the affairs of men.* And, if a sparrow cannot fall to the ground without His notice, is it probable that an empire can rise without His aid? We have been assured, Sir, in the Sacred Writings, that "except the Lord build the house, they labor in vain that build it." I firmly believe this ; and I also believe that, without His concurring aid, we shall succeed in this political building no better than the builders of Babel, we shall be divided by our little, partial, local interests ; our projects will be confounded and we ourselves shall become a reproach and a byword down to future ages. And, what is worse, mankind may hereafter, from this unfortunate instance, despair of establishing Government by human wisdom and leave it to chance, war, and conquest !

## JOHN QUINCY ADAMS ON THE DECLARATION OF INDEPENDENCE.

THE Declaration of Independence ! The interest which, in that paper, has survived the occasion upon which it was issued—the interest which is of every age and every clime,—the interest which quickens with the lapse of years, spreads as it grows old, and brightens as it recedes,—is in the principles which it proclaims. It was the first solemn declaration by a Nation of the only legitimate foundation of civil Government. It was the corner-stone of a new fabric, destined to cover the surface of the globe. It demolished, at a stroke, the lawfulness of all Governments founded upon conquest. It swept away all the rubbish of accumulated centuries of servitude. It announced, in practical form, to the world, the transcendent truth of

BENJAMIN FRANKLIN

the inalienable sovereignty of the People. It proved that the social compact was no figment of the imagination, but a real, solid, and sacred bond of the social union. From the day of this declaration, the People of North America were no longer the fragment of a distant empire, imploring justice and mercy from an inexorable master, in another hemisphere. They were no longer children, appealing in vain to the sympathies of a heartless mother ; no longer subjects, leaning upon the shattered columns of royal promises, and invoking the faith of parchment to secure their rights. They were a Nation, asserting as of right, and maintaining by war, its own existence. A Nation was born in a day.

> " How many ages hence
> Shall this, their lofty scene, be acted o'er,
> In States unborn, and accents yet unknown ? "

It will be acted o'er, fellow-citizens, but it can never be repeated. It stands, and must forever stand, alone ; a beacon on the summit of the mountain, to which all the inhabitants of the earth may turn their eyes, for a genial and saving light, till time shall be lost in eternity, and this globe itself dissolve, nor leave a wreck behind. It stands forever, a light of admonition to the rulers of men, a light of salvation and redemption to the oppressed. So long as this planet shall be inhabited by human beings, so long as man shall be of a social nature, so long as Government shall be necessary to the great moral purposes of society, so long as it shall be abused to the purposes of oppression,—so long shall this declaration hold out, to the sovereign and to the subject, the extent and the boundaries of their respective rights and duties, founded in the laws of Nature and of Nature's God.

---

## WASHINGTON ON FRANCE AND THE UNITED STATES.

BORN, Sir, in a land of liberty ; having early learned its value, having engaged in a perilous conflict to defend it ; having, in a word, devoted the best years of my life to secure its permanent establishment in my own country,—my anxious recollections, my sympathetic feelings, and my best wishes, are irresistibly excited, whensoever, in any country, I see an oppressed Nation unfurl the banners of freedom. But, above all, the events of the French Revolution have produced the deepest solicitude, as well as the hightst admiration. To call your Nation brave, were to pronounce but common praise. Wonderful people ! Ages to come will read with astonishment the history of your brilliant exploits ! I rejoice that the period of your toils and of your immense sacrifices is approaching. I rejoice that the interesting revolutionary movements of so many years have issued in the formation of a Constitution designed to give permanency to the great object for which you have contended. I rejoice that liberty, which you have so long embraced with enthusiasm,—liberty, of which you have been the invincible defenders,—now finds an asylum in the bosom of a regularly organized government ;—a government, which, being formed to secure the happiness of the French People, corresponds

18

with the ardent wishes of my heart, while it gratifies the pride of every citizen of the United States, by its resemblance to his own.   On these glorious events, accept, Sir, my sincere congratulations.

In delivering to you these sentiments, I express not my own feelings only, but those of my fellow-citizens, in relation to the commencement, the progress, and the issue, of the French Revolution; and they will cordially join with me in purest wishes to the Supreme Being, that the citizens of our sister Republic, our magnanimous allies, may soon enjoy in peace that liberty which they have purchased at so great a price, and all the happiness which liberty can bestow.

I receive, Sir, with lively sensibility, the symbol of the triumphs and of the enfranchisement of your Nation, the colors of France, which you have now presented to the United States.   The transaction will be announced to Congress; and the colors will be deposited with those archives of the United States which are at once the evidence and the memorial of their freedom and independence.   May these be perpetual!   And may the friendship of the two Republics be commensurate with their existence!

## MASSILLON ON IMMORTALITY.

IF we wholly perish with the body, what an imposture is this whole system of laws, manners and usages, on which human society is founded!   If we wholly perish with the body, these maxims of charity, patience, justice, honor, gratitude and friendship, which sages have taught and good men have practised, what are they but empty words, possessing no real and binding efficacy?   Why should we heed them, if in this life only we have hope?   Speak not of duty.   What can we owe to the dead, to the living, to ourselves, if all *are*, or *will* be, nothing?   Who shall dictate our duty, if not our own pleasures,—if not our own passions?   Speak not of morality.   It is a mere chimera, a bugbear of human invention, if retribution terminate with the grave.

If we must wholly perish, what to *us* are the sweet ties of kindred? what the tender names of parent, child, sister, brother, husband, wife or friend?   The characters of a drama are not more illusive.   We have no ancestors, no descendants; since succession cannot be predicated of nothingness.   Would we honor the illustrious dead?   How absurd to honor that which has no existence!   Would we take thought for posterity?   How frivolous to concern ourselves for those whose end, like our own, must soon be annihilation!   Have we made a promise?   How can it bind nothing to nothing?   Perjury is but a jest.   The last injunctions of the dying, —what sanctity have they more than the last sound of a chord that is snapped, of an instrument that is broken?

To sum up all:  If we must wholly perish, then is obedience to the laws but an insensate servitude;  rulers and magistrates are but the phantoms which popular imbecility has raised up;  justice is an unwarrantable infringement upon the liberty of men,—an imposition, a usurpation;  the law of marriage is a vain scruple; modesty, a prejudice ; honor and probity, such stuff as dreams are made of ; and incests, murders, parricides, the most heartless cruelties, and the blackest crimes, are but the legitimate sports of man's irresponsible nature ; while the harsh epithets attached to them are merely such as the policy of legislators has invented, and imposed on the credulity of the people.

Here is the issue to which the vaunted philosophy of unbelievers must inevitably lead. Here is that social felicity, that sway of reason, that emancipation from error, of which they eternally prate, as the fruit of their doctrines. Accept their maxims, and the whole world falls back into a frightful chaos ; and all the relations of life are confounded ; and all ideas of vice and virtue are reversed ; and the most inviolable laws of society vanish ; and all moral discipline perishes ; and the government of states and nations has no longer any cement to uphold it ; and all the harmony of the body politic becomes discord; and the human race is no more than an assemblage of reckless barbarians, shameless, remorseless, brutal, denaturalized, with no other law than force, no other check than passion, no other bond than irreligion, no other God than self ! Such would be the world which impiety would make. Such would be this world, were a belief in God and immortality to die out of the human heart.

## CLAY ON RECOGNIZING THE INDEPENDENCE OF GREECE.

ARE we so low, so base, so despicable, that we may not express our horror, articulate our detestation, of the most brutal and atrocious war that ever stained earth, or shocked high Heaven, with the ferocious deeds of a brutal soldiery, set on by the clergy and followers of a fanatical and inimical religion, rioting in excess of blood and butchery, at the mere details of which the heart sickens? If the great mass of Christendom can look coolly and calmly on, while all this is perpetrated on a Christian People, in their own vicinity, in their very presence, let us, at least, show that, in this distant extremity, there is still some sensibility and sympathy for Christian wrongs and sufferings; that there are still feelings which can kindle into indignation at the oppression of a People endeared to us by every ancient recollection, and every modern tie. But, Sir, it is not first and chiefly for Greece that I wish to see this measure adopted. It will give them but little aid,— that aid purely of a moral kind. It, is, indeed, soothing and solacing, in distress to hear the accents of a friendly voice. We know this as a People. But, Sir, it is principally and mainly for America herself, for the credit and character of our common country, that I hope to see this resolution pass, it is for our own unsullied name that I feel.

What appearance, Sir, on the page of history, would a record like this make : —"In the month of January, in the year of our Lord and Saviour 1824, while all European Christendom beheld with cold, unfeeling apathy the unexampled wrongs and inexpressible misery of Christian Greece, a proposition was made in the Congress of the United States,—almost the sole, the last, the greatest repository of human hope and of human freedom, the representatives of a Nation capable of bringing into the field a million of bayonets,—while the freemen of that Nation were spontaneously expressing its deep-toned feeling, its fervent prayer for Grecian success: while the whole Continent was rising, by one simultaneous motion, solemnly and anxiously supplicating and invoking the aid of Heaven to spare Greece, and to invigorate her arms ; while temples and senate-houses were all resounding with one burst of generous sympathy ;—in the year of our Lord and Saviour,—that Saviour alike of Christian Greece and of us,—a proposition was offered in the American Congress, to send a messenger to Greece, to inquire into her state and condition, with an expression of our good wishes and our sympathies ;—and it was rejected !'' Go home, if you dare,—go home, if you can,—to your constituents, and tell them that you voted it down ! Meet, if you dare, the appalling countenances of those who sent you here, and tell them that you shrank from the declaration of your own sentiments ; that, you cannot tell how, but that some unknown dread, some indescribable apprehension, some indefinable danger, affrighted you ; that the spectres of cimeters and crowns, and crescents, gleamed before you, and alarmed you ; and, that you suppressed all the noble feelings prompted by religion, by liberty, by National independence, and by humanity ! I cannot bring myself to believe that such will be the feeling of a majority of this House.

---

## WEBSTER ON LIBERTY AND UNION.

---

I PROFESS, Sir, in my career hitherto, to have kept steadily in view the prosperity and honor of the whole country, and the preservation of our Federal Union. It is to that Union we owe our safety at home, and our consideration and dignity abroad. It is to that Union that we are chiefly indebted for whatever makes us most proud of our country. That Union we reached only by the discipline of our virtues in the severe school of adversity. It had its origin in the necessities of disordered finance, prostrate commerce, and ruined credit. Under its benign influences, these great interests immediately awoke, as from the dead, and sprang forth with newness of life. Every year of its duration has teemed with fresh proofs of its utility and its blessings ; and, although our territory has stretched out wider and wider, and our population spread further and further, they have not outrun its protection or its benefits. It has been to us all a copious fountain of national, social, and personal happiness.

I have not allowed myself, Sir, to look beyond the Union, to see what might lie hidden in the dark recess behind. I have not coolly weighed the chances of preserving liberty when the bonds that unite us together shall be broken asunder. I have not accustomed myself to hang over the precipice of disunion, to see whether, with my short sight, I can fathom the depth of the abyss below ; nor could I regard him as a safe counsellor in the affairs of this government, whose thoughts should be mainly bent on considering, not how the Union may be best preserved, but how

HENRY IRVING

tolerable might be the condition of the people when it shall be broken up and destroyed.

While the Union lasts, we have high, exciting, gratifying prospects spread out before us, for us and our children. Beyond that I seek not to penetrate the veil. God grant that, in my day at least, that curtain may not rise! God grant that on my vision never may be opened what lies behind! When my eyes shall be turned to behold, for the last time, the Sun in heaven, may I not see him shining on the broken and dishonored fragments of a once glorious Union; on States dissevered, discordant, belligerent; on a land rent with civil feuds, or drenched, it may be, in fraternal blood! Let their last feeble and lingering glance rather behold the gorge-ous ensign of the republic, now known and honored throughout the Earth, still full high advanced, its arms and trophies streaming in their original lustre, not a stripe erased or polluted, nor a single star obscured; bearing for its motto, no such miser-able interrogatory as, "What is all this worth?" nor those other words of delusion and folly, "Liberty first, and Union afterwards"; but everywhere, spread all over in characters of living light, blazing on all its ample folds, as they float over the sea and over the land, and in every wind under the whole heavens, that other sentiment dear to every true American heart—Liberty *and* Union, now and forever, one and inseparable!

## VICTOR HUGO ON UNIVERSAL SUFFRAGE.

UNIVERSAL suffrage!—what is it but the overthrow of violence and brute force—the end of the material and the beginning of the moral fact? What was the Revolution of February intended to establish in France, if not this? And now it is proposed to abolish this sacred right! And what is its abolition, but the reintroduction of the right of insurrection? Ye Ministers and men of State, who govern, wherefore do you venture on this mad attempt? I will tell you. It is because the People have deemed worthy of their votes men whom you judge worthy of your insults! It is because the people have presumed to compare your promises with your acts; because they do not find your Administration altogether sublime; because they have dared peaceably to instruct you through the ballot-box! There-fore it is; that your anger is roused, and that, under the pretence that Society is in peril, you seek to chastise the People,—to take them in hand! And so, like that maniac of whom History tells, you beat the ocean with rods! And so you launch at us your poor little laws, furious but feeble! And so you defy the spirit of the age, defy the good sense of the public, defy the Democracy, and tear your unfor-tunate finger-nails against the granite of universal suffrage!

Go on, Gentlemen! Proceed! Disfranchise, if you will, three millions of voters, four millions, nay, eight millions out of nine! Get rid of all these! It will not matter. What you cannot get rid of is your own fatal incapacity and ignor-ance; your own antipathy for the People, and theirs for you! What you cannot get rid of is the time that marches, and the hour that strikes; is the earth that revolves, the onward movement of ideas, the crippled pace of prejudices; the widening gulf between you and the age, between you and the coming generation, between you and the spirit of liberty, between you and the spirit of philosophy! what you cannot get rid of is the great fact that you and the Nation pass on opposite sides; that what is to you the East is to her the West; and that, while you turn your back on the Future, this great People of France, their foreheads all bathed in light from the day-spring of a new humanity, turn their back on the Past.

Ah! Whether you will it or no, the Past is past. Your law is null, void and dead, even before its birth: because it is not just; because it is not true; because, while it goes furtively to plunder the poor man and the weak of his right of suffrage, it encounters the withering glance of a Nation's probity and sense of right, before which your work of darkness shall vanish; because, in the depths of the conscience of every citizen—of the humblest as well as the highest—there is a sentiment sublime, sacred, indestructible, incorruptible, eternal,—the Right! This sentiment which is the very element of reason in man, the granite of the human conscience, —this Right is the rock upon which shall split and go to pieces the iniquities, the hypocrisies, the bad laws and bad governments of the world. There is the obstacle, concealed, invisible,—lost to view in the soul's profoundest deep, but eternally present and abiding,—against which you shall always strike, and which you shall never wear away, do what you will! I repeat it, your efforts are in vain. You cannot deracinate, you cannot shake it. You might sooner tear up the eternal Rock from the bottom of the sea, than the Right from the heart of the people!

## ROBERT EMMETT'S LAST SPEECH.

WHAT have I to say why sentence of death should not be pronounced on me according to law? I have nothing to say which can alter your predetermination, or that it would become me to say with any view to the mitigation of that sentence which you are here to pronounce, and which I must abide. But I have that to say which interests me more than life, and which you have labored—as was necessarily your office in the present circumstances of this oppressed country—to destroy. I have much to say why my reputation should be rescued from the load of false accusation and calumny which has been heaped upon it. I do not imagine that, seated where you are, your minds can be so free from impurity as to receive the least impression from what I am going to utter. I have no hope that I can anchor my character in the breast of a Court constituted and trammelled as this is. I only wish, and it is the utmost I expect, that your Lordships may suffer it to float down your memories, untainted by the foul breath of prejudice, until it finds some more hospitable harbor, to shelter it from the rude storm by which it is at present buffeted.

Were I only to suffer death, after being adjudged guilty by *your* tribunal, I should bow in silence, and meet the fate that awaits me, without a murmur. But the sentence of the law which delivers my body to the executioner will through the ministry of that law, labor, in its own vindication, to consign my *character* to obloquy: for there must be guilt somewhere,—whether in the sentence of the Court, or in the catastrophe, posterity must determine. A man in my situation, my Lords, has not only to encounter the difficulties of fortune, and the force of power over minds which it has corrupted or subjugated, but the difficulties of established prejudice:—the man dies, but his memory lives: that mine may not perish, that it may live in the respect of my countrymen, I seize upon this opportunity to vindicate myself from *some* of the charges alleged against me. When my spirit shall be wafted to a more friendly port,—when my shade shall have joined the bands of those martyred heroes who have shed their blood, on the scaffold and in the field, in defence of their country and of virtue,—this is my hope: I wish that my memory and name may animate those who survive me, while I look down with complacency on the destruction of that perfidious Government which upholds its dominion by blasphemy of the Most High,—which displays its power over man as over the beasts of the forest—which sets man upon his brother, and lifts his hand, in the name of God, against the throat of his fellow who believes or doubts a little more, or a little less, than the Government standard,—a Government which is steeled to barbarity by the cries of the orphans and the tears of the widows which it has made.

I appeal to the immaculate God,—to the throne of heaven, before which I must shortly appear,—to the blood of the murdered patriots who have gone before,—that my conduct has been, through all this peril, and through all my purposes, governed only by the convictions which I have uttered, and by no other view than that of the emancipation of my country from the superinhuman oppression under which she has so long and too patiently travailed; and that I confidently and assuredly hope that, wild and chimerical as it may appear, there is still union and strength in Ireland to accomplish this noblest enterprise. Of this I speak with the confidence of intimate knowledge, and with the consolation that appertains to that confidence. Think not, my Lords, I say this for the petty gratification of giving you a transitory uneasiness; a man who never yet raised his voice to assert a lie will not hazard his character with posterity by asserting a falsehood on a subject so important to his country, and on an occasion like this. Yes, my Lords; a man who does not wish to have his epitaph written until his country is liberated will not leave a weapon in the power of envy, nor a pretence to impeach the probity which he means to preserve even in the grave to which tyranny consigns him.

Let no man dare, when I am dead, to charge me with dishonor. Let no man attaint my memory by believing that I could have engaged in any cause but that of my country's liberty and independence or that I could have become the pliant minion of power in the oppression and the miseries of my countrymen. The proclamation of the Provisional Government speaks for my views. No inference can be tortured from it to countenance barbarity or debasement at home, or subjection, humiliation or treachery from abroad. I would not have submitted to a foreign oppressor, for the same reason that I would resist the domestic tyrant. In the dignity of freedom I would have fought upon the threshold of my country, and its enemy should enter only by passing over my lifeless corpse. And am I, who lived but for my country—who have subjected myself to the dangers of the jealous and watchful oppressor, and now to the bondage of the grave, only to give my countrymen their rights, and my country her independence,—am I to be loaded with calumny, and not suffered to resent it? No, God forbid!

My Lords, you seem impatient for the sacrifice. The blood for which you thirst is not congealed by the artificial terrors which surround your victim;—it circulates, warmly and unruffled, through the channels which God created for nobler purposes, but which you are bent to destroy, for purposes so grievous that they cry to heaven. Be ye patient! I have but a few words more to say. I am going to my cold and silent grave. My lamp of life is nearly extinguished. My race is run. The grave opens to receive me,—and I sink into its bosom! I have but one request to ask, at my departure from this world;—it is the charity of its silence. Let no man write my epitaph; for, as no man who knows my motives dare *now* vindicate them, let not prejudice or ignorance asperse them. Let them and me repose in obscurity and peace, and my tomb remain uninscribed, until other times and other men can do justice to my character. When my country takes her place among the nations of the earth,—then, and not till then, let my epitaph be written! I have done.

---

### KOSSUTH TO THE HUNGARIANS.

OUR Fatherland is in danger! Citizens! to arms! to arms! Unless the whole Nation rise up, as one man, to defend itself, all the noble blood already shed is in vain; and, on the ground where the ashes of our ancestors repose, the Russian knout will rule over an enslaved people! Be it known to all Hungary, that the Austrian Emperor has let loose upon us the barbarous hordes of Russia; that a Russian army of forty-six thousand men has broken into our country from Gallicia, and is on the march; that another has entered Transylvania; and that, finally we can expect no foreign assistance, as the People that sympathize with us are kept down by their rulers, and gaze only in dumb silence on our struggle. We have nothing to rest our hopes upon, but a righteous God, and our own strength. If we do not put forth that strength, God will also forsake us.

Hungary's struggle is no longer our struggle alone. It is the struggle of popular freedom against tyranny. Our victory is the victory of freedom,—our fall is the fall of freedom. God has chosen us to free the nations from bodily servitude. In the wake of our victory will follow liberty to the Italians, Germans, Poles, Vallachians, Sclavonians, Servians, and Croatians. With our fall goes down the star of freedom over all. People of Hungary! will you die under the exterminating sword of the savage Russians? If not, defend yourselves! Will you look on while the Cossacks of the North tread under foot the bodies of your fathers, mothers, wives and children? If not, defend yourselves! Will you see a part of your fellow-citizens sent to the wilds of Siberia, made to serve in the wars of tyrants, or bleed under the murderous knout? If not, defend yourselves! Will you behold your villages in flames, and your harvests destroyed? Will you die of hunger on the land which your sweat made fertile? If not, defend yourselves!

We call upon the People, in the name of God and the Country, to rise up in arms. In virtue of our powers and duty, we order a general crusade of the People against the enemy, to be declared from every pulpit and from every town-house of the country, and made known by the continual ringing of bells. One great effort, and the country is forever saved! We have, indeed, an army which numbers some two hundred thousand determined men; but the struggle is no longer one between two hostile camps; it is the struggle of tyranny against freedom,—of barbarism against all free Nations. Therefore must all the People seize arms and support the army, that, thus united, the victory of freedom for Europe may be won. Fly, then, united with the army, to arms, every citizen of the land, and the victory is sure.

---

## RUFUS CHOATE ON THE BIRTHDAY OF WASHINGTON.

THE birth-day of the "Father of his Country"! May it ever be freshly remembered by American hearts! May it ever reawaken in them a filial veneration for his memory; ever rekindle the fires of patriotic regard to the country which he loved so well; to which he gave his youthful vigor and his youthful energy, during the perilous period of the early Indian warfare; to which he devoted his life, in the maturity of his powers, in the field; to which again he offered the counsels of his wisdom and his experience, as President of the Convention that framed our Constitution; which he guided and directed while in the Chair of State, and for which the last prayer of his earthly supplication was offered up, when it came the moment for him so well, and so grandly, and so calmly, to die. He was the first man of the time in which he grew. His memory is first and most sacred in our love; and ever hereafter, till the last drop of blood shall freeze in the last American heart, his name shall be a spell of power and might.

Yes, Gentlemen, there is one personal, one vast felicity, which no man can share with him. It was the daily beauty and towering and matchless glory of his life, which enabled him to create his country, and, at the same time, secure an undying love and regard from the whole American people. "The first in the hearts of his countrymen!" Yes, first! He has our first and most fervent love. Undoubtedly there were brave and wise and good men, before his day, in every colony. But the American Nation, as a Nation, I do not reckon to have begun before 1774. And the first love of that young America was Washington. The first word she lisped was his name. Her earliest breath spoke it. It still is her proud ejaculation; and it will be the last gasp of her expiring life!

Yes! Others of our great men have been appreciated,—many admired by all. But him we love. Him we all love. About and around him we call up no dissentient and discordant and dissatisfied elements,—no sectional prejudice nor bias,

—no party, no creed, no dogma of politics. None of these shall assail him. Yes. When the storm of battle grows darkest and rages highest, the memory of Washington shall nerve every American arm, and cheer every American heart. It shall relume that Promethean fire, that sublime flame of patriotism, that denoted love of country, which his words have commended, which his example has consecrated.

> "Where may the wearied eye repose,
>     When gazing on the great,
> Where neither guilty glory glows,
>     Nor despicable state?—
> Yes—one—the first, the last, the best,
> The Cincinnatus of the West,
>     Whom Envy dared not hate,
> Bequeathed the name of Washington,
> To make man blush, there was but one."

## BLACK HAWK'S FAREWELL.

YOU have taken me prisoner, with all my warriors. I am much grieved; for I expected, if I did not defeat you, to hold out much longer, and give you more trouble, before I surrendered. I tried hard to bring you into ambush, but your last General understood Indian fighting. I determined to rush on you, and fight you face to face. I fought hard. But your guns were well aimed. The bullets flew like birds in the air, and whizzed by our ears like the wind through the trees in winter. My warriors fell around me; it began to look dismal. I saw my evil day at hand. The sun rose dim on us in the morning, and at night it sank in a dark cloud, and looked like a ball of fire. That was the last sun that shone on Black Hawk. His heart is dead, and no longer beats quick in his bosom. He is now a prisoner to the white men; they will do with him as as they wish. But he can stand torture, and is not afraid of death. He is no coward. Black Hawk is an Indian.

He has done nothing for which an Indian ought to be ashamed. He has fought for his countrymen, against white men, who came, year affer year, to cheat them, and take away their lands. You know the cause of our making war. It is known to all white men. They ought to be ashamed of it. The white men despise the Indians, and drive them from their homes. They smile in the face of the poor Indian, to cheat him; they shake him by the hand, to gain his confidence, to make him drunk, and to deceive him. We told them to let us alone, and keep away from us; but they followed on and beset our paths, and they coiled themselves among us like the snake. They poisoned us by their touch. We were not safe. We lived in danger. We looked up to the Great Spirit. We went to our father. We were encouraged. His great council gave us fair words and big promises; but we got no satisfaction: things were growing worse. There were no deer in the forest. The opossum and beaver were fled. The springs were drying up, and our squaws and pappooses without victuals to keep them from starving.

We called a great council, and built a great fire.  The spirit of our fathers arose, and spoke to us to avenge our wrongs or die.  We set up the war-whoop, and dug up the tomahawk; our knives were ready, and the heart of Black Hawk swelled high in his bosom, when he led his warriors to battle.  He is satisfied.  He will go to the world of spirits contented.  He has done his duty.  His father will meet him there, and commend him.  Black Hawk is a true Indian, and disdains to cry like a woman.  He feels for his wife, his children, and his friends.  But he does not care for himself.  He cares for the Nation and the Indians.  They will suffer.  He laments their fate.  Farewell, my Nation!  Black Hawk tried to save you, and avenge your wrongs.  He drank the blood of some of the whites.  He has been taken prisoner, and his plans are crushed.  He can do no more.  He is near his end.  His sun is setting, and he will rise no more.  Farewell to Black Hawk.

## LINCOLN'S ADDRESS AT GETTYSBURG.

FOUR-SCORE and seven years ago our fathers brought forth on this continent a new nation, conceived in Liberty, and dedicated to the proposition that all men are created equal.

Now we are engaged in a great civil war, testing whether that nation, or any nation so conceived and so dedicated, can long endure.  We are met on a great battlefield of that war.  We have come to dedicate a portion of that field as a final resting place for those who here gave their lives that that nation might live.  It is altogether fitting and proper that we should do this.

But, in a larger sense, we cannot dedicate—we cannot consecrate—we cannot hallow—this ground.  The brave men, living and dead, who struggled here, have consecrated it, far above our poor power to add or detract.  The world will little note, nor long remember what we say here, but it can never forget what they did here.  It is for us the living, rather, to be dedicated here to the unfinished work which they who fought here have thus far so nobly advanced.  It is rather for us to be here dedicated to the great task remaining before us—that from these honored dead we take increased devotion to that cause for which they gave the last full measure of devotion—that we here highly resolve that these dead shall not have died in vain—that this nation, under God, shall have a new birth of freedom—and that government of the people, by the people, for the people, shall not perish from the earth.

## LINCOLN'S SECOND INAUGURAL.

FELLOW-COUNTRYMEN :  At this second appearing to take the oath of the Presidential office, there is less occasion for an extended address than there was at the first.  Then a statement somewhat in detail, of a course to be pursued seemed fitting and proper.  Now, at the expiration of four years, during which public declarations have been constantly called forth on every point and phase of the great contest which still absorbs the attention and engrosses the energies of the nation, little that is new could be presented.

The progress of our arms, upon which all else chiefly depends, is as well known to the public as to myself, and it is, I trust, reasonably satisfactory and encouraging to all. With high hope for the future, no prediction in regard to it is ventured.

On the occasion corresponding to this, four years ago, all thoughts were anxiously directed to an impending civil war. All dreaded it ; all sought to avert it. While the inaugural address was being delivered from this place, devoted altogether to saving the Union without war, insurgents' agents were in the city seeking to destroy it without war—seeking to dissolve the Union and divide its effects by negotiations.

Both parties deprecated war ; but one of them would make war rather than let the nation survive, and the other would accept war rather than let it perish. And the war came.

The prayer of both could not be answered—those of neither have been answered fully. The Almighty has His own purposes. "Woe unto the world because of offences ! for it must needs be that offences come ; but woe to that man by whom the offence cometh."

If we shall suppose that American slavery is one of those offences which, in the providence of God, must needs come, but which, having continued through His appointed time, He now wills to remove, and that He gives to North and South this terrible war as the woe due to those by whom the offence came, shall we discern therein any departure from those divine attributes which the believers in a living God always ascribe to Him ? Fondly do we hope, fervently do we pray, that this mighty scourge of war may soon pass away.

Yet, if God wills that it continue until all the wealth piled by the bondsman's two hundred and fifty years of unrequited toil shall be sunk, and until every drop of blood drawn by the lash shall be paid by another drawn with the sword, as was said three thousand years ago, so still it must be said : "The judgments of the Lord are true and righteous altogether."

*With malice toward none, with charity for all,* with firmness in the right, as God gives us to see the right, let us strive on to finish the work we are in ; to bind up the nation's wounds; to care for him who shall have borne the battle, and for his widow and for his orphan ; to do all which may achieve and cherish a just and lasting peace among ourselves, and with all nations.

---

### JEFFERSON ON REPUBLICANISM.

DURING the throes and convulsions of the ancient world,—during the agonizing spasms of infuriated man, seeking, through blood and slaughter, his long-lost liberty,—it was not wonderful that the agitation of the billows should reach even this distant and peaceful shore,—that this should be more felt and feared by some, and less by others,—and should divide opinions as to measures of safety. But every difference of opinion is not a difference of principle. We have called by

DANIEL WEBSTER

different names brethren of the same principle. We are all Republicans; we are all Federalists. If there be any among us who would wish to dissolve this Union, or to change its republican form, let them stand, undisturbed, as monuments of the safety with which error of opinion may be tolerated, where reason is left free to combat it. I know, indeed, that some honest men fear a republican Government cannot be strong,—that this Government is not strong enough. But would the honest patriot, in the full tide of successful experiment, abandon a Government which has so far kept us free and firm, on the theoretic and visionary fear that this Government, the world's best hope, may, by possibility, want energy to preserve itself? I trust not. I believe this on the contrary, the strongest Government on earth. I believe it the only one where every man, at the call of the law, would fly to the standard of the law, and would meet invasions of the public order as his own personal concern. Sometimes it is said that man cannot be trusted with the government of himself. Can he, then, be trusted with the government of others? Or have we found angels, in the form of Kings, to govern him? Let history answer this question.

Let us, then, with courage and confidence, pursue our own Federal and Republican principles—our attachment to Union and representative Government. Kindly separated, by nature and a wide ocean, from the exterminating havoc of one-quarter of the globe,—too high-minded to endure the degradations of the others,—possessing a chosen country, with room enough for our descendants to the thousandth and thousandth generation,—entertaining a due sense of our equal right to the use of our own faculties, to the acquisitions of our own industry, to honor and confidence from our fellow-citizens, resulting not from birth, but from our actions, and their sense of them,—enlightened by a benign religion, professed, indeed, and practised in various forms, yet all of them inculcating honesty, truth, temperance, gratitude, and the love of man,—acknowledging and adoring an overruling Providence, which, by all its dispensations, proves that it delights in the happiness of man here, and his greater happiness hereafter; with all these blessings, what more is necessary, to make us a happy and prosperous People?

Still one thing more, fellow-citizens; a wise and frugal Government, which shall restrain men from injuring one another, shall leave them otherwise free to regulate their own pursuits of industry and improvement, and shall not take from the mouth of labor the bread it has earned. This is the sum of good government; and this is necessary to close the circle of our felicities.

---

### FREDERICK DOUGLASS AT ARLINGTON CEMETERY ON DECORATION DAY.

---

FRIENDS and Fellow Citizens: Tarry here for a moment. My words shall be few and simple. The solemn rites of this hour and place call for no lengthened speech. There is, in the very air of this resting-ground of the unknown dead, a silent, subtle and all-pervading eloquence, far more touching, impressive, and thrilling than living lips have ever uttered. Into the measureless depths of every loyal soul it is now whispering lessons of all that is precious, priceless, holiest, and most enduring in human existence.

Dark and sad will be the hour to this nation when it forgets to pay grateful homage to its greatest benefactors. The offering we bring to-day is due alike to the patriot soldier dead and their noble comrades who still live ; for, whether living or dead, whether in time or eternity, the loyal soldiers who imperiled all for country and freedom are one and inseparable.

Those unknown heroes whose whitened bones have been piously gathered here, and whose green graves we now strew with sweet and beautiful flowers, choice emblems alike of pure hearts and brave spirits, reached, in their glorious career, that last highest point of nobleness beyond which human power cannot go. They died for their country.

No loftier tribute can be paid to the most illustrious of all the benefactors of mankind than we pay to these unrecognized soldiers when we write above their graves this shining epitaph.

When the dark and vengeful spirit of slavery, always ambitious, preferring to rule in hell than to serve in heaven, fired the Southern heart and stirred all the malign elements of discord, when our great Republic, the hope of freedom and self-government throughout the world, had reached the point of supreme peril, when the Union of these States was torn and rent asunder at the centre, and the armies of a gigantic rebellion came forth with broad blades and bloody hands to destroy the very foundation of American society, the unknown braves who flung themselves into the yawning chasm, where cannon roared and bullets whistled, fought and fell. They died for their country.

We are sometimes asked, in the name of patriotism, to forget the merits of this fearful struggle, and to remember with equal admiration those who struck at the nation's life and those who struck to save it, those who fought for slavery and those who fought for liberty and justice.

I am no minister of malice. I would not strike the fallen. I would not repel the repentant; but may my "right hand forget her cunning and my tongue cleave to the roof of my mouth," if I forget the difference between the parties to that terrible, protracted, and bloody conflict.

If we ought to forget a war which has filled our land with widows and orphans; which has made stumps of men of the very flower of our youth ; which has sent them on the journey of life armless, legless, maimed and mutilated ; which has piled up a debt heavier than a mountain of gold, swept uncounted thousands of men into bloody graves and planted agony at a million hearthstones—I say, if this war is to be forgotten, I ask, in the name of all things sacred, what shall men remember ?

The essence and significance of our devotions here to-day are not to be found in the fact that the men whose remains fill these graves were brave in battle. If we met simply to show our sense of bravery, we should find enough on both sides to kindle admiration. In the raging storm of fire and blood, in the fierce torrent of shot and shell, of sword and bayonet, whether on foot or on horse, unflinching courage marked the rebel not less than the loyal soldier.

But we are not here to applaud manly courage, save as it has been displayed in a noble cause. We must never forget that victory to the rebellion meant death to the republic. We must never forget that the loyal soldiers who rest beneath this sod flung themselves between the nation and the nation's destroyers. If to-day we have a country not boiling in an agony of blood, like France, if now we have a united country, no longer cursed by the hell-black system of human bondage, if the American name is no longer a by-word and a hissing to a mocking earth, if the star-spangled banner floats only over free American citizens in every quarter of the land, and our country has before it a long and glorious career of justice, liberty, and civilization, we are indebted to the unselfish devotion of the noble army who rest in these honored graves all around us.

## KING ON THE FUTURE OF AMERICA.

I HAVE faith in the future, because I have confidence in the present. With our growth in wealth and in power, I see no abatement in those qualities, moral and physical, to which so much of our success is owing; and, while thus true to ourselves, true to the instincts of freedom, and to those other instincts, which, with our race, seem to go hand in hand with Freedom,—love of order and respect for law (*as* law, and not because it is upheld by force),—we must continue to prosper.

The sun shines not upon, has never shone upon, a land where human happiness is so widely disseminated, where human government is so little abused, so free from oppression, so invisible, so intangible, and yet so strong. Nowhere else do the institutions which constitute a State rest upon so broad a base as here; and nowhere are men so powerless, and institutions so strong. In the wilderness of free minds, dissensions will occur; and, in the unlimited discussion in writing and in speech, in town-meetings, newspapers, and legislative bodies, angry and menacing language will be used; irritations will arise and be aggravated; and those immediately concerned in the strife, or breathing its atmosphere, may fear, or feign to fear, that danger is in such hot breath and passionate resolves. But outside, and above, and beyond all this, is the People,—steady, industrious, self-possessed,—caring little for abstractions, and less for abstractionist, but, with one deep, common sentiment, and with the consciousness, calm, but quite sure and earnest, that, in the Constitution and the Union, as they received them from their fathers, and as they themselves have observed and maintained them, is the sheet-anchor of their hope, the pledge of their prosperity, the palladium of their liberty; and with this, is that other consciousness, not less calm and not less earnest, that, in their own keeping exclusively, and not in that of any party leaders or party demagogues, or political hacks, or speculators, is the integrity of that Union and that Constitution. It is in the strong arms and honest hearts of the great masses, who are not members of Congress, nor holders of office, nor spouters at town-meetings, that resides the safety of the State; and these masses, though slow to move, are irresistible, when the time and the occasion for moving comes.

I have faith, therefore, in the future; and when, at the close of this half century, which so comparatively few of us are to see, the account shall again be taken, and the question be asked, What has New York done since 1850? I have faith that the answer will be given in a City still advancing in population, wealth, morals, and knowledge,—in a City free, and deserving, by her virtues, her benevolent institutions, her schools, her courts and her temples, to continue free, and still part and parcel of this great and glorious Union—which may God preserve till Time shall be no more.

## PRENTISS ON OFFICIAL INTEGRITY.

SINCE the avowal, Mr. Chairman, of the unprincipled and barbarian motto, that "to the victors belong the spoils," office, which was intended for the service and benefit of the People, has become but the plunder of party. Patronage is waved like a huge magnet over the land; and demagogues, like iron-filings, attracted by a law of their nature, gather and cluster around its poles. Never yet lived the demagogue who would not take office. The whole frame of our Government—all the institutions of the country—are thus prostituted to the uses of party. Office is conferred as the reward of partisan service; and what is the consequence? The incumbents, being taught that all moneys in their possession belong, not to the People, but to the party, it requires but small exertion of casuistry to bring them to the conclusion that they have a right to retain what they may conceive to be the value of their political services—just as a lawyer holds back his commissions.

Sir, I have given you but three or four cases of defalcations. Would time permit, I could give you a hundred. Like the fair Sultana of the Oriental legends, I could go on for a thousand and one nights; and even as in those Eastern stories, so in the chronicles of the office-holders, the tale would ever be of heaps of gold, massive ingots, uncounted riches. Why, Sir, Aladdin's wonderful lamp was nothing to it. They seem to possess the identical cap of Fortunatus. Some wish for fifty thousand dollars, some for a hundred thousand, and some for a million—and behold, it lies in glittering heaps before them! Not even

> "The gorgeous East, with richest hand,
> Showers on her kings barbaric pearl and gold"

in such lavish abundance, as does this Administration upon its followers. Pizarro held not forth more dazzling lures to his robber band, when he led them to the conquest of the "Children of the Sun."

And now it is proposed to make up these losses through defaulters by retrenchment! And what do you suppose are to be the subjects of this new and sudden economy? What branches of the public service are to be lopped off, on account of the licentious rapacity of the office-holders? I am too indignant to tell you. Look

HENRY CLAY

into the report of the Secretary of the Treasury, and you will find out. Well, Sir, what are they? Pensions, harbors, and lighthouses! Yes, Sir; these are recommended as proper subjects for retrenchment. First of all the scarred veterans of the Revolution are to be deprived of a portion of the scanty pittance doled out to them by the cold charity of the country. How many of them will you have to send forth as beggars on the very soil which they wrenched from the hand of tyranny, to make up the amount of even one of these splendid robberies? How many harbors will it take—those improvements dedicated no less to humanity than to interest—those nests of commerce to which the canvas-winged birds of the ocean flock for safety? How many light-houses will it take? How many of those bright eyes of the ocean are to be put out? How many of those faithful sentinels, who stand along our rocky coast, and, peering far out in the darkness, give timely warning to the hardy mariner where the lee-shore threatens—how many of these, I ask, are to be discharged from their humane service? Why, the proposition is almost impious! I should as soon wish to put out the stars of heaven! Sir, my blood boils at the cold-blooded atrocity with which the Administration proposes thus to sacrifice the very family jewels of the country, to pay for the consequences of its own profligacy!

## HAYNE ON SOUTHERN PATRIOTISM.

IF there be one State in the Union, Mr. President (and I say it not in a boastful spirit), that may challenge comparisons with any other, for an uniform, zealous, ardent, and uncalculating devotion to the Union, that State is South Carolina. Sir, from the very commencement of the Revolution, up to this hour, there is no sacrifice, however great, she has not cheerfully made,—no service she has ever hesitated to perform. She has adhered to you in your prosperity; but in your adversity she has clung to you with more than filial affection. No matter what was the condition of her domestic affairs,—though deprived of her resources, divided by parties, or surrounded with difficulties,—the call of the country has been to her as the voice of God. Domestic discord ceased at the sound: every man became at once reconciled to his brethren, and the sons of Carolina were all seen crowding together to the temple, bringing their gifts to the altar of their common country.

What, Sir, was the conduct of the South during the Revolution? Sir, I honor New England for her conduct in that glorious struggle. But, great as is the praise which belongs to her, I think at least equal honor is due to the South. They espoused the quarrel of their brethren, with a generous zeal, which did not suffer them to stop to calculate their interest in the dispute. Favorites of the mother country, possessed of neither ships nor seamen to create a commercial rivalship, they might have found in their situation a guarantee that their trade would be forever fostered and protected by Great Britain. But, trampling on all considerations either of interest or of safety, they rushed into the conflict, and, fighting for principle, perilled all, in the sacred cause of freedom. Never was there exhibited, in the history of the world, higher examples of noble daring, dreadful suffering and heroic endurance, than by the Whigs of Carolina, during the Revolution. The whole State, from the mountains to the sea, was overrun by an overwhelming force of enemy. The fruits of industry perished on the spot where they were produced, or were consumed by the foe. The "plains of Carolina" drank up the most precious blood of her citizens. Black and smoking ruins marked the places which had been the habitations of her children! Driven from their homes, into the gloomy and almost impenetrable swamps, even there the spirit of liberty survived; and South Carolina, sustained by the example of her Sumpters and her Marions, proved, by her conduct, that though her soil might be overrun, the spirit of her People was invincible.

## McDUFFIE ON POPULAR ELECTIONS.

WE have been frequently told that the farmer should attend to his plough, and the mechanic to his handicraft, during the canvass for the Presidency. Sir, a more dangerous doctrine could not be inculcated. If there is any spectacle from the contemplation of which I would shrink with peculiar horror, it would be that of the great mass of the American People sunk into a profound apathy on the subject of their highest political interests. Such a spectacle would be more portentous, to the eye of intelligent patriotism, than all the monsters of the earth, and fiery signs of the Heavens, to the eye of trembling superstition. If the People could be indifferent to the fate of a contest for the Presidency, they would be unworthy of freedom.

"Keep the People quiet! Peace! Peace!" Such are the whispers by which the People are to be lulled to sleep, in the very crisis of their highest concerns. Sir, "you make a solitude, and call it peace!" Peace? 'T is death! Take away all interest from the People in the election of their Chief Ruler, and liberty is no more. What, Sir, is to be the consequence? If the People do not elect the President, somebody must. There is no special Providence to decide the question. Who, then, is to make the election, and how will it operate? Make the People indifferent, destroy their legitimate influence, and you communicate a morbid violence to the efforts of those who are ever ready to assume the control of such affairs, the mercenary intriguers and interested office-hunters of the country. Tell me not, Sir of popular violence! Show me a hundred political factionists,—men who look to the election of a President as a means of gratifying their high or their low ambition, —and I will show you the very materials for a mob, ready for any desperate adventure, connected with their common fortunes. The People can have no such motives; they look only to the interest and glory of the country.

There was a law of Athens which subjected every citizen to punishment who refused to take sides in the political parties which divided the Republic. It was founded in the deepest wisdom. The ambitious few will inevitably acquire the ascendency, in the conduct of human affairs, if the patriotic many, the People, are not stimulated and roused to a proper activity and effort. Sir, no Nation on earth has ever exerted so extensive an influence on human affairs as this will certainly exercise, if we preserve our glorious system of Government in its purity. The liberty of this country is a sacred depository—a vestal fire, which Providence has committed to us for the general benefit of mankind. It is the world's last hope. Extinguish it, and the earth will be covered with eternal darkness. But once put out that fire, and I " know not where is the Promethean heat which can that light relume."

---

## BEECHER AT GREELEY'S FUNERAL.

---

THERE is no one that dies whose death is not momentous, if we but behold it as God's angels do ; and yet when men have filled the household with their presence, and society has been made a beneficiary by their kindnesses and by their wisdom, death becomes still more momentous. Every day hundreds and hundreds are borne through your streets and laid away to sleep in yonder Greenwood, leaving behind them sorrow and tears, and many reverent thoughts ; and yet of all that have passed through on their way to their long home, no one, I think, has gone, or for a long time will go, bearing with him so many sympathies, so much kindness, so many tender recollections, so much that should be instructive, as he who lies here before you.

Who is this man, bearing upon him all the civic honors that the land could give him ? Who is this man ? One whose wealth has made him a prince in benevolence ? He was not rich in living, nor in dying rich. Who is this man ? Some one gifted with all kindness of heart, and singular tact of administration, that should make every one his friend who came near him ? But he was a man of war, who for thirty years has filled the land with the racket of various controversies ; and yet to-day, without office, without title, without place except that of the humblest citizen, the Government itself stands still, and the honored representative and Chief Magistrate of this great people is here to bow his head in unfeigned sympathy. Here are also heads of Departments, and men of every style of thought ; here are men who have scarcely yet laid down the bow from which the last arrow has been shot—all gathered to-day by one impulse—the business of the street almost stopped ; private dwellings showing the significant tokens of their sorrow—all gathered in genuine sympathy around about this man who can speak no more, walk in our presence no more, but has gone out from us forever.

Is it that death has made us forget all our differences ? We have not forgotten them. Is it that strained courtesy that lays aside criticism in the presence of death as something too august for man to trifle with ? But we differ to-day as much in theory, as much in philosophy, in the best methods of policy, as we did a month ago. A month ago the whole land was full of clamor. A little while ago men were in fierce battle. There has been no change in it ; and yet he who was the chief mark on one side lies before you ; and you press around him in tears to-day to do him reverence. It is because the man is more than a professional man ; not the candidate, not the editor. The man that lay under them all is honored and honorable. And when the conflicts of life intermit for a moment and you can take off your harness, and look into that which belongs to your essential manhood, you do revere him and love him. And since the circumstances of his going were so wonderfully dramatic, since stroke after stroke resounded through the land to make his death one which in every feature is calculated most deeply to affect all, you are brought together to express here your honor and your reverence for Horace Greeley.

It is given to but very few men, the Divine Jesus chiefly, and in lesser measure to Plato, so to think that their thoughts go on as institutions, working down through the generations. Such men are the masters of men and the masters of minds, and they are but few. Most men are great by their circumstances, and great by the exertions of powers which have an application by reason of transient circumstances ; there are others who are great because they have fertile lives, and it is permitted them to mingle their lives with the lives of others. This has been done by him who can write no more and speak no more. For thirty years he has builded for himself no outward monument, no long line of literary efforts, no mansion, no estate ; but for thirty years that heart that meant well by every human being has been beating, beating, and giving some drops of its blood to countless multitudes, until to-day, between the two oceans, there is hardly an intelligent man or child that does not feel the influence of the life of Horace Greeley. He is lost in his individuality, but his work is as great as the character and the currents and the tendencies of this great American people.

And now what matters it, in your present thought, that in political economy he was on one side and you were on the other ; that in the party divisions of life he was on one side and you were on the other ? That which at this hour beseems you, and that which is in accordance with every man's feeling to-day, is this : Horace Greeley gave the strength of his life to education, to honest industry, to humanity, especially toward the poor and the unfriended. He was feet for the lame ; he was tongue for the dumb ; he was an eye for the blind ; and had a heart for those who had none to sympathize with them. His nature longed for more love than it had, and more sympathy than was ever administered to it. The great heart working through life fell at last. He had poured his life out for thirty years into the life of his time. It has been for intelligence, for industry, for an honester life and a nobler manhood ; and, though he may not be remembered by those memorials which carry other men's names down, his deeds will be known and felt to the latest generations in our land.

The husbandman reaps his wheat and it is threshed, and the straw goes back again to the ground and the chaff. It matters not how much or how little wheat is garnered. Even that perishes. Some of it goes to seed again and into the ground ; more of it becomes the farmer himself. He holds the plow with his hand ; he gathers in again other harvests with his skill ; he becomes the man. It is no longer wheat ; it is the man. The harvest has been garnered, and it reappears in

LINCOLN AT GETTYSBURG

the school-boy, the pioneer settler in the distant West, in the young, thriving men of our cities and towns. To these men Horace Greeley's life has gone out. He has been a national benefactor, and to-day we bear testimony to these under virtues which made his life conspicuous. We were attracted so much to the politics of the times that we gave no notice to those nobler under qualities of true manhood in him ; but to-day we think better. To-day we are all speaking kindly of him—sorrowfully. To-day we are asking what things there may be said of him, and what we may add to praise him fairly and justly.

Oh ! men, is there nothing for you to do—you who with uplifted hands a few short weeks ago were doing such battle ? Look at what you were then, and what you are now. Are there no lessons to be learned, no corrections to be made ? Think of those conflicts, in which you forgot charity, kindliness, goodness ! Think of those fierce battles, almost unto blood—in just such you have mingled, out of just such you have come. What do you think of them now ? Look here at all that remains of this man. Did you not magnify the differences ? Did you not give yourselves to your malign passions, and too little to justice and divine charity? As you stand to-day it is not enough that you should mourn with those that mourn. It is wise that you should carry back with you a tempered and kinder and chastened feeling.

At last, at last ! he rests as one that has been driven through a long voyage by storms that would not abate, but reaches the shore and stands upon the firm earth ; sees again the shady trees and the green fields, and the beaming sun. So he, through a long and not untempestuous voyage, has reached the shore and is at rest. Oh! how sweet the way that leads to the grave, when that grave is God's golden gate to immortality ! How blessed are the dead that die in the Lord ! God grant that, in the solemnity of these thoughts in which we have gathered to-day, it may be ours so to live that when we die angels shall open the gate and receive us into the joy and glory of our Lord.

---

## GARFIELD ON THE READING OF THE EMANCIPATION PROCLAMATION.

LET us pause to consider the actors in that scene. In force of character, in thoroughness and breadth of culture, in experience of public affairs and in national reputation, the Cabinet that sat around that council-board has had no superior, perhaps no equal, in our history. Seward, the finished scholar, the consummate orator, the great leader of the Senate, had come to crown his career with those achievements which placed him in the first rank of modern diplomatists. Chase, with a culture and a fame of massive grandeur, stood as the rock and pillar of the public credit, the noble embodiment of the public faith. Stanton was there, a very Titan of strength, the great organizer of victory. Eminent lawyers, men of business, leaders of states and leaders of men, completed the group.

But the man who presided over that council, who inspired and guided its deliberations, was a character so unique that he stood alone, without a model in

history or a parallel among men.  Born on this day, sixty-nine years ago, to an
inheritance of extremest poverty; surrounded by the rude forces of the wilderness;
wholly unaided by parents; only one year in any school; never, for a day, master
of his own time until he reached his majority; making his way to the profession of
the law by the hardest and roughest road; yet by force of unconquerable will and
persistent, patient work, he attained a foremost place in his profession,

> And, moving up from high to higher,
> Became, on fortune's crowning slope,
> The pillar of a people's hope,
> The centre of a world's desire.

At first, it was the prevailing belief that he would be only the nominal head
of his administration; that its policy would be directed by the eminent statesmen
he had called to his council.  How erroneous this opinion was, may be seen from a
single incident :

Among the earliest, most difficult, and most delicate duties of his administration, was the adjustment of our relations with Great Britain.  Serious complications,
even hostilities were apprehended.  On the 21st of May, 1861, the Secretary of
State presented to the President his draught of a letter of instructions to Minister
Adams, in which the position of the United States and the attitude of Great Britain
were set forth with the clearness and force which long experience and great ability
had placed at the command of the Secretary.

Upon almost every page of that original draught are erasures, additions, and
marginal notes in the handwriting of Abraham Lincoln, which exhibit a sagacity, a
breadth of wisdom, and a comprehension of the whole subject, impossible to be
found except in a man of the very first order.  And these modifications of a great
state paper were made by a man who, but three months before, had entered, for
the first time, the wide theatre of Executive action.

Gifted with an insight and a foresight which the ancients would have called
divination, he saw, in the midst of darkness and obscurity, the logic of events, and
forecast the result.  From the first, in his own quaint, original way, without osten-
tation or offence to his associates, he was pilot and commander of his administration.
He was one of the few great rulers whose wisdom increased with his power, and
whose spirit grew gentler and tenderer as his triumphs were multiplied.

---

### CHAUNCEY M. DEPEW ON THE WASHINGTON CENTENARY.

THE simple and imposing ceremony over, the inaugural read, the blessing of God
prayerfully petitioned in old St. Paul's, the festivities passed, and Washington
stood alone.  No one else could take the helm of state, and enthusiast and doubter
alike trusted only him.  The teachings and habits of the past had educated the people to faith in the independence of their States, and for the supreme authority of the
new Government there stood against the precedent of a century and the passions of
the hour little besides the arguments of Hamilton, Madison and Jay in *"The*

*Federalist,"* and the judgment of Washington. With the first attempt to exercise National power began the duel to the death between State sovereignty, claiming the right to nullify Federal laws or to secede from the Union and the power of the Republic to command the resources of the country, to enforce its authority and protect its life. It was the beginning of the sixty years' war for the Constitution and the Nation. It seared consciences, degraded politics, destroyed parties, ruined statesmen, and retarded the advance and development of the country; it sacrificed thousands of precious lives, and squandered thousands of millions of money; it desolated the fairest portion of the land and carried mourning into every home North and South; but it ended at Appomattox in the absolute triumph of the Republic.

Posterity owes to Washington's Administration the policy and measures, the force and direction, which made possible this glorious result. In giving the organization of the Department of State and foreign relations to Jefferson, the Treasury to Hamilton, and the Supreme Court to Jay, he selected for his Cabinet and called to his assistance the ablest and most eminent men of his time. Hamilton's marvellous versatility and genius designed the armory and the weapons for the promotion of National power and greatness, but Washington's steady support carried them through. Parties crystallized, and party passions were intense, debates were intemperate, and the Union openly threatened and secretly plotted against, as the firm pressure of this mighty personality funded the debt and established credit, assumed the State debts incurred in the war of the Revolution and superseded the local by the National obligation, imposed duties upon imports and excise upon spirits, and created revenue and resources, organized a National Banking system for public needs and private business, and called out an army to put down by force of arms resistance to the Federal laws imposing unpopular taxes. Upon the plan marked out by the Constitution, this great architect, with unfailing faith and unfaltering courage, builded the Republic. He gave to the Government the principles of action and sources of power which carried it successfully through the wars with Great Britain in 1812 and Mexico in 1848, which enabled Jackson to defeat nullification, and recruited and equipped millions of men for Lincoln and justified and sustained his Proclamation of Emancipation.

The French Revolution was the bloody reality of France and the nightmare of the civilized world. The tyranny of centuries culminated in frightful reprisals and reckless revenges. As parties rose to power and passed to the guillotine, the frenzy of the revolt against all authority reached every country and captured the imaginations and enthusiasm of millions in every land, who believed they saw that the madness of anarchy, the overturning of all institutions, the confiscation and distribution of property, would end in a millennium for the masses and the universal brotherhood of man. Enthusiasm for France, our late ally, and the terrible commercial and industrial distress occasioned by the failure of the Government under the Articles of Confederation, aroused an almost unanimous cry for the young Republic, not yet sure of its own existence, to plunge into the vortex. The ablest and purest statesmen of the time bent to the storm, but Washington was unmoved. He stood like the rock-ribbed coast of a continent between the surging billows of fanaticism and the child of his love. Order is Heaven's first law, and the mind of Washington was order. The Revolution defied God and derided the law. Washington devoutly reverenced the Deity and believed liberty impossible without law. He spoke to the sober judgment of the Nation and made clear the danger. He saved the infant Government from ruin, and expelled the French Minister who had appealed from him to the people. The whole land, seeing safety only in his continuance in office, joined Jefferson in urging him to accept a second term. "North and South," pleaded the Secretary, "will hang together while they have you to hang to."

No man ever stood for so much to his country and to mankind as George Washington. Hamilton, Jefferson and Adams, Madison and Jay, each represented some of the elements which formed the Union. Washington embodied them all. They fell at times under popular disapproval, were burned in effigy, were stoned, but he, with unerring judgment, was always the leader of the people. Milton said of Cromwell, "that war made him great, peace greater." The superiority of Washington's character and genius were more conspicuous in the formation of our Government and in putting it on indestructible foundations than in leading armies to victory and conquering the independence of his country. "The Union in any event," is the central thought of his farewell address, and all the years of his grand life were devoted to its formation and preservation. He fought as a youth with Braddock and in the capture of Fort Duquesne for the protection of the whole country. As Commander-in-chief of the Continental Army, his commission was from the Congress of the United Colonies. He inspired the movement for the Republic, was the president and dominant spirit of the Convention which framed its Constitution, and its President for eight years, and guided its course until satisfied that moving safely along the broad highway of time, it would be surely ascending toward the first place among the nations of the world, the asylum of the oppressed, the home of the free.

Do his countrymen exaggerate his virtues? Listen to Guizot, the historian of civilization: "Washington did the two greatest things which in politics it is permitted to man to attempt. He maintained by peace the independence of his country which he conquered by war. He founded a free government in the name of the principles of order and by re-establishing their sway." Hear Lord Erskin, the most famous of English advocates: "You are the only being for whom I have an awful reverence." Remember the tribute of Charles James Fox, the greatest parliamentary orator who ever swayed the British House of Commons: "Illustrious man, before whom all borrowed greatness sinks into insignificance." Contemplate the character of Lord Brougham, pre-eminent for two generations in every department of human activity and thought, and then impress upon the memory of your children his deliberate judgment: "Until time shall be no more will a test of the progress which our race has made in wisdom and virtue be derived from the veneration paid to the immortal name of Washington."

Chatham, who, with Clive, conquered an Empire in the East, died broken-hearted at the loss of the Empire in the West, by follies which even his power and eloquence could not prevent.    Pitt saw the vast creations of his diplomacy shattered at Austerlitz, and fell murmuring:  "My country! how I leave my country!"  Napoleon caused a noble tribute to Washington to be read at the head of his armies, but unable to rise to Washington's greatness, witnessed the vast structure erected by conquest and cemented by blood, to minister to his own ambition and pride, crumble into fragments, and an exile and a prisoner he breathed his last babbling of battle-fields and carnage.    Washington, with his finger upon his pulse, felt the presence of death, and calmly reviewing the past and forecasting the future, he answered to the summons of the grim messenger, "It is well," and as his mighty soul ascended to God the land was deluged with tears and the world united in his eulogy.    Blot out from the page of history the names of all the great actors of his time in the drama of nations, and preserve the name of Washington and the century would be renowned.

We stand to-day upon the dividing line between the first and second century of Constitutional Government.    There are no clouds overhead and no convulsions under our feet.    We reverently return thanks to Almighty God for the past, and with confident and hopeful promise march upon sure ground toward the future.    The simple facts of these hundred years paralyze the imagination, and we contemplate the vast accumulations of the century with awe and pride.    Our population has grown from four to sixty-five millions.    Its centre, moving Westward 500 miles since 1789, is eloquent with the founding of cities and the birth of States.    New settlements, clearing the forests and subduing the prairies, and adding four millions to the few thousands of farms which were the support of Washington's Republic, create one of the great granaries of the world, and open exhaustless reservoirs of National wealth.

The infant industries, which the first act of our first Administration sought to encourage, now give remunerative employment to more people than inhabited the Republic at the beginning of Washington's Presidency.    The grand total of their annual output of seven thousand millions of dollars in value places the United States first among the manufacturing countries of the earth.    One-half the total mileage of all the railroads, and one-quarter of all the telegraph lines of the world within our borders, testify to the volume, variety and value of an internal commerce which makes these States, if need be, independent and self supporting.    These hundred years of development under favoring political conditions have brought the sum of our National wealth to a figure which has passed the results of a thousand years for the Mother-land herself, otherwise the richest of modern empires.

During this generation, a civil war of unequalled magnitude caused the expenditure and loss of eight thousand million of dollars, and killed 600,000 and permanently disabled over a million young men, and yet the impetuous progress of the North and the marvellous industrial development of the new and free South have obliterated the evidences of destruction, and made the war a memory, and have stimulated production until our annual surplus nearly equals that of England, France and Germany combined. The teeming millions of Asia till the patient soil and work the shuttle and loom as their fathers have done for ages; modern Europe has felt the influence and received the benefit of the incalculable multiplication of force by inventive genius since the Napoleonic wars; and yet, only 269 years after the little band of Pilgrims landed on Plymouth Rock, our people, numbering less than one-fifteenth of the inhabitants of the globe, do one-third of its mining, one-fourth of its manufacturing, one-fifth of its agriculture, and own one-sixth of its wealth.

This realism of material prosperity, surpassing the wildest creations of the romancers who have astonished and delighted mankind, would be full of danger for the present and menace for the future, if the virtue, intelligence, and independence of the people were not equal to the wise regulation of its uses and the stern prevention of its abuses. But following the growth and power of the great factors, whose aggregation of capital made possible the tremendous pace of the settlement of our National domain, the building of our great cities and the opening of the lines of communication which have unified our country and created our resources, have come National and State legislation and supervision. Twenty millions, a vast majority of our people of intelligent age, acknowledging the authority of their several churches, 12,000,000 of children in the common schools, 345 universities and colleges for the higher education of men and 200 for women, 450 institutions of learning for science, law, medicine and theology, are the despair of the scoffer and the demagogue, and the firm support of civilization and liberty.

Steam and electricity have changed the commerce not only, they have revolutionized also the governments of the world. They have given to the press its power, and brought all races and nationalities into touch and sympathy. They have tested and are trying the strength of all systems to stand the strain and conform to the conditions which follow the germinating influences of American Domocracy. At the time of the inauguration of Washington, seven royal families ruled as many kingdoms in Italy, but six of them have seen their thrones overturned and their countries disappear from the map of Europe. Most of the kings, princes, dukes and margraves of Germany, who reigned despotically, and sold their soldiers for foreign service, have passed into history, and their heirs have neither prerogatives nor domain. Spain has gone through many violent changes and the permanency of her present government seems to depend upon the feeble life of an infant prince. France, our ancient friend, with repeated and bloody revolutions, has tried the government of Bourbon and Convention, of Directory and Consulate, of Empire and Citizen King, of hereditary Sovereign and Republic, of Empire, and again Republic. The Hapsburg and Hohenzollern, after convulsions which have rocked the foundations of their thrones, have been compelled to concede constitutions to their people and to divide with them the arbitrary power wielded so autocratically and brilliantly by Maria Theresa and Frederick the Great. The royal will of George the Third could crowd the American Colonies into rebellion, and wage war upon them until they were lost to his Kingdom, but the authority of the crown has devolved upon Ministers who hold office subject to the approval of the representatives of the people and the equal powers of the House of Lords have been enlarged in the Commons, leaving to the Peers only the shadow of their ancient privileges. But to-day the American people, after all the dazzling developments of the century, are still happily living under the Government of Washington. The Constitution during all that period has been amended only upon the lines laid down in the original instrument, and in conformity with the recorded opinions of the Fathers. The first great addition was the incorporation of a Bill of Rights, and the last the embedding into the Constitution of the immortal principle of the Declaration of Independence—of the equality of all men before the law. No crisis has been too perilous for its powers, no evolution too rapid for its adaptation, and no expansion beyond its easy grasp and administration. It has assimilated diverse nationalities with warring traditions, customs, conditions and languages, imbued them with its spirit, and won their passionate loyalty and love.

The flower of the youth of the nations of Continental Europe are conscripted from productive industries and drilling in camps. Vast armies stand in battle array along the frontiers, and a Kaiser's whim or a Minister's mistake may precipitate the most destructive war of modern times. Both monarchical and republican governments are seeking safety in the repression and suppression of opposition and criticism. The volcanic forces of Democratic aspiration and socialistic revolt are rapidly increasing and threaten peace and security. We turn from these gathering storms to the British Isles and find their people in the throes of a political crisis involving the form and substance of their Government, and their statesmen far from confident that the enfranchised and unprepared masses will wisely use their power.

But for us no army exhausts our resources nor consumes our youth. Our navy must needs increase in order that the protecting flag may follow the expanding commerce which is successfully to compete in all the markets of the world. The sun of our destiny is still rising, and its rays illumine vast territories as yet unoccupied and undeveloped, and which are to be the happy homes of millions of people. The questions which affect the powers of government and the expansion or limitation of the authority of the Federal Constitution are so completely settled, and so unanimously approved, that our political divisions produce only the healthy antagonism of parties, which is necessary for the preservation of liberty. Our institutions furnish the full equipment of shield and spear for the battles of freedom; and absolute protection against every danger which threatens the welfare of the people will always be found in the intelligence which appreciates their value, and the courage and morality with which their powers are exercised. The spirit of Washington fills the executive office. Presidents may not rise to the full measure of his greatness, but they must not fall below his standard of public duty and obligation. His life and character conscientiously studied and thoroughly understood by coming generations, will be for them a liberal education for private life and public station, for citizenship

and patriotism, for love and devotion to Union and Liberty. With their inspiring past and splendid present, the people of these United States, heirs of
a hundred years marvellously rich in all which adds to the glory and greatness of a nation, with an abiding trust in the stability and elasticity of their
Constitution, and an abounding faith in themselves, hail the coming century with
hope and joy.

## BENJAMIN HARRISON ON INDUSTRY AND ANARCHY.

NOTHING is more fatal to the interest of labor than anarchy. A condition of
society in which law is supreme is for the poor man the only tolerable one.
The law reinforces his weakness and makes him the peer of the strongest. It is his
tower. If he forsakes or destroys it his folly or his fury delivers him a prey to the
strong. In this land of universal suffrage, if he will be wise and moderate, no right
legislation can tarry long. That which is just will not be denied. But fury and
threats and force will not persuade. They provoke their like, and in this clash and
strife all must suffer. One of the most distressing and alarming features of our time
is the growing hostility between capital and labor. Those who should be friends
have been drawing apart and glaring fiercely at each other. There is no real or
necessary antagonism. Capital and labor must unite in every enterprise ; the partnership ought to be a fair one, and the partners friendly. The demagogue is a
potent factor of evil in the settlement of the labor question. His object is to use the
laborer to advance a political ambition. He flatters him with professions of ardent
friendship ; beguiles him into turning the stone for his axe-grinding, and when the
edge is on sends him away without wages. If laboring men would appoint com-
mittees to inquire into the personal history of these self-appointed champions they
would not unlikely find that the noisiest of them do not pay their tailor or shoe-
maker. Their mission is to array one class against another—to foment strife, and
to live themselves without work. They talk largely of the producers, but never
produce anything themselves except a riot, and then they are not at the front.
Their doctrine is that every man who hires labor is an oppressor and a tyrant.
That the first duty of every man who works is to hate the man who gives him
work.

The fruit of this sort of teaching is unrest and fear. . . . . The true
workingmen should shake off these vipers into the fire ; place themselves and
all their protective organizations on the platform of the law, and while demand-
ing their legal rights to the full proclaim their equal deference to the rights of
others. From this platform their cry for help and sympathy will find the public
ear. Let them think and work toward specific and legitimate reforms, for within
the limits of constitutional restriction there is no legislation that will be denied
them.

VICTOR HUGO

## PALMERSTON AGAINST CIVIL WAR.

THEN come we to the last remedy,—civil war. Some gentlemen say that, sooner or later, we must fight for it, and the sword must decide. They tell us that, if blood were but shed in Ireland, Catholic emancipation might be avoided. Sir, when honorable members shall be a little deeper read in this history of Ireland, they will find that in Ireland blood *has* been shed,—that in Ireland leaders have been seized, trials have been had, and punishments have been inflicted. They will find, indeed, almost every page of the history of Ireland darkened by bloodshed, by seizures, by trials, and by punishments. But what has been the effect of these measures? They have, indeed, been successful in quelling the disturbances of the moment; but they never have gone to their cause, and have only fixed deeper the poison barb that rankles in the heart of Ireland. Can one believe one's ears, when one hears respectable men talk so lightly—nay, almost so wishfully—of civil war? Do they reflect what a countless multitude of ills those three short syllables contain? It is well, indeed, for the gentlemen of England, who live secure under the protecting shadow of the law, whose slumbers have never been broken by the clashing of angry swords, whose harvests have never been trodden down by the conflicts of hostile feet,—it is well for them to talk of civil war, as if it were some holiday pastime, or some sport of children:

" They jest at scars who never felt a wound."

But, that gentleman, from unfortunate and ill-starred Ireland, who have seen with their own eyes, and heard with their own ears the miseries which civil war produces, —who have known, by their own experience, the barbarism, aye, the barbarity, which it engenders,—that such persons should look upon civil war as anything short of the last and greatest of national calamities,—is to me a matter of the deepest and most unmixed astonishment. I will grant, if you will, that the success of such a war with Ireland would be as signal and complete as would be its injustice; I will grant, if you will, that resistance would soon be extinguished with the lives of those who resisted; I will grant, if you will, that the crimsoned banner of England would soon wave in undisputed supremacy, over the smoking ashes of their towns, and the blood-stained solitude of their fields. But I tell you that England herself never would permit the achievement of such a conquest; England would reject, with disgust, laurels that were dyed in fraternal blood; England would recoil with loathing and abhorrence, from the bare contemplation of so devilish a triumph!

## MACAULAY ON PUBLIC OPINION.

AT the present moment I can see only one question in the State, the Question of Reform; only two parties—the friends of the Bill, and its enemies. No observant and unprejudiced man can look forward, without great alarm, to the effects which the recent decision of the Lords may possibly produce. I do not predict, I do not expect, open, armed insurrection. What I apprehend is this—that the people may engage in a silent but extensive and persevering war against the law. It is easy to say, "Be bold; be firm; defy intimidation; let the law have its course; the law is strong enough to put down the sedition." Sir, we have heard this blustering before, and we know in what it ended. It is the blustering of little men, whose lot has fallen on a great crisis. Xerxes scourging the waves, Canute commanding the waves to recede from his footstool, were but types of the folly. The law has no eyes; the law has no hands; the law is nothing—nothing but a piece of paper printed by the King's printer, with the King's arms at the top—till public opinion breathes the breath of life into the dead letter. We found this in Ireland. The elections of 1826—the Clare elections, two years later—proved the folly of those who think that Nations are governed by wax and parchment; and, at length, in the close of 1828, the Government had only one plain alternative before it—concession or civil war.

I know only two ways in which societies can permanently be governed—by Public Opinion, and by the Sword. A government having at its command the armies, the fleets, and the revenues of Great Britain, might possibly hold Ireland by the sword. So Oliver Cromwell held Ireland; so William the Third held it; so Mr. Pitt held it; so the Duke of Wellington might perhaps have held it. But to govern Great Britain by the sword—so wild a thought has never, I will venture to say, occurred to any public man of any party; and, if any man were frantic enough to make the attempt, he would find, before three days had expired that there is no better sword than that which is fashioned out of a ploughshare! But, if not by the sword, how are the people to be governed? I understand how the peace is kept at New York. It is by the assent and support of the people. I understand, also, how the peace is kept at Milan. It is by the bayonets of the Austrian soldiers. But how the peace is to be kept when you have neither the popular assent nor the military force,—how the peace is to be kept in England by a Government acting upon the principles of the present Opposition,—I do not understand.

Sir, we read that, in old times, when the *villeins* were driven to revolt by oppression,—when the castles of the nobility were burned to the ground,—when the warehouses of London were pillaged,—when a hundred thousand insurgents appeared in arms on Blackheath,—when a foul murder, perpetrated in their presence, had raised their passions to madness,—when they were looking for some captain to succeed and avenge him whom they had lost,—just then, before Hob Miller, or Tom Carter, or Jack Straw, could place himself at their head, the King rode up to them, and exclaimed, "I will be your leader!"—And, at once, the infuriated multitude laid down their arms, submitted to his guidance, dispersed at his command. Herein let us imitate him. Let us say to the people, "We are your leaders,—we your own House of Commons." This tone it is our interest and our duty to take. The circumstances admit of no delay. Even while I speak, the moments are passing away,—the irrevocable moments pregnant with the destiny of a great people. The country is in danger; it may be saved: *we* can save it. This is the way—this is the time. In our hands are the issues of great good and great evil—the issues of the life and death of the State!

## NAYLOR ON AMERICAN LABORERS.

THE Gentleman, Sir, has misconceived the spirit and tendency of Northern institutions. He is ignorant of Northern character. He has forgotten the history of his country. Preach insurrection to the Northern laborers! Who are the Northern laborers! The history of your country is *their* history. The renown of your country is *their* renown. The brightness of their doings is emblazoned on its every page. Blot from your annals the words and the doings of *Northern laborers,* and the history of your country presents but a universal blank. Sir, who was he that disarmed the Thunderer; wrested from his grasp the bolts of Jove; calmed the troubled ocean; became the central sun of the philosophical system of his age, shedding his brightness and effulgence on the whole civilized world; whom the great and mighty of the earth delighted to honor; who participated in the achievement of your independence, prominently assisted in moulding your free institutions, and the beneficial effects of whose wisdom will be felt to the last moment of "recorded time"? Who, Sir, I ask, was he? A Northern laborer,—a Yankee tallow-chandler's son,—a printer's runaway boy.

And who, let me ask the honorable Gentleman, who was he that, in the days of our Revolution, led forth a Northern army,—yes, an army of Northern laborers, —and aided the chivalry of South Carolina in their defence against British aggression, drove the spoilers from their firesides, and redeemed her fair fields from foreign invaders? Who was he? A Northern laborer, a Rhode Island blacksmith,—the gallant General Greene,—who left his hammer and his forge, and went forth conquering and to conquer in the battle for our independence! And will you preach insurrection to men like these?

Sir, our country is full of the achievements of Northern laborers! Where is Concord, and Lexington, and Princeton, and Trenton, and Saratoga, and Bunker Hill, but in the North? And what, Sir, has shed an imperishable renown on the never-dying names of those hallowed spots, but the blood and the struggles, the high daring, and patriotism, and sublime courage, of Northern laborers? The whole North is an everlasting monument of the freedom, virtue, intelligence, and indomitable independence of Northern laborers! Go, Sir, go preach insurrection to men like these!

## HAMILTON ON THE CONSTITUTION.

AFTER all our doubts, our suspicions and speculations, on the subject of Government, we must return, at last, to this important truth,—that, when we have formed a Constitution upon free principles, when we have given a proper balance to the different branches of Administration, and fixed Representation upon pure and equal principles, we may, with safety, furnish it with all the powers necessary to answer, in the most ample manner, the purposes of Government. The great desiderata are a free Representation, and mutual checks. When these are obtained, all our apprehensions of the extent of powers are unjust and imaginary.

What, then, is the structure of this Constitution? One branch of the Legislature is to be elected by the People—by the same People who choose your State Representatives. Its members are to hold their office two years, and then return to their constituents. Here, Sir, the People govern. Here they act by their immediate Representatives. You have also a Senate, constituted by your State Legislatures, —by men in whom you place the highest confidence,—and forming another Representative branch. Then, again, you have an Executive Magistrate, created by a form of election which merits universal admiration.

In the form of this Government, and in the mode of Legislation, you find all the checks which the greatest politicians and the best writers have ever conceived. What more can reasonable men desire? Is there any one branch in which the whole Legislative and Executive powers are lodged? No! The Legislative authority is lodged in three distinct branches, properly balanced; the Executive authority is divided between two branches; and the Judicial is still reserved for an independent body, who hold their office during good behavior. This organization is so complex, so skilfully contrived, that it is next to impossible that an impolitic or wicked measure should pass the great scrutiny with success. Now, what do Gentlemen mean, by coming forward and declaiming against this Government? Why do they say we ought to limit its powers, to disable it, and to destroy its capacity of blessing the People? Has philosophy suggested, has experience taught, that such a Government ought not to be trusted with everything necessary for the good of society? Sir, when you have divided and nicely balanced the departments of Government; when you have strongly connected the virtue of your rulers with their interests; when, in short, you have rendered your system as perfect as human forms *can* be,—you *must* place confidence; you *must* give power.

"Isn't there any ferry or boat, that takes people over to B——, now?" she said.

"No, indeed!" said the woman; "the boats have stopped running."

There was nothing to do, then, but to wait till the next day. But scarcely had Eliza entered a private room of the house and laid the child down to sleep, than she saw the trader, Haley, approach, in pursuit of her.

A thousand lives seemed to be concentrated in that one moment to Eliza. Her room opened by a side door to the river. She caught her child, and sprang down the steps toward it. The trader caught a full glimpse of her, just as she was disappearing down the bank; and throwing himself from his horse, he was after her like a hound after a deer. In that dizzy moment her feet to her scarce seemed to touch the ground and a moment brought her to the water's edge. Right on behind they came; and, nerved with strength such as God gives only to the desperate, with one wild cry and flying leap, she vaulted sheer over the turbid current by the shore on to the raft of ice beyond. It was a desperate leap—impossible to anything but madness and despair; and Haley and his companions instinctively cried out, and lifted up their hands, as she did it.

The huge green fragment of ice on which she alighted pitched and creaked as her weight came on it, but she stayed there not a moment. With wild cries and desperate energy she leaped to another and still another cake; stumbling—leaping—slipping—springing upward again! Her shoes are gone—her stockings cut from her feet—while blood marked every step; but she saw noth- ing, felt nothing, till dimly, as in a dream, she saw the Ohio side.

Haley returned to the tavern, furious at his defeat. There he presently met two men, Loker, a burly ruffian, and Marks, a sly, foxy lawer, who made a business of hunting fugitive slaves, and entered into a bargain with them for the pursuit and recapture of Eliza and her child. Then he returned to Mr. Shelby's to claim "Uncle" Tom, as his chief purchase was called. He put fetters upon him, to make sure against his escaping, and took him away from his life-long home for shipment to New Orleans.

Meantime Eliza and her boy were in the safe retreat of a Quaker village in Ohio, watching an opportunity to go on to Canada. There, after a time, to her unspeakable joy, her husband joined her, and then preparations were made to send them all on together to the next station on the famous "underground railroad" which led from the land of slavery to the land of freedom. They set out at last, when the slave-hunters were already prowling about close upon their trail. They were in a wagon, with another runaway, Jim, and George's mother, escorted by Phineas Fletcher, a Quaker of a rather more militant disposition than is usual among Friends. After driving for miles across a sparsely settled country, they heard their pursuers, on horseback, close behind. Phineas lashed the horses to a run. The wagon rattled, jumped, almost flew, over the frozen ground; but plainer, and still plainer, came the noise of pursuing horsemen behind. The women heard it, and looking anxiously out, saw, far in the rear, on the brow of a distant hill, a party of men looming up against the red-streaked sky of early

# Book VII.

# Fiction.

---

## UNCLE TOM'S CABIN.

### By Harriet Beecher Stowe.

---

ELIZA'S ESCAPE—ACROSS THE RIVER TO FREEDOM—THE BAFFLED TRADER—FIGHTING
FOR FREEDOM—EVANGELINE—TOM'S NEW MASTER—TOPSY—THE LITTLE
EVANGELIST—DEATH OF EVA—DEATH OF ST. CLARE—IN THE
SLAVE MARKET—CASSY—THE DEATH OF TOM—
EMMELINE'S ESCAPE.

---

LATE in the afternoon of a chilly day in February, two gentlemen were sitting alone over their wine, in a well-furnished dining parlor, in the town of P——, in Kentucky. One was a vulgar swaggerer, a slave-dealer, named Haley; the other a refined gentleman, the owner of the house, named Shelby. They were discussing the sale of one of the latter's slaves, one Tom, to the dealer, and Haley, demurring at the price asked, urged that a bright little negro boy, named Harry, be "thrown in to boot." Mr. Shelby hesitated, but being in business straits was at last compelled to yield, and the bargain was made.

"Wal, now, the thing's *done!*" said the trader, getting up.

"Its' *done!*" said Mr. Shelby, in a musing tone; and, fetching a long breath, he repeated, "*It's done.*"

Of this unholy bargain Eliza, the young mother of Harry, had been an unsuspected witness. Her husband, George Harris, had already run away from his master to escape ill-treatment, and was now a fugitive, on his way to Canada. She quickly determined to follow him with the child. Late at night, a winter's night, she set out on her perilous journey.

All night, and the next day, she struggled on, and then, an hour before sunset, she reached the Ohio river, weary and foot-sore, but still strong in heart. The river was swollen and turbulent; great cakes of floating ice were swinging heavily to and fro in the turbid waters, filling up the whole river, and extending almost to the Kentucky shore.

Eliza stood, for a moment, contemplating this unfavorable aspect of things, which she saw at once must prevent the usual ferry-boat from running, and then turned into a small public house on the bank, to make a few inquiries.

UNCLE TOM

# BOOK VII.

---

## FICTION.

dawn. The pursuers gained on them fast; the wagon made a sudden turn, and brought them near a ledge of a steep overhanging rock, that rose in an isolated ridge or clump in a large lot, which was, all around it, quite clear and smooth. This isolated pile, or range of rocks, rose up black and heavy against the brightening sky, and seemed to promise shelter and concealment. It was a place well known to Phineas, who had been familiar with the spot in his hunting days; and it was to gain this point he had been racing his horses.

A quick halt, a desperate scramble up the rocks, and the fortress was gained just in time. They were on top of a high rock, to which their pursuers could gain access only in single file. Then up came the hunters—Loker and Marks, two constables, and a posse of tavern rowdies. George challenged them, and warned them that they would be shot if they tried to scale the rock. While he spoke, Marks shot at him, but missed. Then Loker started to climb up, loudly avowing he "never was afraid of niggers." As he came near to the edge of a chasm that separated this rock from another, George fired—the shot entered his side —but, though wounded, he would not retreat, but, with a yell like that of a mad bull, he was leaping right across the chasm into the party.

" Friend," said Phineas, suddenly stepping to the front, and meeting him with a push from his long arms, "thee isn't wanted here."

Down he fell into the chasm, crackling down among trees, bushes, logs, loose stones, till he lay, bruised and groaning, thirty feet below.

"Lord help us, they are perfect devils!"

said Marks, heading the retreat down the rocks with much more of a will than he had joined the ascent, while all the party came tumbling precipitately after him.

"I say fellers," said Marks, "you jist go around and pick up Tom, there, while I run and get on to my horse, to go back for help—that's you;" and, without minding the hootings and jeers of his company, Marks was as good as his word, and was soon seen galloping away.

The others found Loker, wounded but not fatally, but presently abandoned him and rode away. Then the fugitives and Phineas went down and cared for him and took him to a place where he would be nursed, and then pursued their way toward freedom in safety.

Meantime Uncle Tom was being borne toward New Orleans on a Mississippi steamer.

Among the passengers on the boat was a young gentleman of fortune and family, resident in New Orleans, who bore the name of St. Clare. He had with him a daughter between five and six years of age, together with a lady who seemed to claim relationship to both, and to have the little one especially under her charge.

Tom often caught glimpses of this little girl. Often and often she walked mournfully around the place where Haley's gang of men and women sat in their chains. She would glide in among them, and look at them with an air of perplexed and sorrowful earnestness; and sometimes she would lift their chains with her slender hands, and then sigh wofully, as she glided away. Several times she appeared suddenly among them, with her hands full of candy, nuts, and oranges, which she would distribute joyfully to them, and then be gone again.

"What's little missy's name?" said Tom, at last, when he thought matters were ripe to push such an inquiry.

"Evangeline St. Clare," said the little one, "though papa and everybody else call me Eva. Now, what's your name?"

"My name is Tom; the little children used to call me Uncle Tom, way back thar in Kentuck."

"Then I mean to call you Uncle Tom, because, you see, I like you," said Eva. "So Uncle Tom, where are you going?"

"I don't know, Miss Eva."

"Don't know?" said Eva.

"No. I am going to be sold to somebody. I don't know who."

"My papa can buy you," said Eva, quickly; "and if he buys you, you will have good times. I mean to ask him to, this very day."

"Thank you, my little lady," said Tom.

The boat here stopped at a small landing to take on wood, and Eva, hearing her father's voice, bounded nimbly away. Tom rose up, and went forward to offer his service in wooding, and soon was busy among the hands.

Eva and her father were standing together by the railings, when, by some sudden movement, the little one suddenly lost her balance, and fell sheer over the side of the boat into the water. Her father, scarce knowing what he did, was plunging in after her, but was held back by some behind him, who saw that more efficient aid had followed his child.

Tom was standing just under her on the lower deck, as she fell. He saw her strike the water, and sink, and was after her in a moment. A broad-chested, strong-armed fellow, it was nothing for him to keep afloat in the water, till, in a moment or two, the child rose to the surface, and he caught her in his arms, and swimming with her to the boat-side, handed her up, all dripping, to the grasp of hundreds of hands, which, as if they had all belonged to one man, were stretched eagerly out to receive her. A few moments more, and her father bore her, dripping and senseless, to the ladies' cabin.

When the boat reached New Orleans, Eva coaxed her father to buy Tom, and that light-hearted and genial young man did so. Augustine St. Clare was a rich and high-bred Louisianian, who had been sorely disappointed in love, and then had married a fashionable but frivolous and selfish woman, who, since Eva's birth, had become a peevish invalid. On the present occasion St. Clare was returning with Eva from a visit to Vermont, and bringing with him his cousin, Ophelia; a precise New Englander, who disapproved of slavery on principle, but disliked all personal contact with negroes. The family lived in a splendid mansion in New Orleans, and thither they now went, taking Tom with them, and there Tom lived and served faithfully, and was kindly treated.

Tom regarded his gay, airy, handsome young master with an odd mixture of fealty, reverence, and fatherly solicitude. That he never read the Bible; never went to church; that he jested and made free with any and everything that came in the way of his wit; that he spent his Sunday evenings at the opera or theater; that he went to wine parties, and clubs, and suppers, oftener than was at all expedient, were all things that Tom could see as plainly as anybody, and on which

ELIZA'S ESCAPE

he based a conviction that "mas'r wasn't a Christian."

So Tom took it upon himself to speak of religious matters to St. Clare, and his unaffected simplicity and earnestness produced a profound impression upon the worldly but good-hearted man.

One day, Miss Ophelia having expressed a desire to educate and cultivate one of the negroes, St. Clare brought her a wild little creature named Topsy, whom Miss Ophelia at once took in hand and began to question.

"How old are you, Topsy?"

"Dun no, missus," said the image, with a grin that showed all her teeth.

"Don't know how old you are? Didn't anybody ever tell you? Who was your mother?"

"Never had none!" said the child, with another grin.

"Never had any mother? What do you mean? Where were you born?"

"Never was born!" persisted Topsy, with another grin, that looked so goblin-like, that, if Miss Ophelia had been at all nervous, she might have fancied that she had got hold of some sooty gnome from the land of Diablerie, but Miss Ophelia was not nervous, but plain and business-like, and she said with some sternness:

"You musn't answer me in that way, child; I'm not playing with you. Tell me where you were born, and who your father and mother were."

"Never was born," reiterated the creature, more emphatically; "never had no father nor mother, nor nothin'. I was raised by a speculator, with lots of others. Old Aunt Sue used to take car on us."

"Have you ever heard anything about God, Topsy?"

The child looked bewildered, but grinned as usual.

"Do you know who made you?"

"Nobody, as I knows on," said the child, with a short laugh.

The idea appeared to amuse her considerably; for her eyes twinkled, and she added:

"I s'pect I grow'd. Don't think nobody never made me."

Miss Ophelia rose from this encouraging colloquy; St. Clare was leaning over the back of her chair.

"You'll find virgin soil there, cousin; put in your own ideas—you won't find many to pull up."

Eva's health, always delicate, at last began to fail, and it was evident that her end was near. To the last she played the part of a ministering angel among the slaves of the household. One day she had them all called to her bedside. All looked sad and apprehensive. Many of the women hid their faces in their aprons.

"I sent for you all, my dear friends," said Eva, "because I love you. I love you all; and I have something to say to you, which I want you always to remember. . . . I am going to leave you. I want to speak to you about your souls. . . . Many of you, I am afraid, are very careless. You are thinking only about this world. I want you to remember that there is a beautiful world, where Jesus is. I am going there, and you can go there. It is for you, as much as me. But, if you want to go there, you must not live idle, careless, thoughtless lives. You must be Christians. You must remember that each one of you can become angels, and be angels forever. . . . If you want to be Christians, Jesus will help you. You must pray to him; you must read—"

The child checked herself, looked piteously at them, and said, sorrowfully:

"O, dear! you *can't* read — poor souls:" and she hid her face in the pillow and sobbed, while many a smothered sob from those she was addressing, who were kneeling on the floor, aroused her.

"Never mind," she said, raising her face and smiling brightly through her tears, "I have prayed for you; and I know Jesus will help you, even if you can't read. Try all to do the best you can; pray every day; ask Him to help you, and get the Bible read to you whenever you can; and I think I shall see you all in heaven."

Not many days later the end came. It was between midnight and morning. The changed look on her face showed St. Clare that she was dying. The house was soon roused, the lights were seen, footsteps heard, anxious faces thronged the veranda, and looked tearfully through the glass doors; but St. Clare heard and said nothing, he saw only *that look* on the face of the little sleeper.

The large blue eyes unclosed, a smile passed over her face; she tried to raise her head, and to speak.

"Do you know me, Eva?"

"Dear papa," said the child, with a last effort, throwing her arms about his neck. In a moment they dropped again; and, as St. Clare raised his head, he saw a spasm of mortal agony pass over the face, she struggled for breath, and threw up her little hands.

Tom had his master's hands between his own; and, with tears streaming down his dark cheeks, looked up for help where he had always been used to look.

"Pray that this may be cut short!" said St. Clare—"this wrings my heart."

"O, bless the Lord! it's over—it's over, dear master," said Tom; "look at her."

The child lay panting on her pillows, as one exhausted—the large clear eyes rolled up and fixed.

"Eva," said St. Clare, gently.

She did not hear.

"O, Eva, tell us what you see! What is it?" said her father.

A bright, a glorious smile passed over her face, and she said, brokenly—"O! love—joy—peace!" gave one sigh and passed from death unto life!

It was not long after the death of Eva that St. Clare himself came to his end. In a café one evening two men quarreled and began to fight. St. Clare joined with others in trying to separate them, and was stabbed by one of them, and taken home to die. Miss Ophelia and Tom attended him in his last moments. He lay with his eyes shut, but it was evident that he wrestled with bitter thoughts. After a while, he laid his hand on Tom's who was kneeling beside him, and said, "Tom! poor fellow!"

"What, mas'r?" said Tom, earnestly.

"I am dying!" said St. Clare, pressing his hand; "pray!"

"If you would like a clergyman—" said the physician.

St. Clare hastily shook his head, and said again to Tom, more earnestly, "Pray!"

And Tom did pray, with all his mind and strength.

When Tom ceased, St. Clare reached out and took his hand, looking earnestly at him, but saying nothing. He closed his eyes, but still retained his hold. He murmured softly to himself, at broken intervals.

"His mind is wandering," said the doctor.

"No! it is coming HOME, at last!" said St. Clare, energetically; "at last! at last!"

The effort of speaking exhausted him. The sinking paleness of death fell on him; but with it there fell, as if shed from the wings of some pitying spirit, a beautiful expression of peace, like that of a wearied child who sleeps.

St. Clare's slaves were presently all sent to the slave market, to be sold. Among the men who came to buy, at public auction, was one repulsive-looking fellow, of coarse appearance and brutal manner. He examined Tom as though he were a horse, or an ox, was pleased with him, bid for him, and purchased him, together with several other slaves. This was Simon Legree, a Red River planter, and he at once set out for his home, taking his purchases with him.

Legree's plantation was a forbidding place. The house was large and had been handsome, but now looked desolate. Three or four ferocious-looking dogs, roused by the sound of the wagon-wheels, came tearing out, and were with difficulty restrained from laying hold of Tom and his companions, by the effort of the ragged servants who came after them.

"Ye see what ye'd get!" said Legree, caressing the dogs with grim satisfaction, and turning to Tom and his companions. "Ye see what ye'd get if ye try to run off. These yer dogs has been raised to track niggers; and they'd jest as soon chaw one on ye up as eat their supper. So, mind yourself! How now, Sambo!" he said, to a ragged fellow, without any brim to his hat, who was officious in his attentions. "How have things been going?"

"Fust rate, mas'r."

"Quimbo," said Legree to another, who was making zealous demonstrations to attract his attention, "ye minded what I telled ye?"

"Guess I did, didn't I?"

The two colored men were the two principal hands on the plantation. Legree had trained them in savageness and brutality as systematically as he had his bull-dogs; and, by long practice in hardness and cruelty, brought their whole nature to about the same range of capacities.

In this hideous place the hapless slaves were treated worse than brute beasts. Legree showered upon them all possible injustice and cruelty. One day, meaning to degrade Tom to his own level, he commanded him to flog one of the other slaves, a frail, feeble woman. Tom respectfully but positively refused, whereupon Legree had him flogged half to death by Sambo and Quimbo. That night Tom was visited by one of his fellow-slaves, a woman named Cassy. She was a quadroon, who had been singularly beautiful, refined, and highly educated. Dragged from the man she loved, and made the property of Legree, she had been forced to become his mistress. She had gained a powerful influence over him, so that he stood in mortal fear of her; but now he was trying to cast her aside and replace her with one Emmeline, a beautiful young woman whom he had purchased in New Orleans, and brought home in the same party with Tom. She told Tom all her tragic story, and ended thus:

"When I was a girl, I thought I was

religious; I used to love God and prayer. Now I'm a lost soul, pursued by devils that torment me day and night; they keep pushing me on and on—and I'll do it, too, some of these days!" she said, clinching her hand, while an insane light glanced in her heavy black eyes. "I'll send him where he belongs—a short way, too—one of these nights, if they burn me alive for it!"

There was a great garret in the top of Legree's house, in which he had once brutally murdered a slave-woman who would not obey his foul will, and which he, in his ignorant superstition, now regarded as haunted, and so shunned with mortal fear. Cassy played upon his fears, with tales of ghosts, until she knew he would never dare to enter the garret. Then she hid Emmeline and herself up there, to be safe from his persecutions. She first gave Legree reason to suppose they had fled to the woods, and he pursued them with bloodhounds, but had to return, baffled.

Legree then turned his wrath against Tom. After reviling and abusing him in all possible ways, he announced his determination to kill him, and accordingly he had him flogged to death. Tom did not die directly under the lash, but lingered a few days longer. During that time an unexpected visitor came. This was George Shelby, the son of Tom's old master in Kentucky. He had come in search of the faithful old servant, to purchase him and take him home to Kentucky. He found Tom dying in awful agony. But Tom recognized him, and the vacant eye became fixed and brightened, the whole face lighted up, the hard hands clasped, and tears ran down the cheeks.

"Bless the Lord! it is—it is—it's all I wanted! They haven't forgot me. It warms my soul; it does my old heart good! Now I shall die content! Bless the Lord, oh my soul!"

Then the end came.

George turned to Legree, who stood near, scowling, and said, pointing to the dead, "You have got all you ever can of him. What shall I pay you for the body? I will take it away, and bury it decently.

"I don't sell dead niggers," said Legree, doggedly. "You are welcome to bury him where and when you like."

A few more contemptuous words spoken by Legree roused the young Kentuckian's wrath, and with one well-directed blow he knocked the brute down. Then he bore Tom's body reverently away and gave it honorable burial.

Legree now felt the place worse haunted than before, and in his abject fear took to drinking heavily, and was soon known to be sick and dying. The inexorable Cassy arrayed herself as a ghost, came down from the garret at night, and tormented his dying hours. Then she and Emmeline slipped out of the house and stole away from the accursed place. Cassy was arrayed as a Spanish Creole, and Emmeline as her servant. Thus they took passage on a river steamer and made their way to the North. George Shelby was on the same boat, and on the way the discovery was made that the runaway Eliza was Cassy's long-lost daughter. So Cassy made her way to Canada, and there succeeded in finding Eliza and George, who were living in peace, freedom and happiness.

# DAVID COPPERFIELD.

## By Charles Dickens.

The Visit to Yarmouth—"Barkis is Willin'"—School and Schoolmates—Barkis Waiting—A Great Change—My Aunt Makes up Her Mind—Early Loves—J. Steerforth—My Profession—"Wickfield and Heep"—Dora—Out with the Tide—A Greater Loss—Betsey Trotwood's Story—Mr. Spenlow—House-keeping Extraordinary—My Child-Wife—Little Em'ly Again—The Home-Coming—Heep—Death of Dora—Closing Scenes.

OF MY early life little needs to be said. I was born at Blunderstone, in Suffolk, six months after the death of my father. My mother was yet a mere girl. The only other relative of whom I need speak was an aunt of my father's, Miss Betsey Trotwood. My father had once been a favorite of hers, but, she was mortally affronted by his marriage on the ground that my mother was "a wax doll." She had never seen my mother, but she knew her to be not yet twenty. My father and Miss Betsey never met again. She visited my mother at the time of my birth ; and, being a man-hater, was grievously disappointed when I proved to be not a girl but a boy. She vanished like a discontented fairy, or like one of those supernatural beings, whom it was popularly supposed I was entitled to see ; and never came back any more.

The first objects that assume a distinct presence before me, as I look far back into the blank of my infancy, are my mother with her pretty hair and youthful shape, and Peggotty, our servant and my nurse. Then a gentleman with black whiskers, a Mr. Murdstone, began to call to see my mother, and aroused my childish suspicion and dislike.

One evening Peggotty asked me how I would like to go with her and visit her brother at Yarmouth, and gave me so pleasant an account of the place that I said I should like to go. So go I did, and made the acquaintance of Mr. Peggotty, and his orphan nephew and niece, Ham and Em'ly, and also Mrs. Gummidge, the widow of his former partner in a fishing-boat.

Of course I was in love with little Em'ly. I am sure I loved that baby quite as truly, quite as tenderly, with greater purity, and more disinterestedness, than can enter into the best love of a later time of life, high and ennobling as it is. We were the admiration of Mrs. Gummidge and Peggotty, who used to whisper of an evening when we sat, lovingly, on our little locker side by side, "Lor'! wasn't it beautiful!" Mr. Peggotty smiled at us from behind his pipe, and Ham grinned all the evening and did nothing else.

The visit ended at last, and I returned home to find my mother married to Mr. Murdstone, who, with his sister, soon began to tyrannize over her and to ill-treat and abuse me. It was a relief to me, after several violent scenes, when they decided to send me away to school.

The carrier, in whose wagon I travelled on the first stage of my journey, was named Barkis. Soon after we had started I gave him one of the cakes with which I had been provided. He swallowed it at a gulp.

"Did *she* make 'em, now?" said Mr. Barkis.

"Peggotty, do you mean, sir?"

"Ah!" said Mr. Barkis. "Her."

"Yes. She makes all our pastry, and does all our cooking."

"Well. I'll tell you what," said Mr. Barkis. "P'rhaps you might be writin' to her?"

"I shall certainly write to her," I rejoined.

"Ah!" he said slowly, turning his eyes toward me. "Well! If you was writin' to her, p'raps you'd recollect to say that Barkis was willin'; would you?"

"That Barkis is willing," I repeated innocently. "Is that all the message?"

"Ye-es," he said, considering. "Ye-s. Barkis is willin'." "But you will be at Blunderstone again to-morrow, Mr. Barkis," I said, faltering a little at the idea of my being far away from it then, "and could give your own message so much better."

As he repudiated this suggestion, however, with a jerk of his head, and once more confirmed his previous request by saying with profound gravity, "Barkis is willin'. That's the message," I readily undertook its transmission.

At the school, Salem House, I found myself treated with suspicion, because of the bad account of me Mr. Murdstone had given. But I made two close friends. One was Tommy Traddles, a good-hearted, honorable boy, who was lacking in self-assertion and forever getting punished for some other's fault. The other was James Steerforth, a brilliant, self-assertive fellow, who exercised a profound fascination over me, and constituted himself in a measure my "guide, philosopher and friend." There was an ease in his manner—a gay and light manner it was, but not swaggering—which I still believe to have borne a kind of enchantment with it.

When holiday time came I travelled home with Barkis again, and told him I had sent his message to Peggotty. He seemed gruff.

"When a man says he's willin'," said Mr. Barkis, turning his glance slowly on me again, "it's as much as to say that man's a-waitin' for a answer."

"Have you told her so, Mr. Barkis?"

"N–no," growled Mr. Barkis, reflecting about it. "I aint got no call to go and tell her so. I never said six words to her myself. *I* aint a-goin' to tell her so."

"Would you like me to do it, Mr. Barkis?" said I doubtfully.

"You might tell her if you would," said Mr. Barkis, with another slow look at me, that Barkis was a-waitin' for a answer. Says you, 'Peggotty! Barkis is a-waitin' for a answer.' Says she, perhaps, 'Answer to what?' Says you, 'To what I told you.' 'What is that?' says she. 'Barkis is willin',' says you."

The next great event was the sudden ending of my school life at Salem House by the death of my mother. I was taken home, and ill-treated again by the Murdstones. Then I went to visit my friends at Yarmouth, and on that occasion Mr. Barkis's strange courtship culminated in his marriage with Peggotty. At last Mr. Murdstone sent me to London, to work as a drudge in his wine-warehouse. There I was put to board with a Mr. and Mrs. Micawber. Of Mr. Micawber I may say that he was singularly pompous and ceremonious in manner, and that he was hopelessly in debt to all manner of tradesmen, who besieged his house day and night. At last his "difficulties," as Mrs. Micawber called them, came to a crisis, and he was lodged in the debtors' prison. In time he was released, and then announced his intention of going away from London. I asked Mrs. Micawber if she would go too. She replied : "I never will desert Mr. Micawber. Mr. Micawber may have concealed his difficulties from me in the first instance, but his sanguine temper may have led him to expect that he would overcome them. But I never will desert Mr. Micawber. No!" cried Mrs. Micawber, more affected than before, "I never will do it ! It's of no use asking me !"

Sick at heart of the dog's life I was compelled to lead, I ran away, and, after selling most of my clothes to buy food by the way, reached my aunt's home. At first she did not recognize me ; then she did not know what to do with me. Finally she asked the advice of Mr.

Dick, a benevolent but eccentric gentleman who lodged at her house, and at his word took me to her heart and home. When Mr. Murdstone and his sister came in search of me, she " gave them a piece of her mind " and sent them about their business. Then she renamed me Trotwood Copperfield, and adopted me as her ward.

The next thing was to send me to school, at Canterbury. There I lived in the home of Mr. Wickfield, a lawyer of genial and benevolent disposition. He had a daughter named Agnes, about my own age ; and a clerk, Uriah Heep, who was a singularly repulsive individual.

" I am well aware that I am the umblest person going," said Uriah Heep modestly; " let the other be where he may. My mother is likewise a very umble person. We live in an umble abode, Master Copperfield, but have much to be thankful for. My father's former calling was umble. He was a sexton."

When I went to Canterbury I was much in love with little Em'ly. While there I began to love Miss Shepherd, a pretty girl at a neighboring girls' school. And because a young butcher of the place aspired to love her too, I fought a duel with him, with bare fists, and got tremendously thrashed. Again I fell in love with the eldest Miss Larkins, a fine woman of thirty or thereabouts, while I was seventeen. At the news of her marriage to another I was terribly dejected, but had consolation in fighting the butcher again and thrashing him.

At last my school days ended. On my way home I met Steerforth in London, quite unexpectedly, and renewed our old friendship. He took me on a visit to his home. There I met his mother, a proud stately lady, and also one Miss Rosa Dartle. The latter was, I thought, about thirty years old, and anxious to be married. She was Mrs. Steerforth's companion, and it did not take long to show that she was almost consumed by the fire of her love for James Steerforth, who did not in the least reciprocate her passion.

Next I took Steerforth down to Yarmouth with me, and introduced him to my old friends there—Mr. Peggotty, Mr. and Mrs. Barkis, Ham, Little Em'ly, and Mrs. Gummidge. There, somewhat to my surprise and embarrassment, I learned that my earliest love, Little Em'ly, was to be married to her cousin Ham. We stayed there a fortnight, and Steerforth, by his easy, cordial manner, quite won the hearts of all the simple folk. We also saw there, one day, a fallen outcast girl, named Martha, who in her better days had been Em'ly's friend, and who now fled from Yarmouth to hide herself and her shame in the dark mazes of London.

My aunt decided to indenture me, at the cost of a thousand pounds, to a law-firm, Spenlow & Jorkins, in London. So I began work at Doctors' Commons. In the city I fell in with Steerforth again, and was led by him into wild dissipations. One night I went to the theatre with him while intoxicated, and acted disgracefully in the presence of Agnes Wickfield. Next day I begged her forgiveness, and when she granted it, called her my good angel.

Then she asked me if I had seen Uriah. "Uriah Heep!" said I. "No. Is he in London?"

"He comes to the office downstairs, every day," returned Agnes. "I believe he is going to enter into partnership with papa."

"What? Uriah? That mean fawning fellow, worm himself into such promotion?" I cried indignantly. "You must prevent it, Agnes, while there's time."

"Uriah," she replied, after a moment's hesitation, "has made himself indispensable to papa. He is subtle and watchful. He has mastered papa's weaknesses, fostered them, and taken advantage of them, until—to say all that I mean in a word, Trotwood, until papa is afraid of him." There was more that she might have said; more that she knew or that she suspected; I clearly saw. I could not give her pain by asking her what it was, for I knew that she withheld it from me to spare her father.

Not long after this I again met Tommy Traddles, now studying law; as of old, conscientious, diligent, and by no means fortunate. Before long, too, Uriah confided in me his ambition to make Agnes his wife, which, I saw, he meant to accomplish by dishonestly getting her father into his power.

Mr. Spenlow after a time invited me to visit his home, at Norwood, and I went thither with him. As we entered the house, "Where is Miss Dora?" said Mr. Spenlow to the servant. "Dora!" I thought. "What a beautiful name!" We turned into a room near at hand and I heard a voice say, "Mr. Copperfield, my daughter Dora." It was, no doubt, Mr. Spenlow's voice, but I didn't know it, and I didn't care whose it was. All was over in a moment. I had fulfilled my destiny. I was a captive and a slave. I loved Dora Spenlow to distraction!

On my next visit to Yarmouth, I found my old friend Barkis rapidly sinking.

"People can't die, along the coast," said Mr. Peggotty, "except when the

MR. MICAWBER

tide's pretty nigh out. They can't be born, unless it's pretty nigh in—not properly born, till flood. He's agoing out with the tide. It's ebb at half arter three, slack water half-an-hour. If he lives till it turns, he'll hold his own till past the flood, and go out with the next tide."

We remained there, watching him, a long time—hours. What mysterious influence my presence had upon him in that state of his senses, I shall not pretend to say; but when he at last began to wander feebly, it is certain he was muttering about driving me to school.

Mr. Peggotty touched me, and whispered with much awe and reverence, "They are both agoing out fast."

I was on the point of asking him if he knew me, when he tried to stretch out his arm, and said to me distinctly, with a pleasant smile:

"Barkis is willin'!"

But before I left Yarmouth, something worse occurred. Ham called me aside one evening, weeping and well nigh distracted. Little Em'ly, so soon to become his wife, had run away!

"For some time past," Ham faltered, "there's been a servant about here at odd times. There's been a gen'lm'n, too. The servant was seen along with—our poor girl—last night. He's been in hiding about here, this week or over. He was thought to have gone, but he was hiding. A strange chay and horses was outside the town, this morning, on the Norwich road, a'most afore the day broke. The servant went to it and come from it, and went to it again. When he went to it again, Em'ly was nigh him. The t'other was in-side. He's the man. Mas'r Davy," exclaimed Ham, in a broken voice, "it aint no fault of yourn—and I am far from laying it to you—but his name is Steerforth, and he's a damned villain."

Meantime, my love for Dora grew, and was reciprocated, and presently, all unknown to and unsuspected by her father, we were engaged. Then came the shock of my aunt's announcement that she had lost the bulk of her property; was, in fact, reduced to poverty. How? She explained it all to Agnes and me. Mr. Wickfield, Agnes' father, had been her man of business; but she had been foolish enough to think some one else could make better investments for her, with the result that she had lost all. This, of course, affected my prospects sorely, and so, to add to our now pitifully small income, I sought my old school-master, at Canterbury, and engaged myself to him, as his secretary. I also got an engagement as reporter of debates in Parliament. But when I came to tell Dora of my reverses, she was frightened half to death.

"Oh, don't be dreadful!" she cried.

"Indeed I am not going to be, my darling," I assured her. "But, Dora, my love, if you will sometimes think,—not despondingly, you know; far from that!—but if you will sometimes think—just to encourage yourself—that you are engaged to a poor man—"

"Don't, don't! Pray don't!" cried Dora. "It's so very dreadful!"

"My soul, not at all!" said I cheerfully. "If you will sometimes think of that, and look about now and then at your papa's housekeeping, and endeavor to acquire a little habit of accounts, for instance—"

Poor little Dora received this suggestion with something that was half a sob and half a scream.

"It will be so useful to us afterward," I went on. "And if you would promise me to read a little—a little Cookery Book, that I would send you, it would be so excellent for both of us. For my path in life, my Dora," said I, warming with the subject, "is stony and rugged now, and it rests with us to smooth it. We must fight our way onward. We must be brave. There are obstacles to be met, and we must meet and crush them!"

A few days later came a double catastrophe. Miss Murdstone, who was a confidential friend of Dora's, had suspected Dora's engagement to me, had spied upon her, and at last by a trick got possession of my love letters to her, which she promptly placed before Mr. Spenlow. That gentleman called me to a private interview with him, and taxed me with having acted most dishonorably in thus courting Dora without his knowledge or consent. He bade me break off the engagement, entirely and at once. I refused. Finally, I agreed to think the matter over for a week.

But the next day Mr. Spenlow was found by the roadside, where he had been driving, dead! He left no will, and on examination it was found that after paying his debts his fortune would be quite exhausted, and Dora, who had thought herself rich, would be as poor as I. So she was taken under the care of her two aunts, maiden ladies of uncertain age, and to them I soon applied for permission to make Dora my wife. They consented to my paying my attentions to her, and once more I was made happy in her presence. And then—and then—after a time, we were married!

I doubt whether two young birds could have known less about keeping house than I and my pretty Dora did. We had a servant of course. She kept house for us. She had a written character, as large as a proclamation; and, according to this document, could do everything of a domestic nature that ever I heard of, and a great many things that I never did hear of.

But she preyed upon our minds dreadfully. We felt our inexperience, and were unable to help ourselves.

"My dearest life," I said one day to Dora, "do you think Mary Anne has any idea of time?"

"Why, Doady?" inquired Dora, looking up innocently from her drawing.

"My love, because it's five, and we were to have dined at four."

Dora glanced wistfully at the clock, and hinted that she thought it was too fast.

"On the contrary, my love," said I, referring to my watch, "it's a few minutes too slow."

My little wife came and sat upon my knee, to coax me to be quiet, and drew a line with her pencil down the middle of my nose; but I couldn't dine off that, though it was very agreeable.

"Don't you think, my dear," said I, "it would be better for you to remonstrate with Mary Anne?"

"Oh, no, please! I couldn't, Doady!" said Dora.

"Why not, my love?" I gently asked.

"Oh, because I am such a little goose," said Dora, "and she knows I am!"

"Will you call me a name I want you to call me?" Dora asked, one day.

"What is it?" I asked with a smile.

"It's a stupid name," she said, shaking her curls for a moment, "Child-wife."

I laughingly asked my child-wife what her fancy was in desiring to be so called.

"I don't mean, you silly fellow, that you should use the name instead of Dora. I only mean that you should think of me that way. When you are going to be angry with me say to yourself, "It's only my child-wife!" When I am very disappointing, say, "I knew, a long time ago, that she would make but a child-wife!" When you miss what I should like to be, and I think can never be, say, "Still my foolish child-wife loves me! For indeed I do."

I was passing Mrs. Steerforth's house one day, when a maid came out and asked if I would oblige Miss Dartle by stepping in for a moment. I complied, and that lady asked me to hear the story which Littimer, James Steerforth's servant, had to tell. This was that worthy's tale about little Em'ly:

"Mr. James and myself had been abroad with the young woman, ever since she left Yarmouth under Mr. James' protection. Very much admired, indeed, the young woman was. What with her dress; what with the air and sun; what with being made much of; what with this, that, and the other; her merits really attracted general notice. The young woman went on in this manner for some time, being occasionally low in her spirits, until I think she began to weary Mr. James by giving way to her low spirits and tempers of that kind; and things were not so comfortable. Mr. James he began to be restless again. The more restless he got, the worse she got; and I must say, for myself, that I had a very difficult time of it indeed, between the two.

"But at last, when we were near Naples, Mr. James set off, and left me to break the news to her, that he was gone. The young woman's violence when she came to, after I broke the fact of his departure, was beyond all expectations. She was quite mad and had to be held by force, or, if she couldn't have got a knife, or got to the sea, she'd have beaten her head against the marble floor.

"It was necessary, in short, for a time, to take away everything nigh her that she could do herself or anybody else an injury with, and to shut her up close. Notwithstanding which, she got out in the night, forced the lattice of a window, that I had nailed up myself; dropped on a vine that was trailed below; and never has been seen or heard of, to my knowledge, since."

"She is dead, perhaps," said Miss Dartle with a smile, as if she could have spurned the body of the ruined girl.

"She may have drowned herself, miss," returned Mr. Littimer, catching at an excuse for addressing himself to somebody. "It's very possible."

Mr. Peggotty was convinced, however, of the truth of a dream he had, that Em'ly was still alive and would be restored to him. So he and I sought out poor Martha, and by kindness won her to devote her life to good, and especially to seeking for the lost girl. She did so, and after a long search her labors were rewarded. Emily was found, and taken home by her uncle with all possible tenderness and love. She had made her way back to London, and there been found and saved by Martha. Her uncle forgave her all that had occurred, and then broke up the old home, and went to Australia with her, where life might be begun anew.

It was not long afterward that, while I was at the seashore one day, a fearful tempest broke. A ship was wrecked before my very eyes. One of her passengers made a desperate struggle with the waves. Ham rushed into the breakers to help him, and did help him. But at last he was dashed upon the beach, dead. And there, close by the ruins of the home he had destroyed, lay Steerforth, with his lifeless head upon his arm, as I had often seen him lie at school!

Exposure of Uriah Heep's rascality was bound to come at last. It came through Mr. Micawber, whom Heep had taken into his service after he had got into partnership with Mr. Wickfield. Mr. Micawber charged him to his face, in my presence, with having deceived and swindled Mr. Wickfield, and with having committed an appalling series of forgeries and other crimes. The evidence against the fellow was overwhelming, and in fear of being handed over to the police, he made, so far as possible, restitution of all his plunder. Included in this latter was my aunt's fortune, which, as she now owned, she had supposed Mr. Wickfield had misappropriated, the real culprit, of course, being Heep.

Of the passing away of my child-wife, it is hard to write. On that last night she said to me as I knelt by her pillow:

"I was very happy, very. But as years went on, my dear boy would have wearied of his child-wife. She would have been less and less a companion for him. He would have been more and more sensible of what was wanting in his home. She wouldn't have improved. It is better as it is."

I went away from England, to forget, if possible, my grief. When, after long absence, I returned, Agnes welcomed me with her old sisterly affection. There were many changes to observe. Not the least interesting was that Uriah Heep and Littimer were now Number 27 and Number 28 in prison, and in their penitence were regarded as quite model prisoners.

The year came round to Christmas-time, and I had been at home above two months. I had seen Agnes frequently. However loud the general voice might be in giving me encouragement, and however fervent the emotions and endeavors to which it roused me, I heard her lightest word of praise as I heard nothing else.

At last one day I told her of the love for her that had risen in my heart. It had always been there, but now made its over-mastering presence felt. And then she was clasped in my arms as she had never been, as I had thought she never was to be.

"When I loved Dora—fondly, Agnes, as you know—"

"Yes," she cried earnestly. "I am glad to know it."

"When I loved her—even then, my love would have been incomplete, without your sympathy. I had it, and it was perfected, and when I lost her, Agnes, what should I have been without you, still! I went away, dear Agnes, loving you. I stayed away, loving you. I returned home loving you."

"I am so blest, Trotwood—my heart is so overcharged—but there is one thing I must say."

"Dearest, what?"

"I have loved you all my life!"

ABOARD THE NAUTILUS

# TWENTY THOUSAND LEAGUES UNDER THE SEA.

## By Jules Verne.

ABOARD THE "NAUTILUS"—SUBMARINE HUNTING—THE FOREST—A DREADFUL SCENE—
SHOCKING THE NATIVES—SHARKS AND PEARLS—FIGHTING A SHARK—THE
TUNNEL OF SUEZ—A SUBMARINE VOLCANO—ATLANTIC—THE SOUTH
POLE—THE DEVIL FISH—A DESPERATE BATTLE—
THE DESTROYER—THE MAELSTROM.

THESE marvellous and exciting adventures of M. Pierre Aronnax, his servant Conseil, and a Canadian whale-harpooner, Ned Land, had their origin in 1866. For some time ocean vessels had been met by "an enormous thing," a long object spindle-shaped, occasionally phosphorescent, and infinitely larger and more rapid in its movements than a whale. Others observed what appeared to be a reef, or sandbank, in mid-ocean, which shifted from place to place. Some ships were injured by collisions with the mysterious object, and others were doubtless destroyed by it, since there were numerous total disappearances of ships. Finally the United States Government sent out a warship, the Abraham Lincoln, to search for and capture or destroy the creature, whatever it might be. On that vessel I, Pierre Aronnax, with Conseil and Land, secured passage.

Thousands of miles were sailed without result. Then, on November 5, not far from the coast of Japan, the object of our quest was sighted. A long chase followed, the unknown object easily keeping ahead of the ship. But one night it lay still upon the water, apparently an enormous narwhal with a luminous eye. The ship stole up to it. Ned Land hurled his harpoon. I heard the sonorous stroke of the weapon, which seemed to have struck a hard body. The light went out suddenly, and two enormous waterspouts broke over the bridge of the frigate, rushing like a torrent from stem to stern, overthrowing men, and breaking the lashing of the spars. A fearful shock followed, and thrown over the rail without having time to stop myself, I fell into the sea.

Conseil flung himself after me, and Ned Land was swept over with me. The frigate steamed away, and after a desperate struggle we three found ourselves alone in mid-ocean, on the back of the strange object we had come to destroy. It proved to be made of iron, and we perceived that it was some kind of a submarine boat. Suddenly a trap-door was opened, and we were drawn within it by eight masked men. Not a word was spoken by them, and for a time we were kept close prisoners in a room. Then the commander of the strange craft made himself known to us. He introduced himself as Captain Nemo, of the "Nautilus," and added: "I have done with society entirely, for reasons which I alone have the right of appreciating. I do not therefore obey its laws, and I desire you never to allude to them before me again!"

Then he showed me through his ship. It was operated by electric machinery, and was capable of going at a high rate of speed, on the surface or at any depth below it. He made us his guests, though, of course, we were practically prisoners, and thus we entered upon our marvellous voyage.

We were then in the Black River, or Japanese current, that great stream which flows through the North Pacific. After a few days of uneventful cruising, Captain Nemo invited us to a hunting expedition at the island of Crespo, a tiny rock in the North Pacific, and we of course accepted. The hunt proved to be a submarine one. We set out from the Nautilus in divers suits, walking on the bottom of the sea, and armed with guns charged with compressed air and firing electric bullets, which were more effective under water than an ordinary rifle in the air. In each man's outfit was included a supply of compressed air in a reservoir, sufficient for a day's breathing.

The light, which lit the soil thirty feet below the surface of the ocean, astonished me by its power. The solar rays shone through the watery mass easily, and dissipated all color, and I clearly distinguished objects at a distance of a hundred and fifty yards. Above me was the calm surface of the sea. We were walking on fine, even sand, not wrinkled, as on a flat shore, which retains the impression of the billows.

The forest at the base of the island of Crespo was composed of large tree-plants. Not an herb which carpeted the ground, not a branch which clothed the trees, was either broken or bent, nor did they extend horizontally; all stretched up to the surface of the ocean.

Then, at a depth of seventy-five fathoms, we began to retrace our steps to the Nautilus, rising nearer and nearer the surface as the water shoaled. At ten yards and a half deep, we walked amid a shoal of little fishes of all kinds, more numerous than the birds of the air, and also more agile; but no aquatic game worthy of a shot had as yet met our gaze, when at that moment I saw the captain shoulder his gun quickly, and follow a moving object into the shrubs. He fired—I heard a slight hissing, and a creature fell stunned at some distance from us. It was a magnificent sea-otter, an enhydrus, the only exclusively marine quadruped. This otter was five feet long, and must have been very valuable. Half an hour later we reached and re-entered the Nautilus, and resumed our cruise.

A few days later we were looking out into the depths of the sea, through one of the glass panels with which the sides of the Nautilus were provided. Suddenly a huge black mass loomed in view, in the electric light of our vessel. It was a sunken ship, which had been wrecked at most some few hours. Three stumps of masts, broken off about two feet above the bridge, showed that the vessel had had to sacrifice its masts. But, lying on its side, it had filled, and it was heeling over to port. This skeleton of what it had once been was a sad spectacle as it lay lost under the waves; but sadder still was the sight of the bridge, where some corpses, bound with ropes, were still lying. I counted five—four men, one of whom was standing at the helm, and a woman standing by the poop holding an infant in her arms. The steersman, alone, calm, with a grave, clear face, his gray hair glued to his forehead, and his hand clutching the wheel of the helm, seemed even then to be guiding the three broken masts through the depths of the ocean.

Our next noteworthy adventure was on the coast of New Guinea. The Nautilus was run close to the shore, and Captain Nemo consented to our going on the land, to shoot game and get fresh meat, for which we were longing. We did so, to our great delight, but after several hours of sport, were attacked by the natives, and had to flee for our lives back to the Nautilus. Once within it we were secure. The natives swarmed over the iron top of the boat, unable to produce the least impression upon it.

Before we sailed away, Captain Nemo ordered the hatches to be opened, regardless of the fact that the savages were ready to swarm in and butcher us.

The port lids were 'pulled down outside. Twenty horrible faces appeared. But the first native who placed his hand on the stair-rail, struck from behind by some invisible force, I know not what, fled, uttering the most fearful cries, and making the wildest contortions.

Ten of his companions followed him. They met with the same fate.

Conseil was in ecstasy. Ned Land, carried away by his violent instincts, rushed on to the staircase. But the moment he seized the rail with both hands, he, in his turn, was overthrown.

"I am struck by a thunderbolt," cried he, with an oath.

This explained all. It was no rail, but a metallic cable, charged with electricity from the deck, communicating with the platform. Whoever touched it felt a powerful shock—and this shock would have been mortal if Captain Nemo had discharged into the conductor the whole force of the current.

After leaving the Pacific we entered the Indian Ocean, and visited the pearl fisheries of Ceylon. There Captain Nemo proposed that we leave the Nautilus and take another tramp on the bottom of the sea, among the oysters, the pearl-fishers, and the sharks. Amid the wonders of the submarine world Captain Nemo led me into a cave where, on a ledge of rock, lay a gigantic oyster, more than two and a half yards across. The shells were a little open; the captain came near, and put his dagger between to prevent them from closing; then with his hand he raised the membrane with its fringed edges, which formed a cloak for the creature. There, between the folded plaits, I saw a loose pearl, whose size equaled that of a cocoanut. Its globular shape, perfect clearness, and admirable lustre made it altogether a jewel of inestimable value. Carried away by my curiosity I stretched out my hand to seize it, weigh it, and touch it; but the captain stopped me, made a sign of refusal, and quickly withdrew his dagger, and the two shells closed suddenly. I then understood Captain Nemo's intention. In leaving this pearl hidden in the mantle of the tridacne, he was allowing it to grow slowly. Each year the secretions of the mollusk would enlarge the pearl.

About five yards from me a shadow appeared and sank to the ground. It was a man, a living man, an Indian, a fisherman, a poor devil, who, I suppose, had come to glean before the harvest. Suddenly, as the Indian was on the ground, I saw him make a gesture of terror, rise, and make a spring to return to the surface of the sea. A gigantic shadow appeared just above the unfortunate diver. It was a shark of enormous size advancing diagonally, his eyes on fire, and his jaws open. The voracious creature shot toward the Indian, who threw himself on one side in order to avoid the shark's fins; but not its tail, for it struck his chest, and stretched him on the ground. The shark returned, and turning on his back, prepared himself for cutting the Indian in two, when I saw Captain Nemo rise suddenly, and then, dagger in hand, walk straight to the monster. Holding himself well together, he waited for the shark with admirable coolness; and when it rushed at him, threw himself on one side with wonderful quickness, avoiding the shock, and burying his dagger deep into its side. But it was not all over. A terrible combat ensued. The blood rushed in torrents from its wound. The sea was dyed red, and through the opaque liquid I could distinguish nothing more. Nothing more, until the moment when, like lightning, I saw the undaunted captain hanging on to one of the creature's fins, struggling, as it were, hand to hand with the monster, and dealing successive blows at his enemy, yet still unable to give a decisive one. The captain fell to the earth, upset by the enormous mass which leaned upon him. The shark's jaws opened wide, like a pair of factory shears, and it would have been all over with the captain; but quick as thought, harpoon in hand, Ned Land rushed toward the shark and struck it with its sharp point. Struck to the heart, it struggled in dreadful convulsions. Ned Land disentangled the captain, who, getting up without any wound, went straight to the Indian, quickly cut the cord which held him to the stone, took him in his arms, and with a sharp blow of his heel, mounted to the surface. Captain Nemo's first care was to recall the unfortunate man to life again. He opened his eyes. What was his surprise, his terror even, at seeing four great copper heads leaning over him! And above all, what must he have thought when Captain Nemo, drawing from the pocket of his dress a bag of pearls, placed it in his hand!

Our course next led us into the Red Sea, and I supposed that after reaching its head we should have to turn back, as the Suez Canal was not yet navigable. But Captain Nemo told me he should go straight through to the Mediterranean, by way of a tunnel which he had discovered under the Isthmus of Suez. It was at night when we sighted the lights of Suez. Down we went to the depths again. The captain himself took the helm. A large gallery, black and deep, opened before us. The Nautilus went boldly into it. A strange roaring was heard round its sides. It was the waters of the Red Sea, which the incline of the tunnel precipitated violently toward the Mediterranean. The Nautilus went with the torrent, rapid as an arrow in spite of the efforts of the machinery, which, in order to offer more

SUBMARINE HUNTING

effective resistance, beat the waves with reversed screw. At length Captain Nemo quitted the helm; and turning to me, said:

"The Mediterranean!"

In less than twenty minutes, the Nautilus, carried along by the torrent, had passed through the Isthmus of Suez.

Among the Greek islands one day I noticed that it was growing very warm in the Nautilus, and asked the captain for an explanation. For an answer he opened the covers of the glass panels and I saw the sea entirely white all round. A sulphurous smoke was curling amid the waves, which boiled like water in a copper. I placed my hand on one of the panes of glass, but the heat was so great that I quickly took it off again.

"Where are we?" I asked.

"Near the island of Santorin, sir," replied the captain, " and just in the canal which separates Nea Kamenni from Pali Kamenni. I wished to give you a sight of the curious spectacle of a submarine eruption."

"We can remain no longer in this boiling water," said I to the captain.

"It would not be prudent," replied the impassive Captain Nemo.

An order was given; the Nautilus tacked about and left the furnace it could not brave with impunity. A quarter of an hour after we were breathing fresh air on the surface.

From the Mediterranean we went into the Atlantic Ocean, and there one day came to what seemed a sunken continent. There, ruined, destroyed, lay a town—its roofs open to the sky, its temples fallen, its arches dislocated, its columns lying on the ground, from which one could still recognize the massive character of Tuscan architecture. Further

on, some remains of a gigantic aqueduct; here the high base of an Acropolis, with the floating outline of a Parthenon; there traces of a quay, as if an ancient port had formerly abutted on the borders of the ocean, and disappeared with its merchant vessels and its war galleys. Further on again, long lines of sunken walls and broad deserted streets—a perfect Pompeii escaped beneath the waters. Such was the sight that Captain Nemo brought before my eyes.

Where was I? Where was I? I must know at any cost. I tried to speak, but Captain Nemo stopped me by a gesture, and picking up a piece of chalk-stone advanced to a rock of black basalt, and traced the one word, "Atlantic!"

Southward again we sped, and entered the regions of ice, through which we fought our way. A gigantic iceberg barred our way. We sank to a depth of 900 feet and passed under it. But then we found ourselves under a sea of ice. Hour after hour we sailed on, a thousand feet of ice over our heads! At length the ice grew thinner, then vanished, and we rose to the surface of an open sea. There was a rocky coast not far away, and there we made a landing, and found the exact site of the South Pole. There Captain Nemo, resting with his hand on my shoulder, said:

"I, Captain Nemo, on this 21st day of March, 1868, have reached the South Pole on the ninetieth degree; and I take possession of this part of the globe, equal to one-sixth of the known continents."

Saying which, Captain Nemo unfurled a black banner, bearing an N in gold quartered on its bunting.

Back to the North Atlantic then we sailed, and amid the Bahama Islands met with a tragic episode. Looking through the submarine window one day we saw a horrible monster, worthy to figure in the legends of the marvelous. It was an immense cuttle-fish, being eight yards long. It swam crossways in the direction of the Nautilus with great speed, watching us with its enormous staring green eyes. Its eight arms, or rather feet, fixed to its head, that have given the name of cephalopod to these animals, were twice as long as its body, and were twisted like the Furies' hair. One could see the 250 air-holes on the inner side of the tentacles. The monster's mouth, a horned beak like a parrot's, opened and shut vertically. Its tongue, a horned substance, furnished with several rows of pointed teeth, came out quivering from this veritable pair of shears. What a freak of nature—a bird's beak on a mollusk !

As we gazed at it, the Nautilus stopped. Another such creature had got its horny beak entangled in the screw. So Captain Nemo made the boat rise to the surface, to " slaughter this vermin."

About ten men with boarding hatchets were ready for the attack. Conseil and I took two hatchets ; Ned Land seized a harpoon. One of the sailors, posted on the top ladder-step, unscrewed the bolts of the panels. But hardly were the screws loosed, when the panels rose with great violence, evidently drawn by the suckers of a poulp's arm. Immediately one of these arms slid like a serpent down the opening, and twenty others were above. With one blow of the axe, Captain Nemo cut this formidable tentacle, that slid wriggling down the ladder. Just as we were pressing one on the other to reach the platform, two other arms, lashing the air, came down on the seaman placed before Captain Nemo and lifted him up with irresistible power. Captain Nemo uttered a cry and rushed out. We hurried after him.

What a scene ! The unhappy man, seized by the tentacle, and fixed to the suckers, was balanced in the air at the caprice of this enormous trunk. The unfortunate man was lost. Who could rescue him from that powerful pressure ? However Captain Nemo had rushed to the poulp, and with one blow of the axe, had cut through one arm. His lieutenant struggled furiously against other monsters that crept on the flanks of the Nautilus. The crew fought with their axes.

For one instant I thought the unhappy man tangled with the poulp would be torn from its powerful suction. Seven of the eight arms had been cut off. One only wriggled in the air, brandishing the victim like a feather. But just as Captain Nemo and his lieutenant threw themselves on it, the animal ejected a stream of black liquid. We were blinded with it. When the cloud dispersed, the cuttle-fish had disappeared.

Crossing the ocean to the shores of Europe, we encountered a war-ship, of what nationality, I could not discover. Captain Nemo regarded it, however, as an " accursed ship of an accursed nation," and prepared to attack it. For a time he allowed it to pursue him and expend its shots harmlessly upon the invulnerable back of the Nautilus. Then at last he sank below the surface, and sent his boat at incredible speed against the unprotected side of the ship. I could feel the shock, though it seemed light. I felt the penetrating power of the steel spur. I heard rattlings and scrapings. But the Nautilus, carried along by its propelling power, passed through the mass of the vessel, like a needle through sail-cloth!

I could stand it no longer. Mad, out of my mind, I rushed from my room into the saloon. Captain Nemo was there, mute, gloomy, implacable; he was looking through the port panel. A large mass cast a shadow on the water; and that it might lose nothing of her agony, the Nautilus was going down into the abyss with her. Ten yards from me I saw the open shell through which the water was rushing with the noise of thunder, then the double line of guns and the netting. The bridge was covered with black agitated shadows.

The water was rising. The poor creatures were crowding the ratlings, clinging to the masts, struggling under water. It was a human ant-heap overtaken by the sea. Suddenly an explosion took place. The compressed air blew up her decks, as if the magazines had caught fire. Then the unfortunate vessel sank more rapidly. Her topmast, laden with victims, now appeared; then her spars, bending under the weight of men; and last of all, the top of her mainmast. Then the dark mass disappeared, and with it the dead crew, drawn down by the strong eddy.

I turned to Captain Nemo. When all was over, he turned to his room, opened the door and entered. I followed him with my eyes. On the end wall, beneath his heroes, I saw the portrait of a woman, still young, and two little children. Captain Nemo looked at them for some moments, stretched his arm toward them, and kneeling down, burst into deep sobs. I heard him murmur these words (the last which ever struck my ear):

"Almighty God! enough! enough!"

Was it a confession of remorse which thus escaped from this man's conscience?

The end of our voyage came suddenly. We were off the Norwegian coast. The Nautilus began to whirl about in circles. We were within the grasp of the awful maelstrom. When the catastrophe occurred, Conseil, Ned Land, and I were in the small boat on top of the Nautilus, meaning to make our escape. The whirlpool tore us loose, and then for a time I knew no more. When I regained consciousness we were all safe, in a fisherman's hut, on one of the Loffoden Isles. In ten months we had traveled 20,000 leagues under the sea.

But what has become of the Nautilus? Did it resist the pressure of the maelstrom? Does Captain Nemo still live? Who can tell?

# ROBINSON CRUSOE.

## By Daniel Defoe.

MAKING A HOME—PLANTING A GARDEN—BOAT-BUILDING—EXPLORING THE ISLAND—
A PICTURESQUE OUTFIT—THE FOOTPRINT IN THE SAND—THE RESCUE OF
FRIDAY—ANOTHER BOAT—FIGHTING SAVAGES—SENDING FOR CAST-
AWAYS—THE ENGLISH SHIP—THE MUTINEERS—
HOME AGAIN AT LAST.

I WAS born in the year 1632, in the city of York, of a good family, though not of that country, my father being a foreigner, of Bremen, who settled first at Hull ; he got a good estate by merchandise, and leaving off his trade, lived afterward at York ; from whence he had married my mother, whose relations were named Robinson, a very good family in that country, and from whom I was called Robinson Kreutznaer ; but, by the usual corruption of words in England, we are now called, nay, we call ourselves, and write our name, Crusoe ; and so my companions always called me.

Being the third son of the family, and not bred to any trade, my head began to be filled very early with rambling thoughts ; my father, who was very ancient, had given me a competent share of learning, as far as house-education and country free-school generally goes, and designed me for the law ; but I would be satisfied with nothing but going to sea ; and my inclination to this led me ultimately to run away from home and take passage on a ship.

After several voyages, with various shipwrecks and other adventures, I set out on a voyage from Brazil to Guinea. The ship was driven far out of its course by storms, and at last went aground near the shore of an unknown island. The entire company put off in a boat, but the waves were too furious.. The boat was swamped, and every man perished save myself, who with vast difficulty got ashore.

When the storm abated, I could see our ship standing upright where she ran aground, not a mile away, and I reflected that if we had all remained aboard, all my companions would still be living.

As soon as possible I made a raft, and conveyed from the ship to the shore all possible supplies of food, clothing, tools, arms and ammunition, and everything that was likely to prove of use to me. For a time I lived in a tent on the shore, but finding the place neither wholesome nor easily defended against savages, I searched for a better one. I found a little plain on the side of a rising hill, whose front towards this little plain was steep as a house-side, so that nothing could come down on me from the top. On the side of the rock there was a hollow place, worn a little way in, like the entrance or door of a cave; but there was not really any cave, or way into the rock, at all.

On the flat of the green, just below this hollow place, I resolved to pitch my tent. This plain was not above a hundred yards broad, and about twice as long, and lay like a green before my door; and, at the end of it, descending irregularly every way down into the low ground by the seaside. It was on the N. N. W. side of the hill; so that it was sheltered from the heat every day, till it came to the W. and by S. sun, or thereabouts, which, in those countries, is near the setting.

Before I set up my tent, I drew a half-circle before the hollow place, which took in about ten yards in its semi-diameter, from the rock, and twenty yards in its diameter from its beginning and ending.

In this half-circle I pitched two rows of strong stakes, driving them into the ground till they stood very firm like piles, the biggest end being out of the ground above five feet and a half, and sharpened on the top. The two rows did not stand above six inches from one another.

Then I took the pieces of cable which I had cut in the ship, and laid them in rows, upon one another, within the circle, between these two rows of stakes, up to the top, placing other stakes in the inside, leaning against them, about two feet and a half high, like the spur to a post; and this fence was so strong that neither man nor beast could get into it or over it. This cost me a great deal of time and labor, especially to cut the piles in the woods,

bring them to the place, and drive them into the earth.

The entrance into this place I made to be, not by a door, but by a short ladder to go over the top; which ladder, when I was in, I lifted over after me; and so I was completely fenced in and fortified, as I thought, from all the world, and consequently slept secure in the night, which otherwise I could not have done; though, as it appeared afterwards, there was no need of all this caution from the enemies that I apprehended danger from.

Into this fence, or fortress, with infinite labor, I carried all my riches, all my provisions, ammunition, and stores.

When I had done this, I began to work my way into the rock, and bringing all the earth and stones that I dug down, out through my tent, I laid them up within my fence in the nature of a terrace, so that it raised the ground within about a foot and a half; and thus I made me a cave, just behind my tent, which served me like a cellar to my house.

Among the goods which I brought from the ship there were a few grains of corn and barley, which I carefully planted and cultivated, as I did also some rice. Thus I was enabled to make a little farm, which would supply me with food. I caught and tamed some wild goats and soon had quite a herd of them, which supplied me with milk and meat, and with skins for clothing. Birds of various kinds abounded, and so did great turtles, and with these I was enabled to keep my larder well supplied.

It cost me many experiments and much labor to make earthenware vessels which would hold liquids and stand the heat of the fire, but at last succeeded in doing so, and also a stone mortar, or mill, in which to grind my corn.

Imagining my island to be not very far from the coast of Brazil, I set about plans for making a boat, in which I might effect my escape. I decided to make it of the log of a great tree, as the Indians do. So I went to work and felled a cedar tree. I question much whether Solomon ever had such a one for building the Temple at Jerusalem; it was five feet ten inches diameter at the lower part next the stump, and four feet eleven inches diameter at the end of twenty-two feet; after which it lessened for a while, and then parted into branches. It was not without infinite labor that I felled this tree. I was twenty days hacking and hewing at it at the bottom; I was fourteen more getting the branches and limbs and the vast spreading head of it cut off, which I hacked and hewed through with my ax and hatchet, and inexpressible labor; after this, it cost me a month to shape it and dub it to a proportion, and to something like the bottom of a boat, that it might swim upright as it ought to do. It cost me near three months more to clear the inside, and work it out so as to make an exact boat of it; this I did, indeed, without fire, by mere mallet and chisel, and by the dint of hard labor, till I had brought it to be a very handsome periagua, and big enough to have carried six-and-twenty men, and consequently big enough to have carried me and all my cargo.

But all my devices to get it into the water failed me; though they cost infinite labor too. It lay about one hundred yards from the water, and not more; but the first inconvenience was, it was up hill towards the creek. Well,

to take away this discouragement, I resolved to dig into the surface of the earth, and so make a declivity. This I began, and it cost me a prodigious deal of pains (but who grudge pains that have their deliverance in view?); but when this was worked through, and this difficulty managed, it was still much at one, for I could no more stir the canoe than I could the other boat. Then I measured the distance of the ground, and resolved to cut a dock or canal, to bring the water up to the canoe, seeing I could not bring the canoe down to the water. Well, I began this work; and when I began to enter into it, and calculate how deep it was to be dug, how broad, how the stuff was to be thrown out, I found that, by the number of hands I had, being none but my own, it must have been ten or twelve years before I could have gone through with it; for the shore lay so high that at the upper end it must have been at least twenty feet deep; so at length, though with great reluctancy, I gave this attempt over also.

After this failure I lived for five years without any striking incident. Then I succeeded in finishing a smaller boat, or canoe, and in getting it to the water. It was not big enough to venture to go to Brazil in, but I made bold to set out in it for a voyage of discovery around my island. This I did and made many interesting discoveries, but found no traces of man, nor any prospect of escaping from my island prison.

My appearance at this time would have astonished any civilized man who might have seen me.

I had a great high shapeless cap, made of goat's skin, with a flap hanging down behind, as well to keep the sun from me as to shoot the rain off from running into my neck.

My beard I had once suffered to grow till it was about a quarter of a yard long; but as I had both scissors and razors sufficient, I had cut it pretty short, except what grew on my upper lip, which I had trimmed into a large pair of Mahometan whiskers, such as I had seen worn by some Turks at Sallee, for the Moors did not wear such, though the Turks did; of these moustachios, or whiskers, I will not say they were long enough to hang my hat upon them, but they were of a length and shape monstrous enough, and such as in England would have passed for frightful.

One day after a violent storm, I discovered near the beach, the wreck of a Spanish ship, and managed to secure some articles from it, and some bits of money, but of the ship's company, saw no survivors.

And now I come to a new scene of my life. It happened one day, about noon, going towards my boat, I was exceedingly surprised with the print of a man's naked foot on the shore, which was very plain to be seen on the sand. I stood like one thunderstruck, or as if I had seen an apparition. I listened, I looked round me, but I could hear nothing, nor see anything; I went up to a rising ground, to look farther; I went up the shore, and down the shore, but it was all one: I could see no other impression but that one. I went to it again to see if there were any more, and to observe if it might not be my fancy; but there was no room for that, for there was exactly the print of a foot—toes, heel, and every part of a foot. How it came thither I knew not, nor could in the least imagine.

But after innumerable fluttering thoughts like a man perfectly confused and out of himself, I came home to my fortification, not feeling, as we say, the ground I went on, but terrified to the last degree, looking behind me at every two or three steps, mistaking every bush and tree, and fancying every stump at a distance to be a man. Nor is it possible to describe how many various shapes my affrighted imagination represented things to me in; how many wild ideas were formed every moment in my fancy, and what strange unaccountable whimseys came into my thoughts by the way.

Not long after that, I found that my island was a resort of cannibals, who brought their victims thither to kill and eat them. It is impossible for me to express the horror of my mind, at seeing the shore spread with skulls, hands, feet, and other bones of human bodies; and particularly, I observed a place where there had been a fire made, and a circle dug in the earth, like a cockpit, where I supposed the savage wretches had sat down to their inhuman feastings upon the bodies of their fellow-creatures.

I was now in the twenty-third year of residence in this island, and was so naturalized to the place and the manner of living, that, could I but have enjoyed the certainty that no savages would come to the place to disturb me, I could have been contented to have capitulated for spending the rest of my time there. But that was not to be.

About a year and a half later I discovered, one morning, a party of about thirty savages, landed on the island for a cannibal feast. They brought two captives from a boat, and killed and began to cook one. The other suddenly broke from them and ran for life, straight toward me. As he got near me, closely pressed by two pursuers, I went out to meet him, gun in hand. One of his pursuers I knocked down with the butt of my gun. The other stopped, as if he had been frightened, and I advanced towards him; but as I came nearer, I perceived presently he had a bow and arrow, and was fitting it to shoot at me; so I was then obliged to shoot at him first, which I did, and killed him at the first shot. The poor savage who had fled, but had stopped, though he saw both his enemies fallen and killed, as he thought, yet was so frightened with the fire and noise of my piece that he stood stock still, and neither came forward nor went backward, though he seemed rather inclined still to fly than to come on. I hallooed again to him, and made signs to come forward, which be easily understood, and came a little way; then stopped again, and then a little farther, and stopped again; and I could then perceive that he stood trembling, as if he had been taken prisoner, and had just been to be killed, as his two enemies were. I beckoned to him again to come to me, and gave him all the signs of encouragement that I could think of; and he came nearer and nearer, kneeling down every ten or twelve steps, in token of acknowledgment for saving his life. I smiled at him, and looked pleasantly, and beckoned to him to come still nearer; at length, he came close to me; and then he kneeled down again, kissed the ground, and laid his head upon the ground, and, taking me by the foot, set my foot upon his head; this, it seems, was in token of swearing to be my slave forever. The other savages were soon put to flight. As for the one I had rescued, I called him Friday, for it was on that day of the week that I first met him. He proved amiable and affectionate, and I succeeded in educating him to a degree, and in making of him an excellent servant and agreeable companion.

With Friday's help I now set to work to make another large boat, and this time succeeded in getting it launched. It was big enough to carry twenty men, and I fitted it with mast and sails, rudder and anchor.

I was now in the twenty-seventh year of my residence on the island, and I eagerly pressed preparations for a serious attempt to get away. Then one day Friday, terribly frightened, told me that three canoes full of savages had landed on the island. I quickly armed him, for I had taught him to be expert in the use of firearms, and we set out to see what the savages were doing. To my horror I saw that they had for a captive a white man, whom they were evidently about to kill and eat. We crept up hastily and opened fire upon the wretches, killing and wounding many of them. Then we released the captive, who happily was unharmed, and gave him weapons. He joined us in attacking the rest of the savages with incredible fury, and we soon made an end of them, nearly all. The account of the whole is as follows: Three killed at our first shot from the tree; two killed at the next shot; two killed by Friday in the boat; two killed by Friday, of those at first wounded; one killed by Friday in the wood; three killed by the Spaniard; four killed, being found dropped here and there, of the wounds, or killed by Friday in his chase of them; four escaped in the boat,

ROBINSON CRUSOE

whereof one wounded if not dead—twenty-one, in all.

When we came to search the canoes they had left, we found another captive in one of them, bound hand and foot but living, and in him, to his unspeakable delight, Friday recognized his own father.

My island was now peopled, and I thought myself very rich in subjects; and it was a merry reflection, which I frequently made, how like a king I looked. First of all, the whole country was my own mere property, so that I had an undoubted right of dominion. Secondly, my people were perfectly subjected; I was absolute lord and lawgiver; they all owed their lives to me, and were ready to lay down their lives, if there had been occasion for it, for me.

It was remarkable, too, I had but three subjects, and they were of three different religions: my man Friday was a Protestant, his father was a Pagan and a cannibal, and the Spaniard was a Papist. However, I allowed liberty of conscience throughout my dominion.

In a little time, no more canoes appearing, the fear of their coming wore off; and I began to take my former thoughts of a voyage to the main into consideration; being likewise assured by Friday's father that I might depend upon good usages from their nation, on his account, if I would go. But my thoughts were a little suspended when I had a serious discourse with the Spaniard, and when I understood that there were sixteen more of his countrymen and Portuguese, who having been cast away and made their escape to that side, lived there at peace, indeed, with the savages, but were very sore put to it for necessaries, and, indeed, for life.

And now, having a full supply of food for all the guests expected, I gave the Spaniard leave to go over to the main, to see what he could do with those he had left behind him there. I gave him a strict charge not to bring any man with him who would not first swear, in the presence of himself and the old savage, that he would no way injure, fight with, or attack the person he should find in the island, who was so kind as to send for them in order to their deliverance; but that they would stand by him and defend him against all such attempts, and wherever they went, would be entirely under and subjected to his command; and that this should be put in writing, and signed with their hands. How they were to have done this, when I knew they had neither pen nor ink—that, indeed, was a question which we never asked. Under these instructions, the Spaniard and the old savage, the father of Friday, went away in one of the canoes which they might be said to have come in, or rather, were brought in, when they came as prisoners to be devoured by the savages. I gave each of them a musket, with a firelock on it, and about eight charges of powder and ball, charging them to be very good husbands of both, and not to use either of them but upon urgent occasion.

Eight days after they had gone, while I was still sleeping in the morning, Friday came running in to me, and called aloud, "Master, master, they are come, they are come!" I jumped up, and regardless of danger, I went out as soon as I could get my clothes on, through my little grove, which, by the way, was by this time grown to be a very thick wood; I say regardless of danger, I went without my arms, which was not my custom to do : but I was surprised, when, turning my eyes to the sea, I presently saw a boat at about a league and a half distance, standing in for the shore, with a shoulder-of-mutton sail, as they call it, and the wind blowing pretty fair to bring them in ; also I observed, presently, that they did not come from that side which the shore lay on, but from the southernmost end of the island. Upon this I called Friday in, and bade him lie close, for these were not the people we looked for, and that we might not know yet whether they were friends or enemies. In the next place, I went in to fetch my perspective-glass, to see what I could make of them ; and, having taken the ladder out, I climbed up to the top of the hill, as I used to do when I was apprehensive of anything, and to take my view plainer, without being discovered. I had scarce set my foot upon the hill, when my eye plainly discovered a ship lying at an anchor, about two leagues and a half distance from me, S.S.E., but not above a league and a half from the shore. By observation, it appeared plainly to be an English ship, and the boat appeared to be an English longboat.

As we watched them at a distance, we saw three men put ashore with much ill-treatment. The rest of the company went off to see the island, leaving the boat aground with two men in it, both intoxicated. We then advanced cautiously to the three ill-treated men, and found them to be the captain, mate, and a passenger. The crew had mutinied, and meant to kill them, but finally decided to put them ashore, and abandon them to their fate.

I gave the three men arms, and joined forces with them. Then we attacked the mutineers, surprising them as they lay asleep. Some were killed, others wounded, and all quickly reduced to submission. The boat was secured, and the captain was soon in possession of his ship again.

Some of the mutineers became obedient, and were taken back on the ship. Five others begged to be left on the island, and to this I consented. Accordingly, I gave them the whole history of the place, and of my coming to it; showed them my fortifications, the way I made my bread, planted my corn, cured my grapes, and, in a word, all that was necessary to make them easy. I told them the story also of the sixteen Spaniards, that were to be expected, for whom I left a letter, and made them promise to treat them in common with themselves.

When I took leave of this island, I carried on board, for relics, the great goatskin cap I had made, my umbrella, and one of my parrots ; also I forgot not to take the money I formerly mentioned, which had lain by me so long useless that it was grown rusty and tarnished, and could hardly pass for silver till it had been a little rubbed and handled, and also the money I found in the wreck of the Spanish ship. And thus I left the island, the 19th of December, as I found by the ship's account, in the year 1686, after I had been upon it eight-and-twenty years, two months, and nineteen days ; being delivered from this second captivity the same day of the month that I first made my escape in the longboat from among the Moors of Sallee. In this vessel, after a long voyage, I arrived in England the 11th of June, in the year 1687, having been thirty-five years absent.

# LES MISERABLES.

### By Victor Hugo.

M. MADELEINE—FANTINE—THE TRIAL—DEATH OF FANTINE—THE ESCAPE—ARREST AND ESCAPE—COSETTE—MARIUS—THE DEATH TRAP—THE BARRICADES—THE LAST OF JAVERT—THE TRIUMPH OF MARIUS—TWO EXPLANATIONS—THE END.

EARLY in October, 1815, an hour before sunset, a footsore wanderer entered the French town of Digne. He sought lodging at the inn, but at a hint from the Mayor the landlord refused to receive him. "I know you," he said. "You are Jean Valjean, an ex-convict. Now be-gone!" The wanderer sought shelter at other houses, public and private, but was rudely repulsed. There seemed nothing for him but to spend the night in the open air. But some one finally directed him to the house of the good Bishop Myriel. Thither he went. He told who he was and how he had been treated, and warned the Bishop that he was a rough customer, a dangerous man. The good bishop un-hesitatingly received him as an honored guest. "My brother," he called him.

Jean Valjean was astounded at such treatment. It was the first time in nine-teen years he had slept in a bed. In the middle of the night he awoke and thought of his past life. He had come of a poor rustic family at Brie, and had not been taught even to read. In child-hood he was left an orphan, and in pov-erty. He worked hard to keep himself and his younger brothers and sisters from starvation. One day, in utter despera-tion, he snatched a loaf of bread from a baker's shop. For that he was sent to the galleys for five years! He tried to escape, and got three years more. Again he tried to escape, and got five more. Two more attempts, with penalties, made the total nineteen years. Now he was out at last, an embittered enemy of society.

Before daylight he rose, put the silver plate of the bishop's table in a bag, and stole away! At breakfast time he was caught by the police and brought back. The good bishop told the police they had made a mistake.

"I suppose," took up the bishop, smil-ing, "that he told you that it was given him by a good old priest in whose house he passed the night? I can see what occurred. And you brought him back to verify? You made a mistake."

"Does your lordship mean that we are to let him go?" asked the corporal.

"Of course," replied the bishop.

They went away.

The felon seemed about to swoon as the bishop approached him and said to him in an undertone:

"Jean Valjean, my brother, you no longer belong to evil, but unto good. It is your soul that I have bought; I redeem it from black thoughts and the Spirit of Perdition, and I offer it to God."

A few weeks later a stranger entered the town of Montreuil and opened a shop for the manufacture of black glass jewelry. He had invented an improved method, by means of which he greatly prospered. When he began he had only a few hundred francs. In a few years he counted them by hundreds of thousands, and was the head of great manufacturing enterprises. He was a benevolent, thoughtful man, who was known as Father Madeleine. The government appointed him Mayor. He declined. It made him a Knight of the Legion of Honor. He declined it. A second time it made him Mayor, and now he reluctantly accepted that he might do more good to the town than he otherwise could. One day news came of the death of Bishop Myriel. Thereupon M. Madeleine put crape upon his hat.

All men loved and respected M. Madeleine but one, who suspected him. This was one Javert, a police inspector. He was a man possessed of only two dominant ideas, respect for authority and hate for rebellion. In his sight there could be no forgiveness for any crime. He suspected M. Madeleine of having been a convict, and watched him to detect him.

To M. Madeleine's factories there came Fantine, a young woman who had been betrayed and deserted by a young student. She sought to earn an honest living and redeem her life. Her infant child, Cosette, she had left with a family named Thenardier, in a distant town. Her beauty made her fellow-workers jealous. They pried into her business, found that she had a child, and raised a scandal about her. In shame and confusion she left the factory. Nowhere else could she obtain employment. Driven to despair, for money to support Cosette she sold her clothes, then her hair, then two of her teeth! At last she became a woman of the town, selling herself for her child's sake. One night a stranger brutally assaulted her on the street. She turned upon him, and was arrested, and condemned by Javert to the workhouse. M. Madeleine interfered and set her at liberty. She was ill, and he sent her to a hospital to be cared for tenderly.

One day Javert came to M. Madeleine and told him a man who called himself Champmathieu had been arrested, charged with being Jean Valjean, and with having committed a theft since his release from the galleys. This profoundly affected M. Madeleine, in whom, of course, we have already recognized the real Jean Valjean.

After a hard mental struggle, M. Madeleine hastened to Arras, where Champmathieu was being tried. He entered the court, and was received with all honor as the Mayor of Montreuil. He found Champmathieu about to be convicted; intervened, and denounced himself as the real Jean Valjean.

"Gentlemen of the jury, you will have to release the prisoner, if you please. My lord the judge, order me to be taken into custody. The man whom you are seeking for is here, not there—I am Jean Valjean."

Not a voice, not a hand was raised to stay him as he proceeded towards the exit. All drew aside. Something divine

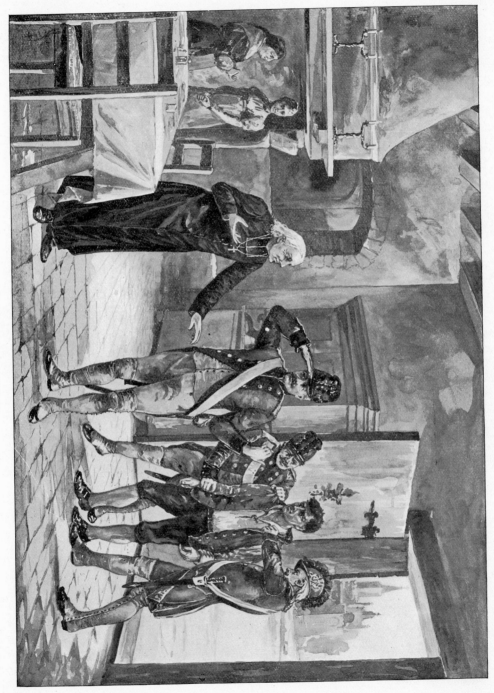

JEAN VALJEAN

made the multitude stand back, and form a line before that single man. He went through the crowd with a slow step. None knew who opened the doors, but they were wide open when he came up to them.

He went forth, and the doors closed as they had opened, for those who do sovereign acts are sure to be forwarded by their fellow-men in the mob.

Less than an hour subsequently, the verdict discharged Champmathieu as free from all fault.

M. Madeleine returned to Montreuil and found Fantine dying. As he was at her bedside, Javert entered to arrest him. In terror at Javert's approach, Fantine screamed aloud, and fell back dead.

Valjean arranged her head on the pillow as a mother does a child's, drew the string of her night-dress close, and enclosed her locks with her cap. One of her hands dropped over the bedside. He knelt to it, lifted it softly and kissed it. Then he drew himself up and turned to Javert, saying :

"Now, I am your man."

Javert lodged Valjean in the town jail.

But that night Valjean broke the bars of his window and escaped. He fled to the rooms occupied by Sister Simplice, a nun of renowned purity and truthfulness, and concealed himself in a closet. Sister Simplice fell on her knees and engaged in prayer. The door opened and Javert entered.

It was this Sister Simplice who had never told a lie in her life ; Javert knew this and venerated her on account of it.

"Sister, are you alone here? " he demanded.

Lifting her eyes the nun said :

" I am."

22

Oh, holy maid ! may this falsehood be recorded in paradise !

An hour after, a man, walking through fog and among the trees, rapidly left Montreuil in the direction of Paris. This was Jean Valjean.

A little later Jean Valjean was rearrested in Paris, tried, sentenced to death, and then the sentence commuted to life imprisonment in the galleys. He had not been there long, when, by almost superhuman exertion he saved the life of a sailor ; then himself fell into the sea and was apparently drowned. He was recorded as dead. But he made his escape, and was soon back near his old home, in quest of Fantine's child, whom he had promised to care for.

He found her at Thenardier's in rags and poverty, brutally treated as a slave. By the offer of a large sum of money he got them to surrender her to him, and took her with him to Paris. He called her his grandchild—she was yet scarcely out of infancy—and lodged with her for a time in a ramshackle old house in the slums, known as the Gorbeau House, thinking they would be safe from detection. But Javert was on his track and found him there. So Valjean and Cosette fled at night ; were pursued by Javert and the police ; by a desperate struggle got over a wall just in time, and hid themselves in a garden. It was the garden of a convent. The gardener, the only man there, proved to be a man whom Valjean, while Mayor of Montreuil, had befriended. He gave them shelter, and got Valjean engaged as his assistant, and Cosette taken in as a scholar in the convent school. In that safe retreat a life of peace and happiness began, and lasted for some years.

M. Marius, or, in full, Marius Pont-mercy, was the son of a Bonapartist officer who had fallen at Waterloo. Because he revered his father's memory, he was repudiated by the rest of the family, who were staunch Royalists. Thus cast out to make his own way, he found himself in poverty, and came to lodge in the old Gorbean House. In his daily walks in the Luxemborg Gardens, he presently began to notice an elderly man of kindly and stalwart appearance, accompanied by a young girl. For a year he saw them frequently, and the girl was then growing toward womanhood, and was ravishingly beautiful. In fine, he found himself in love with her, and she seemed not indifferent to him, though no word had passed between them.

Then Valjean and Cosette—for it was they—took alarm. Valjean even imagined Marius to be a police spy, on their track. So one day they were missing from the garden, and Marius saw them no more, nor could he find them, though he searched and watched for them long and earnestly.

In a room adjoining Marius's in the old house lived the Thenardiers, now in abject poverty, and calling themselves Jondrette. They devoted themselves to begging and crime, especially to wheedling charity out of rich people by false pretences. One day Marius, made suspicious by strange noises, spied upon them through a crevice in the wall. He saw Valjean and Cosette come in and give them alms, having been decoyed thither by a begging letter. When they went away, Valjean promised to return in the evening, with money for their relief. Thereupon they called in a gang of four desperadoes, to rob him. Marius quickly hurried off to the police, and gave information of what he had seen and heard.

Evening came. Valjean came. While he was solicitously inquiring after the needs of the beggars, four cut-throats entered, and after a desperate struggle bound him fast. Then Jondrette, or Thenardier, made him write a note to Cosette, asking her to come to him. Valjean did so, and Thenardier's wife went off with it to fetch her; and came back in an hour to report that she had been sent to a false address. Valjean had done this to gain time, during which he had secretly loosened his bonds and freed himself. The ruffians were for a moment doubtful what to do. Then, to their consternation, the door opened, and Javert entered! A platoon of police followed. The cut-throats were quickly pinioned. Then Javert turned to see the man who was to have been their victim, only to find that he had disappeared.

So again Marius lost all track of his idol, for a weary time. But at last he found her, in the garden of the quiet home where she and her guardian lived in seclusion. He made bold to speak to her, to remind her of his long adoration, to tell her of his love for her. With her eyes she confessed her love for him. Then their lips met, and they were happy.

It was for only a moment. The next, and the two fugitives were again driven to flight, and Marius was left disconsolate. He sought the grandfather who had repudiated him, begged for forgiveness and for aid that he might marry Cosette. The old man refused. Then Marius flung himself into a revolt in the streets of Paris and sought death at the barricades, but in vain. Thenardier's oldest daughter, disguised as a man, fell at his side, but he was unharmed. Then he wrote a farewell note to Cosette, telling her he must surely die in the next day's attack upon the barricade, and sent it to her by the hand of Gavroche, a street gamin. Gavroche delivered it, came back, and was killed in the fight. Valjean also came, and fought by the side of Marius. Javert had been taken prisoner, and doomed to death, and Valjean was appointed his executioner. Instead of killing him, he set him at liberty.

"I would rather you killed me!" said Javert.

At last the barricade was taken. But Valjean, carrying the wounded and unconscious Marius in his arms, escaped, descended into the sewers for a hiding place from the relentless Javert, who was again on his track, and finally reached an open place on the river-bank, where he imagined himself secure.

Then he turned and beheld Javert at his heels. He was so covered with dirt that Javert did not recognize him, but asked "Who are you?"

"I am Jean Valjean!"

"What are you doing here? Who is this man?"

He did not speak with his former contempt and rudeness.

"It was about him that I was going to speak," said Valjean, his peculiar tone seeming to arouse Javert. "Dispose of me as you please, but help me to have him taken home. That is all I beg of you."

Javert called a cab-driver. They found in Marius's pocket the address of his grandfather, M. Gillenormand, and took him thither, leaving him there almost dead. Then Valjean asked Javert another favor, that he might revisit his own home for a few minutes. Javert assented, and when they reached the house, said, "Go in; I will wait here." But when Valjean returned the street was deserted. Javert had disappeared.

The police inspector walked away, slowly and half-dazed, to one of the bridges of the Seine. He was astounded by one thing, that Valjean should forgive him, and another petrified him, that he should pardon the convict.

What was he to do now? To liberate Valjean was bad, and so to leave him free. In the first case, the officer of authority fell lower than the galleyslave; in the second, a jail-bird soared higher than the trained hawk and struck his talons into him. In both cases, dishonor to Javert. There was a fall in any course he chose.

He suffered the strange pains of a conscience suddenly cured of dim vision. He saw what it was repugnant for him to see. He felt vacant, useless, wrenched from his former lines, diverted, discharged. For his authority was dead. There was no reason for him to exist.

All at once he took off his hat and laid it on the flags this side of the balustrade.

In the moment after, a tall, black figure, which might be taken by the beholder at a distance as a shade, appeared standing on the parapet, bent toward the Seine, then rose and fell straight into the shadows; a dull splash was heard, the night alone was in the secret of the spasms of the obscurely struggling form disappearing under the surge.

For a long time Marius lay near death. Then convalescence set in. His grandfather became perfectly reconciled with him, loved him enthusiastically; then one day enraptured him with the announcement that he would consent to his marriage.

"Yes; you shall have your pretty little loved one," continued the old gentleman. "She has been calling every day, in the form of an old gentleman, eager to have the latest news of you. Since you were shot down, she has been spending her time weeping her eyes out and scraping lint for you. I have inquired about it. She lives in Homme-armée Street, at No. 7. Ha! ha! d'ye see the point we are at? You long for her? It shall not be for long! You shall have her."

So in due time Marius and Cosette were married, and installed in the best rooms of the Gillenormand mansion.

Valjean endowed Cosette with a fortune of 600,000 francs. But under a pretext of illness did not attend the wedding, and after it went to live alone in his old home.

Then, after a desperate battle with himself, he told Marius who he was—an ex-convict, now liable to be sent back to the galleys. Marius recoiled from him in horror. But it was finally agreed that Valjean should come every day, if he wished, to call on Cosette, and that the secret should be inviolably kept. Marius supposed that Valjean had murdered "M. Madeleine" and stolen his fortune, and had also killed Javert, and he accordingly regarded him with loathing, and thought of returning to him all the fortune with which he had endowed Cosette.

But one day Thenardier called upon him, to demand money for telling him a great secret about Valjean. Marius scornfully told him he knew it all, already. Then, in his confusion, Thenardier blurted out the truth, that Valjean had not murdered "M. Madeleine," but was himself identical with him, and had not killed Javert, who had been found drowned. Marius could not restrain a cry of delight.

"Well, then, this wretch is an admirable man! That fortune was truly his! He is Madeleine, the saver of the country—its providence! He is Javert's deliverer! He is a hero—a saint!"

Forthwith Marius and Cosette hastened to Valjean, to atone with their love for all the doubts and ill-feelings Marius had cherished. They found him ill, indeed dying. Marius told him all he had learned, and begged forgiveness for his doubts. Valjean, happy in their perfect confidence and love, took them to his heart and blessed them.

"I am dying happy," he said. "Let me lay my hands on your beloved heads—"

Cosette and Marius fell on their knees, suffocated with tears, and on each guided a hand of Valjean's. Those august hands did not move again.

He had thrown his head back, and the lustre from the two candles, illumined it; the white face was upturned to the heavens. He let them cover his hands with kisses. He was dead.

DON QUIXOTE CHARGING THE WINDMILL

# DON QUIXOTE.

## By Miguel de Cervantes.

THE FIRST ADVENTURE—THE WINDMILLS—MAMBRINO'S HELMET—DULCINEA
DEL TOBOSO—THE KNIGHT OF THE WOODS—MONTESINOS' CAVE
—THE COUNTESS OF TRIFALDI—SANCHO AND HIS
ISLAND—THE ENCHANTED HEAD—THE END
OF THE KNIGHT'S CAREER.

IN a certain village of La Mancha there lived in former years an old-fashioned gentleman who was much given to poring over books of romance and reading the doings of knights in the days of chivalry. His name was Quixada, which signifies Lantern-Jaws. His whole household consisted of a housekeeper of about forty years, a niece of twenty, and a man of all work. He was a worthy man, but he read these romances by day and night until they seemed as true to him as the most authentic history, and until he resolved himself to enter upon the career of a knight-errant, in emulation of Amadis de Gaul.

So he scoured up an old suit of armor that had belonged to his great-grandfather, filling out a lacking part of the helmet with pasteboard and bits of iron. Then he got his old horse out of the stable, an ancient rack of skin and bones, and gave him the name of Rozinante, from Rozin, a common pack-horse, and ante, before. He began to call himself Don Quixote de la Mancha. Finally, since every knight must have a lady in whose name to fight, he selected a young peasant girl of that neighborhood, named Aldonza Lorenzo, and called her the Lady Dulcinea del Toboso.

Thus prepared for a chivalric career, he set forth and traveled all day without meeting with any adventure.

Toward the evening he and his horse being heartily tired and almost famished, Don Quixote looked about him, in hopes to discover some castle, or at least some shepherd's cottage, there to repose and refresh himself ; and at last, near the road which he kept, he espied an inn, a most welcome sight to his longing eyes. Hastening toward it with all the speed he could, he got thither just at the close of the evening. There stood by chance at the inn-door two young female adventurers, who were going to Seville with some carriers that happened to take up their lodgings there that very evening ; and as whatever our knight-errant saw, thought, or imagined was all of a romantic cast, and appeared to him altogether after the manner of his favorite books, he no sooner saw the inn but he fancied it to be a castle fenced with four towers, and lofty pinnacles glittering with silver, together with a deep moat, drawbridge, and all those other appurtenances peculiar to such kind of places.

When he came near it he stopped awhile at a distance from the gate, expecting that some dwarf would appear on the battlements and sound his trumpet to give notice of the arrival of a knight; but finding that nobody came, and that Rozinante was for making the best of his way to the stable, he advanced to the inn-door, saw there the two country girls, who appeared to him to be beautiful damsels or lovely dames taking their pleasure at the castle-gate.

It happened just at this time that a swineherd, who in a stubble hard by was tending a drove of hogs, blew his horn, as was his custom, to call them together; and instantly Don Quixote's imagination represented to him that a dwarf gave the signal of his arrival. With great satisfaction, therefore, he rode up to the inn. The women, perceiving a man armed with lance and buckler, were frightened, and about to retreat into the house. But Don Quixote, guessing at their fear by their flight, lifted up his pasteboard visor, and discovering his withered and dusty visage, with gentle voice and respectful demeanor thus accosted them:

"Fly not, ladies, nor fear any discourtesy; for the order of knighthood, which I profess, forbids my offering injury to any one, much less to damsels of such exalted rank as your presence denotes you to be." The women stared at him with all their eyes, endeavoring to find out his face, which the sorry beaver almost covered, and could not help laughing so loudly that Don Quixote was offended, and said to them, "Modesty is becoming in beauty, and excessive laughter, proceeding from a slight cause, is folly. This I mention not as a reproach, by which I may incur your resentment; on the contrary, I have no wish but to do you service."

This language, which they did not understand, and the extraordinary appearance of the knight, increased their laughter, which also increased his displeasure, and he would probably have shown it in a less civil way but for the timely arrival of the innkeeper. He was a man whose burden of fat inclined him to peace and quietness, yet when he observed such a strange disguise of human shape in his old armor and equipage, he could hardly forbear laughter; but, having fear of such a war-like appearance before his eyes, he resolved to give him good words, and therefore accosted him civilly.

"Sir Knight," he said, "if your worship be disposed to alight, you will fail of nothing here but of a bed; as for all other accommodations, you may be supplied to your mind."

So they took the would-be knight in and entertained him well, and in turn his curious ways gave them much entertainment in return. It was a source of great mirth to see him eat; for his hands being occupied in keeping his helmet on and the beaver up, he had no means of feeding himself, and the office was performed by one of the ladies. To give him drink would have been utterly impossible, had not the innkeeper bored a reed, and, putting one end to the knight's mouth, poured in the wine leisurely at the other; but all this Don Quixote patiently endured rather than cut the lacings of his helmet. While he was at supper a pig-driver happened to sound his cane-trumpet, or whistle of reeds, four or five times as he came near the inn, which made Don Quixote the more positive that he was in a famous castle, where he was entertained with music at supper, that the country girls were great ladies, and the innkeeper the governor of the castle, which made him applaud himself for his resolution, and his setting out on such an account.

A few days later, as the knight, now attended by his faithful man of all work, Sancho Panza, whom he had made his squire, he discovered some thirty or forty windmills in the plain ; and as soon as the knight had spied them, "Fortune," cried he, " directs our affairs better than we could have wished ; look yonder, Sancho, there are at least thirty outrageous giants, whom I intend to encounter ; and having deprived them of life, we will begin to enrich ourselves with their spoils ; for they are lawful prize ; and the extirpation of that cursed brood will be an acceptable service to heaven."

"What giants ? " quoth Sancho Panza.

"Those whom thou seest yonder," answered Don Quixote, "with their long extended arms ; some of that detested race have arms of so immense a size that sometimes they reach two leagues in length."

"Pray, look better, sir," quoth Sancho; " those things yonder are not giants, but windmills, and the arms are their sails, which, being whirled about by the wind, make the mill go."

"'Tis a sign," cried Don Quixote, "thou art but little acquainted with adventures ! I tell thee they are giants ; and therefore if thou art afraid, go aside and say thy prayers, for I am resolved to engage in combat with them all."

This said, he clapped spurs to his horse without giving ear to his squire, who bawled out to him, and assured him that they were windmills, and not giants. But he was so fully possessed with a strong conceit of the contrary that he did not so much as hear his squire, nor was he sensible of what they were, although he was already very near them.

"Stand, cowards ! " cried he as loud as he could ; " stand your ground, ignoble creatures, and fly not basely from a single knight, who dares encounter you all."

At the same time, the wind rising, the mill-sails began to move, which, when Don Quixote spied, "Base miscreants," cried he, "though you move more arms than the giant Briareus, you shall pay for you arrogance."

He most devoutly recommended himself to his Lady Dulcinea, imploring her assistance in this perilous adventure ; and so, covering himself with his shield and couching his lance, he rushed with Rozinante's utmost speed upon the first windmill he could come at, and running his lance into the sail, the wind whirled it about with such swiftness that the rapidity of the motion presently broke the lance into shivers, and hurled away both knight and horse along with it, till down he fell, rolling a good way off in the field. Sancho Panza ran as fast as his ass could drive to help his master, whom he found lying, and not able to stir.

"Did not I give your worship fair warning ? " cried he ; " did not I tell you they were windmills, and that nobody could think otherwise, unless he had also windmills in his head ? "

"Peace, friend Sancho," replied Don Quixote ; "there is nothing so subject to the inconstancy of fortune as war. I am verily persuaded that cursed necromancer Freston, who carried away my study and my books, has transformed these giants into windmills, to deprive me of the honor of the victory: such is his inveterate malice against me: but in the end, all his pernicious wiles and stratagems shall prove ineffectual against the prevailing edge of my sword."

"So let it be," replied Sancho.

The knight's fancy now began to run altogether on finding his lady, Dulcinea del Toboso, and Sancho determined to try to persuade him that the next peasant girl they might meet was she. So presently, while riding a little ahead of his master, he espied three country girls coming toward him, each mounted on a young ass. He hastened back, and exclaimed in joy:

"Your worship has only to clap spurs to Rozinante, and get out upon the plain to see the lady Dulcinea del Toboso, who, with a couple of her damsels, is coming to pay your worship a visit."

"Gracious Heavens!" exclaimed Don Quixote, "what dost thou say? Take care that thou beguilest not my real sorrow by a counterfeit joy."

"What should I get," answered Sancho, "by deceiving you worship, only to be found out the next moment? Come, sir, put on, and you will see the princess, our mistress, all arrayed and adorned— in short, like herself. She and her damsels are one blaze of flaming gold; all strings of pearls, all diamonds, all rubies, all cloth of tissue above ten hands deep; their hair loose about their shoulders, like so many sunbeams blowing about in the wind; and, what is more, they come mounted upon three pied belfreys, the finest you ever laid eyes on."

"Palfreys, thou wouldst say, Sancho," quoth Don Quixote.

"Well, well," answered Sancho, "belfreys and palfreys are much the same thing; but let them be mounted how they will, they are sure the finest creatures one would wish to see, especially my mistress the princess, Dulcinea, who dazzles one's senses."

"Let us go, son Sancho," answered Don Quixote; "and, as a reward for this welcome news, I bequeath to thee the choicest spoils I shall gain in my next adventure."

They were now got out of the wood, and saw the three girls very near. Don Quixote looked eagerly along the road toward Toboso, and seeing nobody but the three girls, he asked Sancho, in much agitation, whether they were out of the city when he left them.

"Out of the city!" answered Sancho; "are your worship's eyes in the nape of your neck that you do not see them now before you, shining like the sun at noonday?"

"I see only three country girls," answered Don Quixote, "on three asses."

"Now keep me from mischief!" answered Sancho; "is it possible that three belfreys, or how do you call them, white as the driven snow, should look to you like asses? As I am alive, you shall pluck off this beard of mine if it be so."

"I tell thee, friend Sancho," answered Don Quixote, "that it is as certain they are asses, as that I am Don Quixote and thou Sancho Panza; at least so they seem to me."

"Sir," quoth Sancho, "say not such a thing; but snuff those eyes of yours, and come and pay reverence to the mistress of your soul."

So saying he advanced forward to meet the peasant girls; and, alighting from Dapple, he laid hold of one of their asses by the halter and, bending both knees to the ground, said to the girl, "Queen, princess and duchess of beauty, let your haughtiness and greatness be pleased to receive into your grace and good-liking your captive knight, who stands there turned into stone, all disorder and without any pulse, to find himself before your magnificent presence. I am Sancho Panza, his squire, and he is that wayworn knight Don Quixote de la Mancha, otherwise called the Knight of the Rueful Countenance."

Don Quixote had now placed himself on his knees by Sancho, and with wild and staring eyes surveyed her whom Sancho called his queen, and seeing nothing but a peasant girl, with a broad face, flat nose, coarse and homely, he was so confounded that he could not open his lips. The girls were also surprised to find themselves stopped by two men so different in aspect, and both on their knees; but the lady who was stopped, breaking silence, said in an angry tone, "Get out of the road, plague on ye!" and let us pass by, for we are in haste."

"O princess and universal lady of Toboso!" cried Sancho, "is not your magnificent heart melting to see, on his knees before your sublimated presence, the pillar and prop of knight-errantry?"

"Haydey! what's here to do?" cried another of the girls; "look how your small gentry come to jeer us poor country girls as if we could not give them as good as they bring. Go, get off about your business, and let us mind ours, and so speed you well."

So the girls hastened on their way, leaving the knight disconsolate, for he was now persuaded that he was bewitched and thus prevented from seeing his lady in her own proper shape.

Not long after this they fell upon a strange knight in a great wood who was sighing over his love for his lady, Casildea. Don Quixote engaged him for a time in pleasant converse, but soon the Knight of the Woods assumed a boastful tone.

"I have," he said, "traversed the greatest part of Spain, and have vanquished divers knights who have had the presumption to contradict me. But what I value myself most upon is having vanquished, in single combat, that renowned knight Don Quixote de la Mancha, and made him confess that my Casildea is more beautiful than his Dulcinea; and I reckon that, in this conquest alone, I have vanquished all the knights in the world; for this Don Quixote has conquered them all, and I, having overcome him, his glory, his fame, and his honor are consequently transferred to me. All the innumerable exploits of the said Don Quixote I therefore consider as already mine, and placed to my account."

Don Quixote was amazed at the assertions of the Knight of the Wood, and had been every moment at the point of giving him the lie; but he restrained himself, that he might convict him of falsehood from his own mouth; and therefore, he said very calmly, "That you may have vanquished, Sir Knight, most of the knights-errant of Spain, or even of the whole world, I will not dispute; but that you have conquered Don Quixote de la Mancha I have much reason to doubt. Some one resembling him, I allow, it might have been; though, in truth, I believe there are not many like him."

"How say you?" cried he of the Wood; "as sure as I am here alone, I fought with Don Quixote, vanquished him, and made him surrender to me! He is a man of an erect figure, withered face, long and meagre limbs, grizzle-haired, hawk-nose, with large black moustachios, and styles himself the Knight of the Rueful Countenance. The name of his squire is Sancho Panza; he oppresses the back and governs the reins of a famous steed called Rozinante—in a word the mistress of his thoughts is one Dulcinea del Toboso, formerly called Aldonza Lorenzo, as my Casildea, being of Andalusia, is now distinguished by the name of Casildea de Vandalia. And now, if I have not sufficiently proved what I have said, here is my sword, which shall make incredulity itself believe."

"Softly, Sir Knight," said Don Quixote, "and hear what I have to say. You must know that this Don Quixote you speak of is the dearest friend I have in the world, insomuch that he is, as it were, another self; and notwithstanding the very accurate description you have given of him, I am convinced, by the evidence of my senses, that you have never subdued him. It is, indeed, possible that, as he is continually persecuted by enchanters, some one of these may have assumed his shape, and suffered himself to be vanquished, in order to defraud him of the fame which his exalted feats of chivalry have acquired him over the whole face of the earth. A proof of their malice occurred but a few days since,

when they transformed the figure and face of the beautiful Dulcinea del Toboso into the form of a mean rustic wench. And now if, after all, you doubt the truth of what I say, behold the true Don Quixote himself before you, ready to convince you of your error by force of arms, on foot or on horseback, or in whatever manner you please."

He then rose up, and grasping his sword, awaited the determination of the Knight of the Wood, who very calmly said in reply, "A good paymaster wants no pledge: he who could vanquish Signor Don Quixote under transformation may well hope to make him yield in his proper person. But as knights-errant should by no means perform their feats in the dark, like robbers and ruffians, let us wait for daylight, that the sun may witness our exploits; and let the condition of our combat be, that the conquered shall remain entirely at the mercy and disposal of the conqueror; provided that he require nothing of him but what a knight may with honor submit to."

When the morning was come Don Quixote perceived his opponent to be clad in armor set all over with mirrors, whence he was properly to be called the Knight of the Mirrors. They met in battle, and Don Quixote quickly overthrew his opponent, and would have slain him had not the latter revealed himself as one of his old friends and neighbors, who had played this trick upon him in hope of curing him of his folly. Don Quixote then let him go, and pursued his own way as before.

Don Quixote one day placed himself under the guidance of a young student who promised to show him the wonders of the famous cave of Montesinos.

Sancho tried in vain to dissuade him from entering so dangerous a place. The knight had himself bound to the end of a stout rope and lowered into the cave, which was a dreadful black abyss. After half an hour they pulled him up again, and found him fast asleep. With much difficulty they awakened him, whereupon he complained that they had disturbed him in the most delightful life man ever led, which he now perceived to have been only a dream.

"About twelve or fourteen men's depths," said he, "in the profundity of this cavern, on the right hand, there is a concavity wide enough to contain a large wagon, mules and all. I entered, and coiling up the cord, sat upon it very melancholy, and thinking how I should most conveniently get down to the bottom, having nobody to guide or support me. While I thus sat pensive, and lost in thought, insensibly, without any previous drowsiness, I found myself surprised by sleep; and after that, not knowing how nor which way I wakened, I unexpectedly found myself in the finest and most delightful meadow that ever nature adorned with her beauties, or the most inventive fancy could ever imagine. Now, that I might be sure this was neither a dream nor an illusion, I rubbed my eyes, felt several parts of my body, and convinced myself that I was really awake with the use of all my senses, and all the faculties of my understanding sound and active as at this moment.

"Presently I discovered a sumptuous palace, of which the wall seemed all of transparent crystal. The spacious gates opening, there came out toward me a venerable old man, clad in a sad-colored robe, so long that it swept the ground; on his breast and shoulders he had a green satin tippet, after the manner of those worn in colleges. On his head he wore a black Milan cap, and his broad hoary beard reached down below his middle. He had no kind of weapon in his hands, but a rosary of beads about the bigness of walnuts, and his credo beads appeared as large as ordinary ostrich-eggs. The awful and grave aspect, the pace, the port and goodly presence of this old man, each of them apart, and much more altogether, struck me with veneration and astonishment. He came up to me, and, without any previous ceremony, embracing me close, 'It is a long time,' said he, 'most renowned knight, Don Quixote de la Mancha, that we who dwell in this enchanted solitude have hoped to see you here; that you may inform the upper world of the surprising prodigies concealed from human knowledge in this subterranean hollow, called the cave of Montesinos—an enterprise reserved alone for your insuperable heart and stupendous resolution. Go with me, then, thou most illustrious knight, and behold the wonders inclosed within the transparent castle, of which I am the perpetual governor and chief warden, being the same individual Montesinos from whom this cavern took its name.'

"No sooner had the reverend old man let me know who he was, but I entreated him to tell me whether it was true or no, that, at his friend Durandarte's dying request, he had taken out his heart with a small dagger, the very moment he expired, and carried it to his mistress Belerma, as the story was current in the world.

"'It is literally true,' answered the old gentleman, 'except that single circumstance of the dagger; for I used neither a small nor a large dagger on this occasion, but a well-polished poniard, as sharp as an awl.'

"The venerable Montesinos having conducted me into the crystal palace, led me into a spacious ground-room, exceeding cool, and all of alabaster. In the middle of it stood a marble tomb, that seemed a masterpiece of art; upon it lay a knight extended all at length, not of stone or brass, as on other monuments, but pure flesh and bones; he covered the region of his heart with his right hand, which seemed to me very full of sinews, a sign of the great strength of the body to which it belonged. Montesinos, observing that I viewed the spectacle with surprise, 'Behold,' said he, 'the flower and mirror of all the living and valiant knights of his age, my friend Durandarte, who, together with me and many others, of both sexes, are kept here enchanted by Merlin, the British magician. Here, I say, we are enchanted; but how and for what cause no man can tell, though time, I hope, will shortly reveal it. But the most wonderful part of my fortune is this: I am as certain as that the sun now shines that Durandarte died in my arms; and that with these hands I took out his heart, which weighed above two pounds, a sure mark of his courage; for, by the rules of natural philosophy, the most valiant men have still the biggest hearts. Nevertheless, though this knight really died, he still complains and sighs sometimes as if he were alive.'

"Scarce had Montesinos spoke these words, but the miserable Durandarte cried out aloud, 'O! cousin Montesinos, the last and dying request of your departing friend was to take my heart out of my breast with a poniard or a dagger, and carry it to Belerma.' The venerable Montesinos, hearing this, fell on his knees before the afflicted knight, and with tears in his eyes, 'Long, long ago,' said he, 'Durandarte, thou dearest of my kinsmen, have I performed what you enjoined me on that bitter fatal day when you expired. I took out your heart with all imaginable care, and hasted away with it to France, as soon as I had committed your dear remains to the bosom of the earth. To confirm this truth yet further, at the first place where I stopped from Roncesvalles, I laid a little salt upon your heart, to preserve it, till I presented it into the hands of Belerma, who, with you and me, and Guadiana your squire, as also Ruydera (the lady's woman) with her seven daughters, her two nieces, and many others of your friends and acquaintance, is here confined by the necromantic charms of the magician Merlin; and though it be now above five hundred years since we were first conveyed into this enchanted castle we are still alive, except Ruydera, her daughters and nieces, who by the favor of Merlin, that pitied their tears, were turned into so many lakes, still extant in the world of the living, and in the province of La Mancha, distinguished by the name of the lakes of Ruydera. But now I have other news to tell you, which, though perhaps it may not assuage your sorrows, yet I am sure it will not increase them. Open your eyes, and behold in your presence that mighty knight, of whom Merlin the sage has foretold so many wonders: that Don Quixote de la Mancha, I mean, who has

SANCHO PANZA IN THE HALL OF THE DUCHESS

not only restored to the world the function of knight-errantry, that has lain so long in oblivion, but advanced it to greater fame that it could boast in any former age. It is by his power that we may expect to see the charm dissolved, which keeps us here confined; for great performances are properly reserved for great personages.'

"'And should it not be so?' answered the grieving Durandarte, with a faint and languishing voice; 'should it not be so, I say? Oh, cousin! patience, and shuffle the cards.'

"Then turning on one side, without speaking a word more, he relapsed into his usual silence.

"After this I was alarmed with piteous howling and crying, which, mixed with lamentable sighs and groans, obliged me to turn about to see whence it proceeded. Then through the crystal wall I saw a mournful procession of most beautiful damsels, all in black, marching in two ranks, with turbans on their heads after the Turkish fashion; and last of all came a majestic lady, dressed also in mourning, with a long white veil that reached from her head down to the ground. Montesinos informed me that the procession consisted of Durandarte's and Belerma's servants, who were enchanted there with their master and mistress; but that the last was Belerma herself, who with her attendants used four days in the week constantly thus to sing their dirges over the heart and body of his cousin; and that though Belerma appeared a little haggard at that juncture, occasioned by the grief she bore in her own heart, for that which she carried in her hand; yet had I seen her before her misfortunes had sunk her eyes and tarnished her complexion, I must have owned that even the celebrated Dulcinea del Toboso, so famous in La Mancha, and over the whole universe, could scarce have vied with her in gracefulness and beauty.

"'Hold there, good Signor Montesinos, said I. 'You know that comparisons are odious, therefore no more comparing, I beseech you; but go on with your story. The peerless Dulcinea del Toboso is what she is, and the Lady Belerma is what she is, and has been; so no more upon that subject.'

"'I beg your pardon,' answered Montesinos; 'Signor Don Quixote, I might have guessed you were the Lady Dulcinea's knight, and therefore I ought to have bit my tongue off sooner than to have compared her to anything lower than heaven itself.'

"This satisfaction, which I thought sufficient from the great Montesinos, stifled the resentment I else had shown, for hearing my mistress compared to Belerma."

"Nay, marry," quoth Sancho, "I wonder you did not give the old fellow a hearty kicking! How could you leave one hair on his chin?"

"No, no, Sancho," answered Don Quixote, "there is always a respect due to our seniors, though they be no knights; but most when they are such, and under the oppression of enchantment. However, I am satisfied that in what discourse passed between us, I took care not to have anything that looked like an affront fixed upon me."

"But, sir," asked the scholar, "how could you see and hear so many strange things in so little time? I cannot conceive how you could do it."

"How long," said Don Quixote, "do you reckon that I have been in the cave?"

"A little above an hour," answered Sancho.

"That is impossible," said Don Quixote, "for I saw morning and evening, and evening and morning, three times since; so that I could not be absent less than three days from this upper world."

"Ay, ay," quoth Sancho, "my master is in the right; for these enchantments, that have the greatest share in all his concerns, may make that seem three days and three nights to him which is but an hour to other people."

"It must be so," said Don Quixote.

"I hope, sir," said the scholar, "you have eaten something in all that time."

"Not one morsel," replied Don Quixote; "neither have had the least desire to eat, or so much as thought of it all the while."

"Do not they that are enchanted sometimes eat?" asked the scholar.

"They never do," answered Don Quixote.

"Do they never sleep either?" said Sancho.

"Never," said Don Quixote; "at least they never closed their eyes while I was among them, nor I either."

"This makes good the saying," quoth Sancho, "'Tell me thy company, and I will tell thee what thou art.' Troth! you have all been enchanted together. No wonder if you neither eat nor slept, since you were in the land of those that always watch and fast. But, sir, would you have me speak as I think? and pray do not take it in ill part, for if I believe one word of all you have said—"

"What do you mean, friend?" said the student. "Do you think the noble Don Quixote would be guilty of a lie? and if he had a mind to stretch a little, could he, think you, have had leisure to frame such a number of stories in so short a time?"

"I do not think that my master would lie neither," said Sancho.

"What do ye think then, sir?" said Don Quixote.

"Well, truly, sir," quoth Sancho, "I do believe that this same cunning man, this Merlin, that bewitched or enchanted, as you call it, all that rabble of people you talk of, may have crammed and enchanted, some way or other, all that you have told us, and have yet to tell us, into your noddle."

Our worthy pair one day met at the palace of a duke a veiled lady who called herself the Countess Trifaldi, and who related a long story of grievances. She was in the power of a wicked magician, who had condemned her and her ladies to wear great beards upon their faces, and they were to be freed from the spell only by some gallant knight undertaking a journey to the distant land where the conjuror dwelt and overcoming him. This journey was to be accomplished on a magical horse, which would carry both the knight and his squire, and would fly through the air in obedience to their will. Don Quixote and Sancho mounted. The attendants forced air upon them from a great bellows, and thus persuaded the Don that he was flying through the air at a prodigious pace. Other shrewd devices increased the delusion, and as the knight never once looked down he was convinced that he had ridden thousands of miles through the air, though the image of a horse on which he sat did not really move an inch. At last the horse, which was filled with gas, was made to explode. The two riders were gently thrown to the ground, and then the knight was made to understand that his mission had succeeded through the mere attempt to carry it out.

The success of this trick mightily pleased the duke and duchess, and they resolved to try another upon the credulous pair. So they told Sancho he was to be made governor of a certain island, to which the duke would send him. The fat squire was much pleased at this, and was eager to depart.

Don Quixote gave Sancho much good advice about the manner in which he should administer the government of his island, and ended with saying :

"If, Sancho, thou wilt observe these precepts and rules thy days will be long, and thy fame eternal, thy recompense full, and thy felicity unspeakable. Thou shalt match thy children as it may please thee ; they and their children shall inherit titles ; thou shalt live in peace and in favor with all men : and at the end of thy life death shall find thee in a sweet and mature old age, and thy eyes shall be closed by the tender and pious hands of thy children's grandchildren."

After many other marvellous adventures the knight determined to become a shepherd and end his days in quiet pastoral pursuits. At this his old neighbors were rejoiced, for they hoped thus to see an end made of his romantic follies which were continually bringing him into danger of life and limb. But before he could carry his resolution into effect he fell ill with a fever. In spite of all the doctor could do he steadily failed and his end seemed near at hand. One day he awoke as if from a sound sleep and began to praise God.

The niece, hearkening very attentively to these words of her uncle, and finding more sense in them than there was in his usual talk, at least since he had fallen ill, "What do you say, sir ? " said she ; "has anything extraordinary happened ? What mercies are these you mention ?"

"Mercies, " answered he, "that Heaven has this moment vouchsafed to show me, in spite of all my iniquities. My judgment is returned, clear and undisturbed, and that cloud of ignorance is now removed which the continual reading of those books of knight-errantry had cast over my understanding. I am only sorry the discovery happens so late, when I want time to make amends by those studies that should enlighten my soul, and prepare me for futurity. I find, niece, my end approaches; but I would have it such, that though my life has got me the character of a madman, I may deserve a better at my death. I am no longer Don Quixote de la Mancha, but Alonzo Quixano, the same whom the world, for his fair behavior, had been formerly pleased to call The Good. I now declare myself an enemy to Amadis de Gaul, and his whole generation; all foolish stories of knight-errantry I detest. I have a true sense of the danger of reading them, and of all my past follies; and, through Heaven's mercy and my own experience, I abhor them."

Thus being at last freed from his follies and delusions he called for a clergyman and made his will, disposing of his estate in a sensible and proper fashion. He left the bulk of his property to his niece, but with this proviso:

"Item, It is my will, that if my niece Antonia Quixano be inclinable to marry, it be with none but a person who, upon strict inquiry, shall be found never to have read a book of knight-errantry in his life; and in case it appears that he has been conversant in such books, and that she persists in her resolution to marry him, she is then to forfeit all right and title to my bequest, which, in such case, my executors are hereby empowered to dispose of to pious uses, as they shall think most proper."

Having finished the will, he died in his bed quietly, and like a good Christian.

Thus died that ingenious gentleman, Don Quixote de la Mancha, whose native place Cid Hamet has not thought fit directly to mention, with design that all the towns and villages in La Mancha should contend for the honor of giving him birth, as the seven cities of Greece did for Homer.

# BOOK VIII.

---

## HISTORY OF THE WORLD.

BUILDING OF THE PYRAMIDS

# Book VIII.

# History of the World.

## CHAPTER I.

### BEFORE THE CHRISTIAN ERA.

ASSYRIA—MEDIA—BABYLON—ASIA MINOR—SYRIA—EGYPT—CARTHAGE—PERSIA—WAR
WITH GREECE—THE FALL OF PERSIA—EARLY GREECE—THE AGE OF PERICLES—
THE FALL OF GREECE—ALEXANDER THE GREAT—END OF THE MACE-
DONIAN EMPIRE—ORIGIN OF ROME—THE KINGS—THE REPUBLIC—
CORIOLANUS AND CINCINNATUS—THE GAULS—WAR
WITH CARTHAGE—DOMESTIC TROUBLES—
THE TRIUMVIRS—THE EMPIRE.

WHERE the human race was cradled, and where civilization had its origin, is a secret of the unknown past. Asia, Africa and Central America all have claims to the distinction. The consensus of accessible evidence, however, places the earliest organized society on the shores of the Eastern Mediterranean Sea and of the Persian Gulf. The earliest of the Asiatic Monarchies sprang up in the great plane at the head of the Persian Gulf. Here Moses places the first "kingdom," and a Chaldean Monarchy was established probably as early as 2000 B. C. The Hebrew records give Nimrod as the founder of this kingdom. There were forty-nine Chaldean monarchs, whose reigns covered the space of from about 2000 to 1543 B. C. They were the builders of the most ancient edifices now existing in that country, and their date was long before the time of Sennacherib and Nebuchadnezzar.

After the years had borne sway they were succeeded by Arabs, who held the dominion for 245 years, when they too were superseded by the Assyrians. These ruled for 526 years, and then the Chaldeans became free and independent again.

### Assyria.

The beginning of the Assyrian Empire is lost in the mists of antiquity. The first great king of whom much is known was Sardanapalus. He was a great conqueror, who fought many foreign wars in Armenia, Syria and Babylonia, received the submission of the chief Phœnican towns and built a great palace at Calah. Ivalush, about 800 B. C., was another warlike monarch. He conquered Damascus, and received tribute from Samaria, Philistia and Edom. Babylon also acknowledged his sovereignty. His wife bore the name of Semiramis. The closing era of the Assyrian monarchy was a splendid one, but came to a sudden end. Among its kings were Sargon, Sennacherib and the second Sardanapalus. Another was the second Tiglath-pileser, who is mentioned in the Bible. Distant expeditions were resumed and the arms of Assyria carried into new regions. Naval expeditions were undertaken in both the Mediterranean and the Persian Gulf. Cyprus was conquered and the Assyrian monarchs numbered Greeks among their subjects. Almost all the kings of this period came into contact with the Jews. But at last great hordes of Scythians invaded the Empire from the north and almost prostrated it. Before it could recover from this blow its old enemy, Media, fell upon it, and with the assistance of Babylon effected its downfall about 625 B. C.

## Media.

Little is known of the early history of Media. About the ninth century B. C. it was attacked by the Assyrians, and in the time of Sargon, about 710 B. C., it was partially conquered, and some of the Jews who had been taken captive by the Assyrians were settled in it. About 650 B. C. the Medes began to assume the aggressive against Assyria, and at the fall of Nineveh they shared with the Babylonians supreme power in the western Asia. The revolt of the Persians under Cyrus brought the Median Empire to an end in 558 B. C., but Media remained thereafter for many years the most important of the Persian provinces.

## Babylon.

After the conquest of Babylonia by the Assyrians, about 1250 B. C., an Assyrian dynasty was established at Babylon and the country was long subject to the Kings of Nineveh. Later Babylonia was not only an independent kingdom, but was the head of a great empire. At the fall of Nineveh it seized upon a large share of the spoils of the Assyrian Empire, taking the Euphrates Valley, Syria, Phœnicia and Palestine. A brilliant period followed. Attacked by Egypt, the Babylonians not only repelled the aggressor, but actually invaded the Egyptian Empire and inflicted severe blows upon it. The Babylonian Empire flourished until the rise of Cyrus, the Persian. At that time its ruler, Belshazzar, was a weak and effeminate prince, who neglected properly to defend his capital. Cyrus gained an easy victory and Babylon became a province of the Persian Empire.

## Asia Minor.

The most powerful state in Asia Minor in early times seems to have been Phrygia. Its people were brave but somewhat brutal. Its monarchs bore alternately the two names of Gordias and Midas. It was conquered and became a province of Lydia about 560 B. C. Cilicia was likewise the seat of a monarchy before the time of Cyrus, but became subject to Persia in the reign of Cambyses. Ultimately the most important of all the kingdoms of Asia Minor was Lydia. According to the accounts which Herodotus followed, a Lydian Kingdom existed from very ancient times. The last Lydian monarch, Crœsus, was conquered by Cyrus B. C. 554.

Phœnicia was one of the most important countries of the ancient world. In her the commercial spirit first showed itself as the dominant spirit of a nation. She was the carrier between the East and the West, in the ages before the first appearance of the Greeks as navigators. Her chief cities were Tyre, Sidon, Berytus, Byblus, Tripolis and Aradus. Of these Sidon was the most ancient, and prior to 1050 B. C. was the most flourishing of all. The precedency enjoyed by Sidon afterward devolved upon Tyre. The defeat of Sidon by the Philistines caused the transfer of power. About 743 B. C. the passive submission of Phœnicia to the Assyrian yoke began to be exchanged for an impatience of it, and frequently efforts were made from this date until the fall of Nineveh to establish Phœnician independence. Nebuchadnezzar added Phœnicia to Babylon and the country remained thus subjected until the conquest of Babylon by Cyrus.

## Syria.

Until it was made a province of the Persian Empire, Syria was a mere cluster of semi-independent states. The chief of these was Damascus, the capital city of which was at least as old as the time of Abraham. This state was powerful enough to escape absorption into the Jewish Empire of Solomon, but finally fell before the attacks of Tiglath-pileser, about 732 B. C.

The story of Palestine and its inhabitants, the Jews, need not be rehearsed in this place as it is fully given in the stories of the Bible.

## Egypt.

One of the most ancient of all nations was Egypt—how old it is impossible to say. The early establishment of a monarchical government there is indicated in the Bible by the mention of a Pharaoh as contemporary with Abraham. The Egyptian priests themselves claimed for the monarchy in the time of Herodotus an age of more than 11,000 years. In early times Egypt was divided into a number of kingdoms each with its own separate dynasty, so that of the thirty dynasties recorded before the Macedonian conquest several were all the time ruling simultaneously. It was during the first six dynasties that the most noted pyramids were built, as tombs of the Kings. The fourth dynasty, which had its seat at Memphis, is especially known as the pyramid dynasty, and its date is variously set at from 2440 to 3209 B. C.

About 2080 B. C., or a little later, a powerful enemy entered Egypt from the northeast and subdued the greater part of the Empire. These were the so-called Shepherd Kings, wanderers from Syria or Arabia, who destroyed most of the Egyptian cities and nearly exterminated the male population, making slaves of the women and children. Native Egyptian dynasties continued, however, to hold their own in the far south. The city of Thebes accordingly rose at this time to preeminence, and after many years headed a movement for the expulsion of the

Shepherd Kings. This was accomplished about 1525 B. C. Thebes then became the capital of all Egypt and the most flourishing period of Egyptian history followed. The great temple palaces of Thebes were built, and the obelisks were erected. Ethiopia, Arabia and Syria were invaded, the Euphrates was crossed, and a portion of Mesopotamia was added to the Egyptian Empire.

Thothmes III was one of the greatest rulers of this dynasty. He was the invader of Mesopotamia and he built the great temples at Karnak, Thebes, Memphis and elsewhere. Thothmes IV was another great sovereign who led many military expeditions and constructed the famous Sphinx. Amunoph III also deserves notice as a military conqueror and the maker of the great statue of Memnon.

Under the nineteenth dynasty Egypt reached the height of her power and glory. Under the twentieth she rapidly sank, and after 1100 B. C. played a comparatively small part in the history of the world. After that date Egypt was conquered successively by the Ethiopians and the Assyrians.

## Carthage.

The foundation of Carthage was probably about 850 B. C. It was a colony of Tyre, founded because of political differences in the mother country. It rapidly rose to commercial and military importance and extended its influence over Western Sicily, nearly all the other islands of the Western Mediterranean, and the northern coast of Africa. Toward the middle of the sixth century B. C. jealousies and conflicts arose between Carthage and Greece, and then to strengthen herself against the rising power of Greece, Carthage made an alliance with Rome, the latter being then under the Tarquins. The extent of Carthaginian commerce was enormous. It reached northward to England, eastward to Phœnicia, westward to the Canary Islands, and southward almost to the Soudan.

## Persia.

The Persians appeared to have formed a part of the great host which migrated westward from Bokhara in very early times. About a century before Cyrus the Persian monarchy was established by a chieftain named Achamenes, who founded an important dynasty. Until the time of Cyrus, however, the Persian Kings were in some measure subject to the Medians. Cyrus himself lived at first as a sort of hostage at the Median Court, and could not leave it without permission. But at length, seeing the weak character of the King of Media and the decay of the military spirit among the Medes he determined to revolt and make Persia an independent power. Finding this easily accomplished he went further and subdued the Medes, and made Persia the head of a new empire.

His successor was Cambyses, a warlike prince who greatly extended his realm. He conquered Egypt, and marched against Carthage, but was overwhelmed by sandstorms in the desert and driven back. A similar disaster in the Nubian Desert checked his march against Ethiopia. Then a revolt arose against him in Persia and he committed suicide. After a revolutionary interregnum of a few months, Darius

ROMAN CHARIOT RACE

came to the Persian throne. He was the greatest of all the Persian Monarchs. He greatly extended the empire, and consolidated and strengthened it by a reformed system of government. He carried his power as far as Northwestern India and into Southern Russia.

## War with Greece.

His ambitious schemes were checked by a revolt of his Greek subjects in Asia Minor. Two states of European Greece, Athens and Eretria, joined the rebels. After a hard struggle Darius conquered the insurrection in his own realm, and then set out to punish Athens. His first expedition was unfortunate. The fleet was shattered by a storm off Mount Athos and his land army was crippled by a night attack. A second expedition was defeated by the Greek General Miltiades, at Marathon. The third would have been led by Darius himself had not his death prevented. He left his Empire and the legacy of revenge to his son Xerxes.

The latter promptly proceeded with preparations for the invasion of Greece. An army of a million men was collected, and an enormous fleet. The advance through Thessaly was unresisted. But 400 ships were lost in a storm off Cape Sepias, and Leonidas, King of Sparta, with only three hundred men, held the entire army at bay for a time at the narrow pass of Thermopylæ. At last through treachery the pass was carried and all the Spartans slain. Then came another disaster with the loss of 200 ships off the coast of Eubœa. The army continued to advance, however, and captured and destroyed Athens. Then the Greek commander, Themistocles, brought about the naval battle of Salamis, in which the remainder of the Persian fleet was destroyed. Xerxes returned home in despair, leaving his army behind him. The next year it was utterly routed in the battle of Platæa, on September 25, 479 B. C., and the Persians never again attempted to invade European Greece. But the Greeks took the aggressive against Persia, drove them from the sea, and wrested from them many islands and colonies on the Asiatic coast.

## The Fall of Persia.

After the death of Xerxes, the power of Persia began to decline. Weak kings occupied the throne and revolutions were frequent. In the reign of Artaxerxes II, about 400 B. C., a formidable revolt was headed by the king's younger brother, Cyrus, who engaged the assistance of 10,000 Greek mercenaries and invaded the Empire. Cyrus was killed and his army defeated in the battle of Cunaxa. The 10,000 Greeks under Xenophon then made a masterly retreat and reached home in safety. Their observation of the military weakness of Persia increased the feeling of Greek superiority and opened the way for a Greek conquest of Asia.

About seventy years later, in 336-330 B. C., Darius III occupied the Persian throne. He was an amiable but weak prince, and was unable to cope with the Greek, or Macedonian, invasion which then took place. Alexander the Great defeated the Persian army at the Granicus, then at Issus, and finally at Arbela, on October 1, 331 B. C. In the last named battle Darius was utterly routed and the Persian Empire came to an end.

## Early Greece.

The Greeks of historical times had no traditions of a migration from Asia. They held that their ancestors had always occupied their country. The original Greek tribes seemed to have been only two, the Dorians and the Achæans. In early times the latter were the more powerful, but at last the Dorians became dominant and were the true founders of historic Greece. The first Greek state that rose to importance was Argos, which for several centuries was the leading power. Next, about 743 B. C., arose Sparta, ruled conjointly by two kings under the code of laws prepared by Lycurgus. This was a rude, aggressive and warlike state, which fought with its neighbors and soon became master of all Southern Greece.

The traditional history of Athens begins with a dynasty of kings. Heroic monarchs are said to have governed the country from long before the Trojan War down to 1050 B. C. Then an aristocracy arose and Athens was ruled by magistrates called Archons, chosen for life, down to 752 B. C.; then to 684 B. C., by Archons chosen for ten years each; then for a short time by an oligarchy of nine Archons. Next arose a demand for a written code of laws, which was answered by Draco, 624 B. C., with a code of almost inconceivable severity and despotism. Agitation continued and in 594 B. C. Solon framed the first constitution of Athens. The dictatorship of Pisistratus followed, and then under the new constitution of Clisthenes, a republic was established. This gave a great impetus to the spirit of patriotism, and Athens soon rose to a commanding place in Greece, conquering even the Spartans.

The other Greek states were generally inferior, in military and political importance, to Sparta and Athens, and were allied with one or the other of the latter. Greek colonies were planted on nearly all the coasts of the Mediterranean and at some points far inland.

## The Age of Pericles.

After the Persian War Athens was the leading state of Greece and its capital city the most splendid city in the world. Among its leading men were Pericles, Cimon, Aristides, Themistocles and others. The Parthenon and other famous buildings were constructed, and there was collected in Athens a galaxy of intellectual and artistic lights scarcely paralleled in the history of the world.

Then came on the desperate struggle with Sparta known as the Peloponnesian War. This lasted from 431 to 404 B. C., and extended over nearly the whole Grecian world. It ended in the downfall of Athens, which was due largely to the treachery of Alcibiades. He was a brilliant but dissolute Athenian General who, in the furtherance of a selfish ambition, went over to the Spartans and brought about the overwhelming defeat of the Athenians at Syracuse in Sicily. From this blow Athens never recovered.

## The Fall of Greece.

The triumph of Sparta was the ruin of Greece. War after war followed between the various states, all steadily weakening the whole Hellenic race.

Thebes rose in determined resistance to Spartan tyranny. Under the leadership of Epaminondas she crushed the Spartans in the great battle of Leuctra, 371 B. C., and the power of Sparta was broken forever. Sparta actually sought an alliance with Athens against Thebes, and rallied several other states to the same side. They succeeded at last in causing the decline of Thebes, but not in building up any other strong state or league of states. At last Thebes, driven to despair by her enemies, called in Philip of Macedonia to help her. He readily responded, entered Greece, and soon achieved the conquest of practically all the states, in spite of the heroic and eloquent efforts of the great orator, Demosthenes, to rouse the Athenians against him. That was the end of Greece. Thereafter the various states were mere provinces of the Macedonian Empire, and on the assassination of Philip his son, Alexander, became the unchallenged lord of the whole Greek world.

## Alexander the Great.

Having made himself master of the Greek states, and of Egypt, Alexander invaded Asia, crossing the Hellespont in 334 B. C. with 35,000 men. After conquering Persia, as already told, he marched as far as India. Following the course of the Indus in ships built for the purpose, while his army marched along the banks, he conquered the valley as he descended, and, having reached the ocean, proceeded with the bulk of his troops westward through Beloochistan into Persia. Meanwhile his admiral, Nearchus, sailed from the Indus to the Euphrates.

It was the intention of Alexander, after taking the measures which he thought advisable for the consolidation of his empire, and the improvement of his intended capital, Babylon, to attempt the conquest of the peninsula of Arabia. But these plans were brought to an end by the sudden death of their projector at Babylon, in the thirteenth year of his reign and the thirty-third of his age, June, B. C. 323.

## End of the Macedonian Empire.

After the death of Alexander, the Macedonian empire was divided into four distinct kingdoms, viz., Egypt, under Ptolemy ; Macedonia, including Greece, under Cassander ; Thrace, under Lysimachus, and Syria, under Seleucus. Thrace soon became subject to Syria, and not long after, Macedonia was annexed to the Roman empire.

Syria, for a period of 247 years, was governed by twenty-three kings, the successors of Seleucus, who were called the Seleucidæ. It was then conquered by Pompey, and united with the Roman empire. Egypt under a race of kings called Ptolemy, lasted 293 years, and was then added by Octavius (afterwards called Augustus) to the Roman empire. Thus the whole Macedonian empire finally became subject to Rome.

After the fall of the Macedonian empire the other Grecian states made several attempts to recover their liberty and independence ; the last of which was made by a confederacy called the Achæan League. But the Roman empire, which had become the most powerful in the world, soon extended its mighty arm over the divided states, and reduced the whole of Greece to a Roman province under the name of Achaia.

## Origin of Rome.

Rome is said to have been founded by a colony of Trojans, under Æneas, after the fall of Troy. But the Roman people, in the earliest historic times, evidently belonged to the aboriginal race of Italy, the Latins. Procas, King of Alba, left two sons, Numitor and Amulius. The latter seized the throne, and murdered Numitor's son and made his daughter become a vestal virgin. But that daughter, Sylvia, was loved by Mars, the god of war, and by him became the mother of twin sons, Romulus and Remus. Then Amulius had her and the twins thrown into the River Tiber. She was drowned, but the twins were succored and nursed by a she-wolf. When they grew to manhood they killed Amulius and put Numitor on the Alban throne. Then, with his permission, they set out to build a city of their own. They had a quarrel over it, and Remus was killed, so Romulus became the founder of the city and gave it his own name, Rome.

But he and his comrades were without wives; and the neighboring tribes scornfully declined intermarriages. Romulus then proclaimed a great festival; and the neighboring people, especially the Latins and Sabines, came in numbers, with their wives and daughters, to witness the ceremonies; but while they were intent on the spectacle, the Roman youths rushed in, and forcibly bore off the maidens, to become wives of the captors. War followed, and the forces of three Latin cities were successively defeated. At last the Sabine king brought a powerful army against Rome, which Romulus was unable to resist in the open field, and he therefore retreated to the city, while he fortified and garrisoned the Capitoline hill, over against the Palatine on the north, intrusting the command of it to one of his most faithful officers. But Tarpeia, the daughter of the commander, dazzled by the golden bracelets of the Sabines, agreed to open a gate of the fortress to the enemy on condition that they should give her what they bore on their left arms—meaning their golden ornaments. Accordingly the gate was opened, but the traitress expiated her crimes by her death; for the Sabines overwhelmed her with their shields as they entered, these also being carried on their left arms. Soon after peace was made, and the Romans and Sabines became one nation.

## The Kings.

After the death of Romulus, the country was ruled by a succession of kings, to wit.: Numa Pompilius, Tullus Hostilius, Ancus Martius, Tarquin the Elder, Servius Tullius, and Tarquin the Proud. The son of the latter, Sextus, brought about the fall of the dynasty by shamefully violating the person of Lucretia, wife of Collatinus, his cousin. She killed herself in her despair, and a popular revolt, headed by Lucius Junius Brutus, expelled the Tarquins and decreed the perpetual abolition of the kingship. Several attempts were made by the Tarquins, aided by neighboring tribes, to regain the throne. Once they nearly succeeded, but Horatius Cocles and two companions defended the sole entrance to the city, over a bridge of the Tiber, against an army of 80,000 men, until the bridge was torn down behind them. His two comrades retreated just before the bridge fell, but Horatius remained until it had fallen, and then swam back to the city.

## The Republic.

Rome was now governed by a Senate and two Consuls, though in times of great need the supreme authority was given to a single Dictator. Frequent conflicts arose between the two classes into which Romulus had divided the people, the Patricians, or aristocrats, and Plebeians, or common people. After a time the office of Tribune was created, to guard the interests of the Plebeians.

The office of Decemvirs was established in Rome, under the Consuls, to prepare a body of written laws, and to put them into execution for one year. They were ten in number, and each one in turn was invested with absolute power for a day. During the time for which they were appointed, all other magistrates were suspended. For three years the Decemvirs, or "Wicked Ten," were tyrants over Rome. Then one of them, Appius Claudius, fell in love with Virginia, daughter of Virginius, a veteran soldier; but finding her betrothed to another, he procured a base dependant to claim her as his slave. Virginia was brought before the tribunal of Appius himself, who, by an iniquitous decision, ordered her to be surrendered to the claimant. It was then that the distracted father, having no other means of preserving his daughter's honor, stabbed her to the heart in the presence of the court and the assembled people. A general indignation against the Decemvirs spread through the city; the army took part with the people; the power of the Decemvirs was overthrown; and the ancient forms of government were restored.

## Coriolanus and Cincinnatus.

During this time occurred wars with the Volscians and Æquians. In these Caius Marcius, a Roman nobleman, acquired the surname of Coriolanus from his bravery at the capture of the Volscian town of Corioli, and that Lucius Quinctius, called Cincinnatus, acquired great distinction by his conduct of the war against the Æquians. Coriolanus afterwards aroused the wrath of the Plebeians, who had him exiled. He fled to Corioli, led the Volscians against Rome, and would have captured it had not his wife and mother begged him to spare it. But for sparing it he was murdered at Corioli.

In the Æquian war the Senate and people chose Cincinnatus Dictator, and sending in haste to inform him of his election, the deputies found him at work in his field, dressed in the habit of a Roman farmer. He soon raised an army, surrounded the enemy, and took their whole force prisoners, and at the end of sixteen days, having accomplished the deliverance of his country, resigned his power, and returned to private life.

## The Gauls.

The existence of Rome was next threatened by the Gauls, who, under Brennus, took all the city save the Palatine Hill. They tried to take it, too, by climbing up the rocks in the night, but the cackling of the sacred geese in the temple of Juno awoke Marcus Manlius, who hurled the foremost Gaul headlong down the precipice, and prevented the ascent of those who were mounting after him. At length famine began to be felt in the garrison. But the host of the besiegers was gradually melting away by sickness and want, and Brennus agreed, for a thousand pounds of gold, to quit Rome and its territory. According to the old Roman legend, Camillus entered the city with an army while the gold was being weighed, and rudely accosting Brennus, and saying, "It is the custom of us Romans to ransom our country, not with gold, but with iron," ordered the gold to be carried back to the temple, whereupon a battle ensued and the Gauls were driven from the city.

A war with Tarentum, in Southern Italy, followed, in which the Tarentines were aided by Pyrrhus, King of Ephirus. The Romans were successful, and were thus encouraged later to invade Epirus and conquer all Greece.

## War with Carthage.

The first war with Carthage occurred in 263 B. C. A Carthaginian fleet of sixty ships ravaged the coast of Italy; and the Romans saw the necessity of being able to meet the enemy on their own element. Unacquainted with the building of large ships, they must have been obliged to renounce their design had not a Carthaginian ship of war been thrown upon the Italian coast by a storm. From the model thus furnished a hundred and thirty ships were built within sixty days after the trees had been felled, and the Romans soon mastered their foes on sea as well as on land.

In the next war the Carthaginians were led by Hannibal, one of the greatest of generals. He marched though Spain and France, crossed the Alps, invaded Italy, and laid siege to Rome itself. But after a desperate campaign he was driven off. Then the Roman commander Scipio invaded Africa, and Hannibal had to return to the defence of Carthage. The Romans were successful in this war, and Hannibal went into exile, and there died.

The third Carthaginian war ended in 146 B. C., in the total destruction of Carthage.

## Domestic Troubles.

Now arose fresh troubles at Rome. The feuds of Patricians and Plebeians were renewed. Tiberius Gracchus and his brothers, grandsons of Scipio, became champions of the people and effected great reforms, but were presently murdered by the Patricians. An aristocratic despotism was established, and the way opened for the downfall of the Republic itself. A war with Jugurtha, King of Numidia, followed, in which the Romans under the Consul Marius were successful. Marius also defeated the Germans, who attacked Rome in great force. Then Sylla, a colleague of Marius, went to Asia to conquer Pontus and other lands.

After that, a contest arose between Marius and Sylla for supreme power in Rome. First Marius declared himself Consul, and had the friends of Sylla massacred. But sixteen days later Marius died. Then Sylla returned, massacred the partisans of Marius, and made himself master of Rome.

The next great leader was Pompey, who conquered the Kingdom of the Seleucidæ in Asia, and captured Jerusalem. His rival, Crassus, meanwhile crushed the insurrection of slaves and gladiators, led by the famous Spartacus.

Catiline, a dissolute nobleman, organized a deadly conspiracy at Rome, but was exposed and baffled by the great orator, Cicero, and finally fell in battle.

## The Triumvirs.

Then Pompey and Crassus became friends, and formed with Julius Cæsar a triumvirate, ruling the whole Roman world. In a few years Cæsar conquered all of Gaul, part of England, and some of Germany. Crassus invaded Parthia, and was killed, leaving Cæsar and Pompey to divide the world between them. Then Cæsar and Pompey fell out, and went to war with each other. Pompey was defeated in the great battle of Pharsalia, and was soon after murdered.

Cæsar was now supreme. After putting Cleopatra in her brother's place on the Egyptian throne, he marched against the King of Pontus, and overthrew him so quickly that he reported to the senate, "Veni, Vidi, Vici," ("I came, I saw, I conquered"). On his return to Rome he reformed the calendar, made many useful changes in the laws, and was created Dictator for ten years. He had vast projects for the improvement of the empire in view, when a conspiracy was formed against him, led by Brutus and Cassius. They charged him with aspiring to be king, and assassinated him in the senate chamber, March 15, B. C. 44.

## The Empire.

At the death of Julius Cæsar, a second triumvirate was formed by Mark Antony, Lepidus, and Octavius. But Brutus and Cassius, who were anxious to restore the former government of Rome, and re-establish its republican character, raised a large army against the triumvirs. The efforts of the conspirators were unsuccessful, and Brutus and Cassius were defeated at the memorable battle of Philippe. The triumvirs, however, did not long live in harmony. Lepidus was deposed and banished, and the contest between Anthony and Octavius was finally terminated at the memorable battle of Actium, in which Octavius was completely successful, and became sole master of the Roman empire. Thus finally terminated the Commonwealth, or republican form of government of Rome, and it was never again restored.

Octavius soon proclaimed himself Emperor, under the name of Augustus Cæsar. His empire extended from the Rhine and the Danube on the north, to the Euphrates on the east; and from the Atlantic Ocean on the west, to the desert of Arabia and Africa on the south. Literature and the arts flourished wonderfully during his reign. For a time Rome was at peace with all nations, and in that year of universal peace, Jesus Christ was born at Bethlehem, in Judea, a province of the Roman Empire.

# CHAPTER II.

---

## FROM ROME TO AMERICA.

THE EMPIRE AT ITS ZENITH—CONSTANTINE—GOTHS AND VANDALS—
THE SARACENS—CHARLEMAGNE—THE RISE OF ENGLAND—THE
NORMAN CONQUEST—THE CRUSADES—FRANCE AND ENGLAND
—THE WARS OF THE ROSES—THE MOGULS—GERMANY—
SPAIN AND PORTUGAL—VARIOUS STATES—THE
AGE OF DISCOVERY—DISCOVERY OF AMERICA.

---

JULIUS Cæsar, of whom we have already spoken, is commonly reckoned the first Emperor of Rome. Octavius, or Augustus Cæsar, was therefore the second. He was succeeded by Tiberius, in whose reign the crucifixion of Jesus Christ occurred. After Tiberius came nine other Emperors, all like himself of savage and profligate character, with the exceptions of Vespasian and Titus, who were men of fine natures. The others were Caligula, Claudius, Nero, Galba, Otho, Vitellius, and Domitian all abandoned wretches. During the reign of Vespasian the city of Jerusalem was taken and destroyed and the Jews scattered abroad throughout the world. In the reign of Titus occurred the eruption of Vesuvius which destroyed the cities of Pompeii and Herculaneum. Under Claudius the British Isles were added to the empire. Nero had the city of Rome burned and charged the crime against the Christians, whom he then persecuted with unrivalled savagery. Among his victims was St. Paul.

## The Empire at its Zenith.

The succeeding Emperors varied in character. Trajan, under whom the empire reached its greatest extent, Hadrian, A. Severus, and the Antonines were all worthy princes, who are to be held in lasting honor. The rest were either weak or dissolute, or both. Commodus was one of the worst, but the palm for utter vileness must be given to Heliogabalus. Diocletian was an able ruler, but after reigning for more than twenty years he voluntarily retired to private life—the first sovereign who ever thus resigned his power.

## Constantine.

The first Christian emperor was Constantine, who is said to have been converted by a miracle, much as was St. Paul. He found himself unpopular at Rome, and so changed the seat of government to Byzantium, which he renamed Constantinople. That city afterward became the capital of the Eastern Empire, while Rome was the capital of the Western.

After Constantine had publicly embraced Christianity, the Emperor Julian renounced it, and restored the old Roman worship for a time. The last emperor who ruled over the entire empire was Theodosius. Before he died he divided it and gave the eastern half to his son Arcadius, and the western half to his son Honorius.

## Goths and Vandals.

The Western Empire was soon invaded by the Goths under their king, Alaric; then by the Huns under Attila; and by the Vandals, under Genseric. It was much ravaged and despoiled, and finally abolished altogether by Odoacer, king of the Heruli, who deposed the last Roman Emperor, Romulus Augustus, and proclaimed himself King of Italy. Thus ended, in the year 476, the Roman Empire, which in one form or another, had lasted about 1,200 years.

The Eastern Empire lasted a thousand years longer, and then was overthrown by the Ottoman Turks, and Constantinople was made the capital of the Turkish Empire.

After the fall of Rome there came upon Europe what are known in history as the Dark Ages. The masses of the people were sunk in ignorance. The Feudal System of government prevailed in all its tyranny, and finally the principles of chivalry began to prevail and to usher in a better age.

## The Saracens.

A new power arose to commanding ranks. This was the Saracen Empire, which had its origin in the Arabian Peninsula, the only country of the world which has never suffered conquest. The founder of the empire was Mohammed, a camel-driver. He professed to have received a revelation from Heaven and to be a prophet of God. At first he was treated with contempt, but at last gained a host of followers and founded one of the greatest empires in history. Arabia, Syria, Persia, Egypt, and indeed all of northern Africa and western Asia fell under his sway. Later the Eastern Roman Empire, Spain, Hungary, and much of Austria were seized, and all Europe was threatened.

Soon after the death of Mohammed a great division occurred in the empire on religious lines, and in the thirteenth century the empire was shattered by the Moguls, but out of its ruins three great monarchies were formed, which still exist.

## Charlemagne.

Next a new empire was formed in Western Europe by various tribes known as Franks, or Freemen. They were chiefly centered in Gaul, which then became known as France. The greatest Frankish emperor was Charlemagne, who was crowned at Rome in the year 800. His rule extended over France, Germany, the Netherlands, Switzerland, and most of Spain and Italy. An inestimable service was rendered to the Christian world by the Franks under the grandfather of Charlemagne, Charles Martel, in the decisive defeat of the Saracens, who were then trying to overrun and subdue all Europe. Charles Martel gave them a repulse from which they never recovered and drove them out of France.

The new western empire fell to pieces after the death of Charlemagne, and became divided into several states, of which France and Germany were the chief.

At this time Denmark, Sweden aed Norway began to rise to importance. The Slavs pushed their way into Europe, and Italy fell to the rank of a mere province of the rising German Empire.

## The Rise of England.

England, under the name of Britain, first appeared in history about fifty years before the Christian Era, when Julius Caesar, after conquering Gaul, attempted to subdue it. In the reign of Claudius, A. D. 41, the Romans made it a Roman province, and held it for about five hundred years thereafter. When the Roman Empire declined, the Saxons invaded, conquered and colonized the island, and divided it into seven kingdoms, known as the Saxon Heptarchy. This state of affairs lasted for about two hundred years. Then, in 828, all the kingdoms were united into one under Egbert, who thus became the first King of England.

The greatest of the early kings of England was Alfred, who reigned in the latter part of the ninth century. He was the first great English law-giver ; he divided England into counties, introduced the art of building with brick and stone, translated many foreign books into Saxon, began ship-building, introduced trial by jury, established schools, and founded the University of Oxford.

## The Norman Conquest.

The last of the Saxon kings of England was Harold, whose right to the throne was disputed by William, Duke of Normandy. Harold was overthrown and killed at the battle of Hastings in 1066, and the Norman Conquest of England was then effected. A series of Norman kings followed, and the crown then went to the Plantagenets under Henry II., who was sovereign not only of England but of the western part of France as well. After him came Richard the Lion-hearted, who was a great leader of the Crusades. Under his brother, John, the English crown lost much of its French realm, and Magna Charta was granted to the nobles of England, the latter being the foundation of constitutional government in that country.

## The Crusades.

The Crusades were military expeditions, in which the Christian nations of Europe were engaged for the purpose of recovering Palestine from the dominion of the Turks. The Turks were of the Mohammedan religion, and cruelly treated the Christian pilgrims who resorted from pious motives to the city of Jerusalem. The Crusaders obtained possesion of Jerusalem for a short time, but it was soon retaken by the Mohammedans, who still retain possession of it.

The crusading spirit lasted from the eleventh to the thirteenth century, and during this period of about 200 years, in which ten different expeditions were undertaken, it is computed that more than two million of Europeans found their graves in the East.

## France and England.

King John of England was succeeded by his son Henry, and after him came the three Edwards. Edward I. conquered Wales. Edward II. tried to conquer Scotland. He invaded that country with an army of a hundred thousand men; which immense force was met at Bannockburn by the Scots, under their king, Robert Bruce, with an army of only thirty thousand, and entirely defeated. This victory secured the independence of Scotland.

Edward III. being the son of a French princess, claimed the crown of France and went to war with Philip of Valois who held it. His son, the Black Prince, was the foremost leader of his army. In the battles of Crecy and Poictiers the French vastly outnumbered the English but were utterly routed. In this war Edward III. adopted the motto still borne by the sovereigns of England "Dieu et Mon Droit," or "God and my right," and the Black Prince adopted as the crest the three plumes and the motto "Ich Dien" or "I serve," still borne by the Prince of Wales.

Under Henry V. and VI. the war with France was resumed and was continued in all for a hundred years. The French were routed at Agincourt, and Orleans was besieged. Charles, king of France, was not yet crowned. At this juncture appeared Joan of Arc, a beautiful maiden of eighteen years of age, and of obscure parentage, commanded, as she asserted, by a vision, to raise the siege of Orleans, and to conduct Charles to Rheims to be crowned. After some neglect, her services were accepted: she was mounted on horseback in male attire, and at the head of the French troops compelled the English to retire from Orleans. She then conducted Charles to Rheims; and, after seeing him crowned, declared that her mission was accomplished, and wished again to retire to private life. But her countrymen, finding her presence so animating to the troops, detained her still in arms. She afterwards fell into the hands of the English, and, at the instigation of her own ungrateful countrymen, was condemned by the church as a sorceress and a heretic, and was finally burned at the stake.

## The Wars of the Roses.

The "Wars of the Roses" in England were contests between the houses of York and Lancaster for the crown. A white and a red rose were adopted as a badge, respectively, by the houses of York and Lancaster; that of York being known by the white rose, that of Lancaster by the red. These contests involved the kingdom in civil wars and commotions, for many years, from the reign of Henry IV. to that of Henry VII., the second branch of the house of Lancaster; who, at the battle of Bosworth, overthrew Richard III., the last sovereign of the house of York; and marrying Elizabeth, the daughter of Edward IV., of the same house, united the houses of York and Lancaster. As Elizabeth was the rightful heir of the throne, Henry VII. thus united all the claims, and terminated "the wars of the roses."

Richard III. was a usurper, murderer, and tyrant. But in his short reign several important laws were enacted, and the laws of England were first written in English and published.

## The Moguls.

The Moguls, or Tartars, had their origin somewhere in north central Asia. In the thirteenth century they moved westward and southward under their famous leader Genghis Khan, and overran a large part of Asia and Europe. They established a strong dynasty in southeastern Russia, which greatly delayed the civilization of that country. In 1258 they captured Bagdad and shattered the Mohammedan empire.

In the next century they were successfully opposed by the Ottoman Turks. Their last great leader was Tamerlane, and after his death, in 1405, their empire came to an end. Russia finally got rid of them in 1477, but did not until much later herself enter the community of European states.

## Germany.

In the eleventh century the German Empire, which included Austria, Burgundy, Switzerland and Italy, was the leading power in Europe. In the twelfth century it began to decline and to be divided into independent states. The cities of northern Italy, such as Venice, Genoa and Florence, secured their independence and rose to great distinction. These cities in the fourteenth century began to fall under the power of tyrannical families, and to be combined into larger states. Florence under the Medici family reached in the fifteenth century the height of its splendor. In that century Germany lost Burgundy to France and became in other respects much weakened.

## Spain and Portugal.

In the tenth century the southern two-thirds of the Spanish Peninsula belonged to the Saracens, whose civilization there was then at its height. The kingdoms of Leon, Castile, and Navarre were founded in the north in the tenth century and Aragon was added to their number in the eleventh. Portugal became a kingdom in the twelfth century, and then the five steadily pushed the Saracens southward until only the small kingdom of Granada remained to them. It fell in 1492. Portugal then occupied about its present territory, and practically all the rest of the peninsula belonged to Spain.

## Various States.

Denmark, Norway, and Sweden reached the height of their power in the eleventh and twelfth centuries, and were united under one monarch in the fourteenth.

Russia, Servia and Hungary became Christian powers in the eleventh century. Ireland was conquered by England in 1172.

The Swiss Confederation was founded in 1308, and a century later became an important power. Poland also rose to importance in the fifteenth century. Mention must also be made of Rienzi, a Roman patriot of noble birth, who, in the fourteenth century, for a time re-established the Roman Republic in something of its ancient form. His success was, however, short-lived, and he fell a victim to his own ambition.

RETREAT FROM MOSCOW

## The Age of Discovery.

And now the time was ripe for the dawning of a new era. Gunpowder had been invented, and the art of printing. The properties of the magnetic needle had also been discovered, and this latter gave a great impetus to navigation of the sea. Under the patronage of Prince Henry of Portugal various expeditions were sent out, with noteworthy results. The first voyages were made down the west coast of Africa, in quest of a sea route to the East Indies. Thus the Cape of Good Hope was finally reached and rounded. These adventures moved Christopher Columbus, a Genoese navigator, to conceive the bold project of sailing westward from the European coast across the Atlantic Ocean. Thus he believed it would be possible to circumnavigate the globe and reach the East Indies from the other side. He met at first with little encouragement and many obstacles, but at last received some limited patronage from Isabella, Queen of Castile, and in 1492 set out with three small vessels upon his wondrous voyage.

## Discovery of America.

To the importance of that voyage no words can do full justice. "The departure from Palos," said Everett, "where, a few days before, he had begged a morsel of bread and a cup of water for his wayworn child,—his final farewell to the Old World at the Canaries,—his entrance upon the trade winds, which then, for the first time, filled a European sail,—the portentious variation of the needle, never before observed,—the fearful course westward and westward, day after day, and night after night, over the unknown sea,—the mutinous and ill-appeased crew :—at length, when hope had turned to despair in every heart but one, the tokens of land, —the cloud-banks on the western horizon,—the logs of driftwood,—the fresh shrub, floating with its leaves and berries,—the flocks of land birds,—the shoals of fish that inhabit shallow water,—the indescribable smell of the shore,—the mysterious presentiment that seems to go ever before a great event,—and finally, on that ever-memorable night of the 12th of October, 1492, the moving light seen by the sleepless eye of the great discoverer himself, from the deck of the Santa Maria, and in the morning the real, doubted land, swelling up from the bosom of the deep, with its plains, and hills, and forests, and rocks, and streams, and strange new races of men :—these are incidents in which the authentic history of the discovery of our continent excels the specious wonders of romance, as much as gold excels tinsel, or the sun in the heavens outshines the flickering taper."

# CHAPTER III.

---

## DOWN TO MODERN TIMES.

---

THE close of the fifteenth century saw Spain rising to power as the foremost
nation of Europe. The two kingdoms of Aragon and Castile were
practically united under Ferdinand and Isabella. After the latter's death
they were temporarily separated, but the astute Ferdinand soon reunited them, and
then, by the seizure of Navarre in 1512, made all Spain one kingdom. Naples and
Sicily were also added to the Spanish domain. After a brief regency, Ferdinand
was succeeded by his grandson, Charles I., best known as the Emperor Charles V.,
one of the most famous of European rulers. He was a descendant of Charles the
Bold of France and Maximilan of Austria. He thus was at the same time King of
Spain, Archduke of Austria, Duke of Burgundy and the Netherlands, King of the
Two Sicilies, and Lord of the Spanish Settlements in America and Africa, which
latter were of vast extent. A couple of years after his accession he was made
Emperor of Germany, and thus became by far the greatest sovereign of his times.

## The Wars of France.

The Hundred Years' War between France and England was ended, but the
former nation enjoyed little peace. Under Charles VIII. and Louis XII., it was
almost continually at war. In Italy it made great conquests, but had to surrender
most of them to Spain. Then a quarrel with England arose, and Henry VIII.
invaded France, and routed an army at the famous Battle of the Spurs, so called

because of the precipitate flight of the French. The most noted French warrior of these times was the Chevalier Bayard, who was said to be "without fear and without reproach."

## England's Growing Power.

England was also rapidly growing in power. Henry VII. was a wise and enterprising king. Despite several rebellions at home, the most notable being that of Perkin Warbeck, who claimed the throne, as a son of Edward IV., the influence of England was steadily extended abroad. Much attention was paid to commerce and naval power, and under English commissions John Cabot and others made voyages of discovery and conquest. Cabot first discovered the North American continent and planted an English colony there. Henry VII. married his daughter to James IV. of Scotland, and thus prepared the way for the ultimate union of those countries. Under Henry VIII. the growth of England continued. At the battle of Flodden Field the Scotch army was almost annihilated, and the military power of that country hopelessly broken, after which there was peace between England and Scotland.

## Unhappy Italy.

At this time the condition of Italy was most deplorable. Savonarola for a time effected great reforms at Florence, but was at last led to martyrdom by the very people he strove to benefit. The Papacy became corrupt. Cæsar and Lucretia Borgia distinguished themselves by their crimes. The commercial supremacy of Venice and Genoa was destroyed by the Portuguese, who discovered the route to India around the Cape of Good Hope and built up an empire there. France and Spain invaded Italy and found it an easy prey. Nevertheless, the artistic genius of Leonardo da Vinci, Raphael, and Michael Angelo made this a time of Italian glory.

## Some Other States.

Germany, meanwhile, was too much divided to figure largely in European affairs. The Turks, now established at Constantinople, added Syria and Egypt to their growing empire. Poland was now an important kingdom, and Russia was becoming civilized, and getting into touch with the rest of Europe. Ivan III., who died in 1505, was the first Russian ruler known as Czar. He freed the country from the Tartars and laid the foundation of Russian greatness.

## The Reformation.

Now came one of the greatest movements in history, with its origin and centre in Germany. This was the Reformation led by Martin Luther. Papal corruption reached its climax in the sale of so-called Indulgences, giving their purchaser freedom from the moral law. Against these Luther, then an Augustinian friar in Germany, publicly protested, in 1517, and thus presently became known as a Protestant. At first he aimed at reform of the Roman church from within, but was soon driven out of that church altogether, and became the leader of a separate religious communion.   He was excommunicated by the Pope, and in return himself denounced the Pope as Antichrist.   Various German Princes became converted to the Protestant faith, and so the new movement took on a political as well as a religious aspect.   All Europe was divided between the rival faiths, and an era of religious wars and persecutions began, marked with the utmost bitterness and cruelty on both sides. At last, in 1555 the Religious Peace of Augsburg was concluded, and the next year the great Emperor, Charles V., took the extraordinary step of resigning his crown and retiring to a monastery, where he spent the remainder of his life.

### French Disasters.

Francis I. of France was the bitter foe of Charles V., and made war against him, but was disastrously beaten.   Then he invaded Italy, only to be routed.   At Pavia, Francis was taken prisoner by the Imperial troops, and sent word home to his mother, "All is lost, save honor."   He was released, and resumed the war, and continued it until the end of his life, almost steadily losing and bringing his kingdom near to ruin.   In his reign, however, the great religious reformer John Calvin arose and established Protestantism in France.   He was persecuted by Francis and compelled to seek refuge in Switzerland, where most of his work was thereafter done. In this reign also the satirist Rabelais did his work.

Francis's son and successor, Henry II., was not more fortunate.   He took from the English their last remaining possession in France, but was elsewhere beaten by Spain.   He married Catherine de Medici, and thus introduced her baleful influence into French politics.   He began persecuting the Protestants and started an era of religious wars in France.   In his time arose the Duke of Guise and Admiral Coligny, the leaders of the Catholic and Protestant parties respectively.

### Italy.

The history of Italy at this time was a troubled one.   The country was made a mere fighting ground for others.   Spain finally won, and the enslavement of Italy was completed.   The Medici family was at this time one of the most powerful in Italy.   Doria, the great Genoese admiral, flourished.   Ignatius Loyola founded the famous Order of Jesus, commonly known as Jesuits, and the Inquisition, founded in Spain, was introduced into Italy.   Correggio and Titian enriched Italian art, and Ariosto in literature and Machiavelli in statecraft and philosophy added lustre to the Italian name.

### The English Reformation.

Henry VIII. of England was a proud and masterful prince, and was restless under the Papal authority to which his predecessors had submitted.   Finally, disagreeing with the Roman church on the matter of divorcing his first wife, Katharine of Aragon, he renounced all allegiance to the Pope and espoused the cause of the Lutheran Reformation.   The English church was declared independent of Rome, an English translation of the Bible was authorized for popular use, and an era of religious strife thus begun.   During the short reign of his son and successor, Edward VI., the Reformation was continued, but under Queen Mary, a Catholic

CHARGE AT WATERLOO

reaction set in, and Protestants were savagely persecuted. Mary married Philip of Spain, who aspired to unite the two kingdoms, but she died without issue and that plan came to naught. She was succeeded by her sister, Elizabeth, a Protestant, under whom the Reformation was fully restored.

### Scandinavia.

At about this time the modern history of the Scandinavian kingdoms began. In the reign of the savage monster, Christian II., the union of the three was broken. Sweden revolted and made Gustavus Vasa its king. All three of the kingdoms accepted the Protestant faith.

Meanwhile Ivan IV., the Terrible, greatly extended the Russian empire, making it reach from the Caspian to the Baltic, and gave it its first real code of laws and judicial system.

### Solyman the Magnificent.

In this era flourished Solyman the Magnificent, the greatest of all Turkish rulers and one of the greatest of that time in all the world. He took the island of Rhodes after a memorable struggle; captured Belgrade in 1521; and five years later invaded Hungary, won a great victory and killed the King of Hungary at Mohacz, and occupied Budapest. Next he laid siege to Vienna, but after losing 120,000 men was compelled to retire. He made conquests in other directions and was sought as an ally by Christian sovereigns. He was a great legislator, a fine poet, an eminent warrior, a patron of arts and letters, a great road-maker, and a builder of many splendid edifices.

The first half of the sixteenth century the great Mogul Empire was founded in India by Baber, a descendant of Tamerlane.

### The New World.

Meantime the development of the New World proceeded apace. Fernando Cortez, a Spanish adventurer conquered Cuba, and then, in 1519 and 1520 achieved the conquest of Mexico with almost unparalleled bloodthirstiness. In 1531 Francisco Pizarro did the same in Peru. Others extended the work of conquest elsewhere, until practically the whole of Central and South America, and the southern part of North America, with inestimable riches in gold and silver, belonged to Spain.

In the latter half of the sixteenth century interest was chiefly centered upon France and the Netherlands. Germany led a peaceful existence under the mild and tolerant Emperors Ferdinand and Maximilian. Rudolph II., who came next, was a bigoted Romanist who attempted to suppress Protestantism and started the Anti-Reformation, but no serious conflict arose in his reign.

### Religious Wars in France.

In France civil war soon broke out between the Catholics and the Protestants, or Huguenots. The Duke of Guise was the leader of the former and the Prince of Conde and Admiral Coligny of the latter. After much open fighting the Duke of

Guise was murdered, and then a truce was concluded.  But a second and then a third war followed, the Prince of Conde being slain in the latter.  In the next peace the Huguenots were so favored at court that the Guises determined upon extreme measures against them.  The weak minded King was prevailed upon by his mother, Catherine de Medici, to sign an order for the destruction of the Huguenots.  The mob and soldiery of Paris then rose under the lead of the Guises and massacred them to the number of 20,000, Coligny among them.  This occurred on St. Bartholomew's Day, August 24, 1572.  Another war followed, in which the Huguenot city of Rochelle withstood a memorable siege.

The wretched King, Charles IX., soon died, and was succeeded by his brother, Henry III.  The Guises at once attempted to take Paris by force and depose the King, in order to establish a new dynasty and prevent the next heir, the Protestant Henry of Navarre, from succeeding the childless Henry III.  Strong resistance was made by Henry of Navarre, but the Guises entered Paris and expelled the King, and Henry of Guise was proclaimed King in his stead.  Henry III. fled to the camp of Henry of Navarre, but was murdered by a young monk, an emissary of the Guises.  A few hours earlier his famous mother also died.

### The First Bourbon.

Henry of Navarre then succeeded to the French throne as Henry IV., and founded the famous Bourbon dynasty.  He had to fight for his throne, however, but was successful in so doing.  He crushed the Catholic League in the famous Battle of Ivry, in 1590, and then, deeming it politic thus to please the majority of his subjects, became a Catholic.  He was thereupon loyally accepted as King by all, and the religious wars came to an end.  In the Edict of Nantes he decreed perfect civil equality between members of both faiths, and kept his word to both.

### Italy and the Turks.

Italy at this time was in a bad way.  The power of Venice was declining, and the Turks were seizing outlying possessions and threatening the conquest of the peninsula itself.  The Turks would have succeeded had not a combined Italian and Austrian fleet, under Don John of Austria defeated them utterly in the great sea-fight of Lepanto, in 1571.  This was truly one of the decisive battles of the world.

In this period Sixtus V. was Pope, one of the greatest men that ever filled that exalted place.  Another great Pope was Clement VIII.  The printer Aldus at Venice, the poet Tasso, the painters Titian and Paul Veronese, and St. Charles Borromeo and St. Francis of Sales made this era in Italian history noteworthy.

### Spain's Cruelty and Woe.

At this time Spain was under Philip II., a monster of cruelty.  He at first set out to extirpate Protestantism.  To that end he established the Inquisition in all its severity in Spain, Italy and the Netherlands.  In the last named country he was stubbornly resisted by William of Orange, best known as William the Silent.  This great prince fought against overwhelming odds with valor that has seldom been equalled in history. The cruelties of the Spaniards under the Duke of Alva were hideous beyond description. But in the end the Netherlanders won their independence and established a commonwealth of their own with the colossal genius of William the Silent at its head. William was afterward assassinated by a wretch hired by Philip of Spain, and was succeeded by his worthy son, Maurice. The Dutch were helped by the English in their heroic struggle, and it was in their battle of Zutphen, in 1586, that the famous Sir Philip Sidney fell.

But Philip of Spain met with awful punishment for his cruelty. He was so enraged at England for helping the Dutch and for other reasons that he determined to attempt the conquest of that country. Accordingly he fitted out an enormous fleet, called the Invincible Armada, consisting of 130 ships with nearly 30,000 soldiers and sailors. The much smaller but more active English fleet met it in the Channel and harassed it greatly, destroying many of its ships and throwing all into confusion. Violent storms completed the work, and only 35 of the Spanish ships and less than 10,000 men ever reached home again. This was a terrible blow to Spain, but it was not the only one. Francis Drake and other English captains preyed upon Spanish commerce at will, with most destructive results. Spanish ships were taken wholesale, with the vast treasures they were bringing from America. Spanish cities in the New World were sacked. And Drake even entered the chief port of Spain itself, Cadiz, and destroyed the Spanish warships as they lay at anchor. This he grimly called "singeing the King's beard."

### The Elizabethan Age.

England under Queen Elizabeth was now making great progress in all respects. Religious strife was hushed. Industries, arts and letters prospered. Navigators explored the world and laid the foundations of a great colonial empire. Francis Drake sailed around the world—the first to do so with a single ship. Walter Raleigh planted a colony in Virginia, thus sowing the seed from which the United States has grown. In 1600 the charter of the East India Company was granted, and the first step taken toward conquering an empire there. Mary Stuart, Queen of Scotland, by her vicious courses plunged her own land into anarchy, and was driven out of it for its good. She sought refuge in England, but soon began plotting for the murder of Elizabeth, whom she hoped to succeed. At last Elizabeth was compelled, by the demands of the people, to consent to Mary's execution.

In this notable reign English literature was enriched with the works of Shakespeare, Spenser, Sidney, Marlowe, and Richard Hooker.

### The Stuarts.

Elizabeth was succeeded by her cousin, James VI. of Scotland, son of Mary Stuart. He became James I. of England, established the Stuart dynasty, and effected in his person the union of England and Scotland, being thus the first sovereign of the united kingdom of Great Britain and Ireland. In his reign the great works of the Elizabethan age were continued. The colony of Jamestown was planted in Virginia, a revised version of the Bible was published, and Francis Bacon made his immortal contributions to literature and human learning.

James had numerous disagreements with Parliament, and these were continued and intensified in the reign of his son, Charles I. That monarch tried to levy unlawful taxes, to compel obnoxious changes in the form of public worship, and to do other things in opposition to the will of Parliament. Civil war soon broke out, the Parliamentary party being led by Oliver Cromwell, John Hampden and others. In the end the King was beaten. He was taken prisoner, tried for high treason, and put to death, on January 30, 1649.

## The Thirty Years' War.

Meantime religious strife was renewed in Germany, in the form of the Thirty Years' War. Albert of Wallenstein was the chief Catholic leader in the field, and for a time he carried all before him. But his success and his ambition caused him to be regarded with jealousy by others of his own party. He was presently dismissed by the Emperor and succeeded by Count Tilly, an able but unscrupulous and savage soldier.

Gustavus Adolphus, King of Sweden now came to the help of the Protestants with an army of Swedes. Tilly captured Magdeburg in 1631, sacked it and butchered its inhabitants in the most inhuman fashion. Then Gustavus came up with him at Breitenfeld, or Leipsic, and in a tremendous battle routed him and showed him that his Swedes were the best fighters in Europe.

This made the Protestant cause seem sure of success, and Gustavus at a single step placed himself at the head of military commanders of that age. He again met Tilly, killed him and routed his army. He then captured Munich, the Catholic capital, and occupied the Emperor's palace. The Emperor in desperation recalled Wallenstein, and that great soldier came back to command the Catholic forces. He and Gustavus met at Nuremburg and fought an indecisive battle. Again they met, on November 10, in the great battle of Lutzen. Here Wallenstein was utterly routed and his chief lieutenant, Pappenheim, was killed. But Gustavus too was killed, and in his death the Protestants suffered an irreparable loss. Wallenstein organized another army and, freed from the one man able to cope with him, aimed at seizing the supreme power. His ambitious schemes were cut short by his death at the hands of assassins hired by the Emperor. Thus, in Gustavus and Wallenstein perished two of the greatest men of their time on the continent of Europe. The war then gradually waned, and peace was at last restored, with general religious toleration.

## Richelieu.

The third great man was Cardinal Richelieu, Minister and real ruler of France. Henry IV. and his able Minister, the Duke of Sully, had given France much prosperity. Henry was murdered in 1610, and Louis XIII. came to the throne. He was a mere boy, and the government was for years conducted by others in his name, with the result that the good and wise reign of Henry was followed by one of the worst on record. But at last Richelieu came to the fore, and gave France a worthy government. Catholic though he was, he supported the Protestants in Germany, and greatly assisted Gustavus. He reformed the whole French administration, founded the French Academy, and when he died France lost her ablest Minister and the world its greatest statesman of that age. He was succeeded by his friend and pupil, Cardinal Mazarin, who continued his policy, and raised the French army, under the Prince of Conde, to the foremost rank in Europe.

## Italy and Spain.

In Italy, the Dukedom of Savoy now began to rise into prominence, but elsewhere little of interest occurred. In 1633, the astronomer Galileo was compelled to renounce his theory of the revolution of the earth around the sun; but when he got out of hearing of the Inquisition again he persistently declared, "It does move!"

Spain, under the narrow and cruel Philip III., was now hopelessly on the down grade. Through religious intolerance, the Moriscoes, or Spanish Moors, were expelled. They went away, half a million in number, taking with them five-sixths of the commercial wealth and enterprise of Spain. From that self-inflicted blow the kingdom never recovered.

Nevertheless, this disastrous time was partially redeemed by the literary achievements of Cervantes, author of "Don Quixote," and of Lope de Vega, the great dramatist, who both flourished in the early part of the seventeenth century.

## Eastern Nations.

The early part of the seventeenth century saw the Turkish Empire steadily declining, under a succession of weak or brutal Sultans. Poland was governed most unwisely, and began the quarrels with Russia, which in later times culminated in her ruin. Russia, on the other hand, was making steady progress. In 1598 the long dynasty, founded by Rurik, came to an end, after 700 years of rule. After some troubled years under elected or usurping Czars, the nobles chose Michael Romanoff to be hereditary Emperor, and thus established the present dynasty.

The Mogul Empire in India suffered an irreparable loss in 1606 in the death of its Emperor Akbar, one of the most enlightened rulers of his time. His successors were unworthy princes, and the empire began to decline. The British, Dutch, and French all sought to make conquests there by peaceful means, but for a time the Dutch far outstripped the others.

The Persian Empire, under the great Shah Abbas, was much enlarged and strengthened. Armenia, Mesopotamia, and Georgia were conquered and added to it; Ispahan was made its capital, and the great pilgrimage to the holy city of Meshed was established as a rival to the Turkish pilgrimages to Mecca.

In China this was a momentous era. In 1603 missionaries first preached Christianity in that Empire. In 1627 an attack upon the throne—the latest of a long series—was made by the Tartars of Mantchooria, and was successful. The native Chinese dynasty was deposed, and the Tartar dynasty, which has ever since ruled the Empire, was established. The Chinese were thenceforth compelled to wear their hair in pig-tails as a mark of submission to their conquerors.

In 1620 the Emperor of Japan sent a commission to Europe to study the Christian religion, and report upon the desirability of introducing it into Japan. The report was not favorable, and the preaching of Christianity was forbidden. It is of interest to observe that from 1630 to 1647 the offices of Mikado and Tycoon were both held by women.

## Troubles in France.

The latter half of this century was a troublous time for France. Cardinal Mazarin was the real head of the government, and he soon came into conflicts with the local Parliaments, that then existed, on subjects of taxation and others. The Prince of Conde placed himself at the head of the opposition party, and plunged the country into civil war. For a time the great Marshal Turenne was a partisan of Conde, but on the latter's attempt to overturn the dynasty Turenne arrayed himself against him. Conde then joined the Spanish in a war against France, but was completely beaten by Turenne, who had the assistance of England.

On Mazarin's death, in 1661, the young King, Louis XIV., decided to govern France himself, without a Minister, saying, "The State? I am the State!" An era of despotism followed, but marked with great splendor of arms and letters, entitling Louis to become known as "the Grand Monarch." Colbert, the financier, Vauban, the inventor of the modern methods of military fortification, Turenne, the commander, and Bossuet, Fenelon, Racine, Corneille, and Moliere were some of the great figures of this extraordinary reign.

A bitter war with Holland broke out in 1672, in which the French, under Turenne, were generally victorious on land, and the Dutch, under Admiral De Ruyter, on the sea. Turenne was killed in the battle at Salsbach, in 1675, and was succeeded by Conde, who had returned to his allegiance to France. In 1678 peace was concluded on terms of compromise.

## Persecutions.

At the height of his power, Louis turned his attention to religious affairs. Under the influence of Madame de Maintenon, to whom he was privately married, he began a severe persecution of the Protestants of France. Protestant churches were everywhere shut up, and when the unhappy people ventured to resist they were hunted down and butchered by parties of dragoons, in what were known as the "dragonnades." But even these monstrous cruelties were not enough to satisfy the fanatical Maintenon. In 1685 the Edict of Nantes was revoked, and the last shelter of the Protestants was destroyed. The exercise of the Protestant religion was forbidden, Protestant churches were destroyed, all children of Protestants were to be taken from them and brought up as Catholics, and, in order that no one might escape the rigors of the decree, emigration from the country was forbidden. Nevertheless, some 50,000 families, including most of the industrial leaders of the country, made their escape to England and other countries, and in a few years

France lost 100,000 of her best citizens and $300,000,000, and had her industries almost ruined, as the results of this barbarous policy.

Louis next engaged in war with Germany, and ravaged the Palatinate in the most savage manner. England and Holland joined the league against him, and a bitter campaign ensued, in which Luxembourg and Catinat were the foremost French Generals, and Prince Eugene on the side of the allies.

## Marlborough.

After much indecisive fighting, a truce was made at Ryswick in 1697. But within five years it was broken again, and a still greater war begun. It raged all through Italy, Germany, and the Netherlands. The French were led by Tallard, Vendome, and others. The allied powers had for their leaders Prince Eugene and the Duke of Marlborough. The latter, John Churchill, proved himself the greatest soldier of the age. He routed the French in the tremendous battles of Blenheim, in 1704 ; Ramillies, in 1706 ; Oudenarde, in 1708 ; and Malplaquet, in 1709 ; and left behind him on the continent a name that is still used to conjure with. In 1704, too, the English took possession of the celebrated rock-fortress of Gibraltar, in Spain, which they have ever since held.

Peace came at last in the Treaty of Utrecht, in 1713, with considerable advantages to England and her allies. Two years later Louis, "the Grand Monarch," died. He left France overwhelmed in debts, crushed beneath tyranny, and with industries prostrated—an ominous legacy for his weak and dissolute grandson.

## Spain and Portugal.

Spain continued to decline, under a series of incompetent kings. An effort was made to annex Portugal, but the latter little country stoutly resisted the attacks of her big neighbor, and by means of alliances with France and England, was enabled to hold her own. Indeed, she did more, for she succeeded in planting an extensive colony in Brazil.

Italy, divided into a number of petty states, was still the sport and prey of the greater powers, and often their fighting-ground. The one significant fact with her was the steady growth of Savoy in strength and influence.

Nor was Germany much better off than Italy. Divisions and jealousies among the states kept them from enjoying the rank in European affairs to which they were naturally entitled. But there, too, the age was marked by the growth of a power destined one day to be dominant over all the rest. This was Prussia, which, beginning with the Electorate of Brandenburg, became practically an independent kingdom in 1656, although the royal title was not actually assumed for another half century.

The religious disturbances in Austria and Hungary led to another invasion by the Turks, who came to the succor of the Protestants. In 1683 they laid siege to Vienna, and despite a most heroic defence, would doubtless have captured it had not the famous John Sobieski, King of Poland, come to its relief. Charles, Duke of

Lorraine, also assisted in the rescue of the city, and later, in 1687, broke the power of the Turks in Hungary by a splendid victory at Mohacs. Upon that, the Hungarian Diet conferred upon the House of Austria—the Lorraine family—the hereditary succession to the Hungarian throne. Finally, in 1697, Prince Eugene of Savoy won a brilliant victory over the Turks at Zenta, by which practically the whole of Hungary and Transylvania were redeemed from their control. Thereafter Turkish aggression ceased to be a source of anxiety to Europe.

## Charles XII. of Sweden.

The greatness to which Gustavus Adolphus had raised Sweden was soon sacrificed by his successors. Charles X. became involved in war with Poland. He invaded that country, captured Warsaw, expelled the king, and proclaimed himself king. But a league of Russia, Denmark, Prussia and the rest of Germany was formed against the Swedes and they were driven from Poland wlth much loss. The next year Charles invaded Denmark and defeated its armies, but again was assailed by an overwhelming combination of powers and driven out with disastrous losses. He died in 1660, and under his young son, Charles XI., Sweden suffered further losses. But in the closing years of his reign and of the century this sovereign by wise administration largely restored the prosperity of the country.

In 1697 Charles XII. succeeded to the Swedish throne and quickly showed himself to be one of the greatest soldiers of the age. In 1700, when he was only eighteen years old, he was attacked by Denmark, Poland and Russia together. Undaunted, he first crushed Denmark. Then he conquered Poland and put a new king upon its throne. Then, after deposing the King of Saxony, he prepared to grapple with Russia, while all Europe looked on in wonder. At first he drove the Russians before him. But the dreadful climate proved too much for him, as it has for other invaders of that country. The terrible winter of 1709 so weakened his heroic army that it fell a victim to the overwhelming legions of Peter the Great at Pultowa. Charles was made a fugitive, and sought refuge in Turkey. There his indomitable will soon prepared for another attack upon Russia, which he pressed with such vigor that the Czar was saved from destruction only by the shrewdness of the Empress Catherine, who managed to buy off a large part of Charles' support.

## Peter the Great.

Russia was now emerging from barbarism and beginning to take rank among the nations of civilized Europe. Alexis, the second of the Romanoff Czars, who ascended the throne in 1645, conquered Little Russia from Poland, built a navy, and did much to promote the arts and sciences. In 1696 the famous Peter the Great came to the throne. He was a savage in manners, cruel to the last degree, and a monster of vice and wickedness. But he had unbounded energy and ambition, and very great ability as an administrator. He learned shipbuilding and other useful trades by working as a common laborer in Germany, Holland and England. With the assistance of a Scotch soldier he re-organized his army and established the first real standing army in Russia.

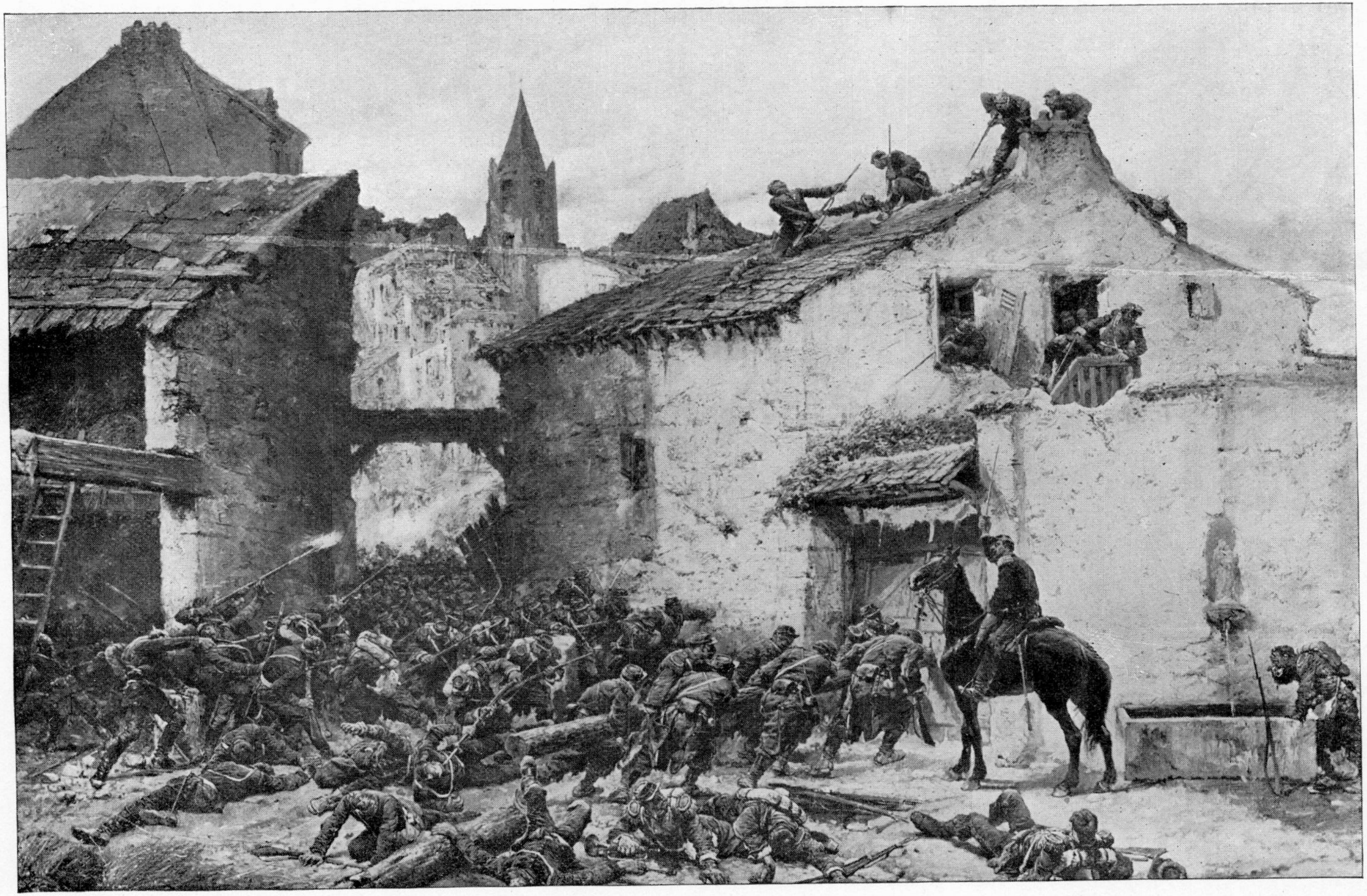

FRANCO-PRUSSIAN WAR

After the battle of Pultowa he seized and annexed to his empire several Swedish provinces on the Baltic, and thus for the first time gave Russia an outlet on that sea. He founded and built the city of St. Petersburg and made it his capital.

## The Times of Cromwell.

After the execution of Charles I. Great Britain became a Commonwealth, or practical republic, under the headship of Oliver Cromwell. But that masterful man soon disagreed with Parliament, as the King had done. Accordingly he arbitrarily dismissed it and formed another entirely subservient to his will, and thereafter was king in all but name. Wars arose, foreign and domestic. The son of King Charles claimed the throne, and invaded the country, gaining a strong following, especially in Scotland. But Cromwell crushed his army at Dunbar and he had to flee to France. The Dutch made war also, and their great Admiral, Van Tromp won some notable victories over the British fleet. The famous Blake retrieved the honor of the British navy, however, and then entered upon a brilliant campaign against the Barbary States of North Africa. He also inflicted great losses upon Spain, and left at his death a name surpassed in British naval annals only by that of Nelson.

During the Protectorate of Cromwell a great impetus was given to British trade and commerce, the British empire in the New World was much extended, and the prestige of British arms and British diplomacy was vastly enhanced throughout the world. Cromwell deserves to rank as one of the greatest of English rulers, in peace and in war.

## The Restoration.

Cromwell died in 1658, and was succeeded by his son Richard. But the latter had no gift for ruling, and soon retired to private life, and the Stuart dynasty was restored in the person of Charles II., one of the most dissolute of monarchs. Under the Commonwealth stern Puritanism had prevailed. A reaction now set in. The court became the most licentious in the world, and society in general was debauched as never before or since in English history. The reign was marked by the acquisition of the province of Bombay, in India, which came to Charles as the wedding-portion of his wife, a Portuguese princess, by the Great Plague in London in 1665, from which over 100,000 persons perished, and by the great fire which destroyed most of London in 1666. In 1667 a Dutch fleet entered the Medway and put England in greater peril of invasion than she had been in for seven centuries.

The kingdom now seemed on the down grade. The king in his greed for money for the gratification of his vices, agreed to sell the honor of the country. He stipulated that if France would aid him, he and his brother James, his heir-presumptive, would become Roman Catholics and forcibly convert England to that faith. James did actually make this change of faith, but Charles hesitated to do so openly, though he was believed to have done so in private. The king produced a financial panic by arbitrarily seizing for his own use more than a million pounds of the public funds. Torture and the burning of heretics were revived, and innumerable acts of gross tyranny were committed.

## Preparing for Revolution.

This state of affairs aroused popular wrath, and a revolutionary spirit began to show itself. A religious war broke out in Scotland, but was soon suppressed. Then the king's illegitimate son, the Duke of Monmouth, joined several other noblemen in a plot to force the king to govern constitutionally. They failed, and all the leaders except Monmouth himself were put to death. In 1685 Charles died, to the great relief of his long-suffering subjects. He was succeeded by his brother James, who was at first regarded with hope by the nation. But he soon showed himself worse even than Charles. The Earl of Argyle raised a rebellion in Scotland, but was defeated and put to death. The same fate attended Monmouth, who led a revolt in the south of England. The infamous Judge Jeffries then went on circuit, and put to death hundreds of persons who were merely suspected of having sympathized with Monmouth.

The next step of the king was to try to force the people to accept the Roman Catholic religion. That brought affairs to a crisis, and the people determined to rebel.

## William of Orange.

In their extremity they turned to the king's daughter, Mary, who was a Protestant and was married to Prince William of Orange. They invited her and her husband to come over and take the throne. James fled to France, and a National Convention met, declared the throne vacant, and elected William and Mary joint sovereigns. The latter accepted the trust, and thus the almost bloodless Revolution of 1689 was effected. Parliament then undid the despotic legislation James had forced upon the country, and enacted a law of succession, providing that thereafter only Protestants should be eligible to the throne.

James made several efforts to regain the crown. One rebellion in his favor was started in Scotland by Grahame of Claverhouse, Viscount of Dundee, but dwindled away after the death of its leader, who fell at the battle of Killecrankie, in the moment of victory. James himself led a rebellion in Ireland, which lasted for some years. It was made memorable by the defence of Londonderry, which withstood a long siege by James's army in the most heroic manner conceivable. In 1690 the Battle of the Boyne was fought, in which William and James confronted each other as rival commanders, and James was utterly routed, largely because of his personal cowardice.

William's reign was largely occupied with wars, in Ireland and on the continent. He was opposed to some of the most renowned generals and to far stronger armies than his own. He was sometimes defeated, and sometimes victorious. But his consummate skill and his great personal valor entitled him to the rank he won, as one of the foremost captains and ablest rulers of his age. He died in 1701, leaving the throne to his daughter Anne.

## "Good Queen Anne."

In the second year of Anne's reign a great continental war was begun, in which the British army was led by John Churchill, Duke of Marlborough. This extraordinary man, who has already been spoken of, was utterly devoid of moral or political principle, and in his greed for gold committed many infamous acts. But as a military genius he must be placed in the very highest rank, along with Hannibal, Cæsar, and Bonaparte. He won every battle in which he was ever engaged, and captured every town he ever besieged. Of no other commander of comparable experience can that be said. He was, moreover, opposed to some commanders who were otherwise quite invincible, but who could make no stand against him.

The most noteworthy event of the reign, in domestic affairs, was the enactment of complete union with Scotland. The reign was made memorable by high literary and scientific achievements of Addison, Newton and others scarcely less famous.

## India.

The Mogul empire in India was now declining. Shah Jehan, grandson of the great Akbar, was a capable ruler, but could not prevent the loss of Afghanistan and other provinces. He was finally deposed by his son, Aurungzebe, and died in prison. Aurungzebe was a strong ruler, but tyrannical and hypocritical. In 1680 his power was disputed by Sivajee, who formed a league of the Mahratta States against him and seriously impaired the strength of his empire. Aurungzebe died in 1707, after a long and magnificent reign, but left no successor able to withstand the disintegrating forces that were already at work, and the condition of the empire thereafter soon became hopelessly chaotic.

At about this time French and English settlers began to find their way into China, and Formosa and Thibet were added to that empire.

## The American Colonies.

The first permanent British colony in America was made at Jamestown, in what is now Virginia, in 1607. This was done under the patronage of the London Company, which sent thither three small ships with about a hundred colonists. The chief man among them was the celebrated Captain John Smith. He had already had a most adventurous and romantic career in the Old World as a soldier and sailor. At Jamestown he fell into the hands of Powhatan, a great Indian chief, who was at first minded to put him to death. But the chief's daughter, Pocahontas, intervened and persuaded her father to spare Smith's life. Thereafter friendly relations were established and maintained between the colonists and the Indians. Smith was made President of the colony, and Pocahontas married Thomas Rolfe, one of the colonists. She returned to England with him, and died there a few years later, leaving a son, from whom many distinguished Virginians have been descended.

The Dutch planted a colony at what is now the city of New York in 1614, and another at Albany. They based their claim to the region upon the discoveries of Henry Hudson, an Englishman in the employ of the Dutch East India Company, who first explored the Hudson River.

## Plymouth Rock.

Most noteworthy of all was the colony planted at Plymouth, Massachusetts, on December 20, 1620. This was established by Englishmen belonging to the Congregational Church. They had been persecuted in England on account of their dissent from the established church, and first sought a refuge in Holland. Finally they came to America to found a colony where they might have freedom to worship God according to the dictates of their own conscience. They sailed from Plymouth, in England on September 16, 1620, in the little ship Mayflower, and reached the American coast on December 20. For many months they had great hardships to endure, and many of them died. But the survivors persevered and made a permanent settlement which ultimately grew into the most important of all the English colonies in America.

At first they got along in friendly fashion with the Indians, especially with the great chiefs Samoset and Massasoit. But the son of the latter, King Philip, was their deadly and unrelenting foe. A bitter war was waged with him which ended with his death and the dispersion of his tribe.

Colonies were planted by the Swedes in Delaware, but these together with the Dutch colonies, presently fell into the hands of the English as spoils of war, and all the north Atlantic coast as far south as Florida, which Spain held, became English territory.

## Dates of Settlement.

As already said, Virginia was settled at Jamestown in 1607, and it may be added that negro slavery was introduced into the North American colonies there in 1620. New York was settled by the Dutch at New York—then called New Amsterdam—and Albany, in 1614. It was taken by the English and its name changed to the present form in 1664. Massachusetts was settled at Plymouth in 1620, by English Puritans. New Hampshire was settled by the English in 1628. New Jersey was settled by the Dutch and was taken by the English in 1664. Delaware was first settled by the Dutch in 1627, and then by Swedes in 1635, and taken by the English in 1664. Maine was settled in 1630 as a dependency of Massachusetts. Maryland was settled by Roman Catholics in 1633. Connecticut was settled by emigrants from Massachusetts in 1635. Rhode Island dates from 1635, and was planted by exiles from Massachusetts who had been driven out because of their religious belief. North Carolina dates from 1659, South Carolina from 1670, and Georgia from 1733. Pennsylvania was settled in 1682 by the Society of Friends, or Quakers. These were the original colonies, from which have grown the United States.

## France Preparing for Revolution.

Louis XV. of France was only five years old when he succeeded his grandfather, Louis XIV. A regency was therefore necessary, and the duties of it were first filled by the Duke of Orleans, a man of singularly depraved morals. After doing all he could to corrupt the young king, he died and was succeeded by the

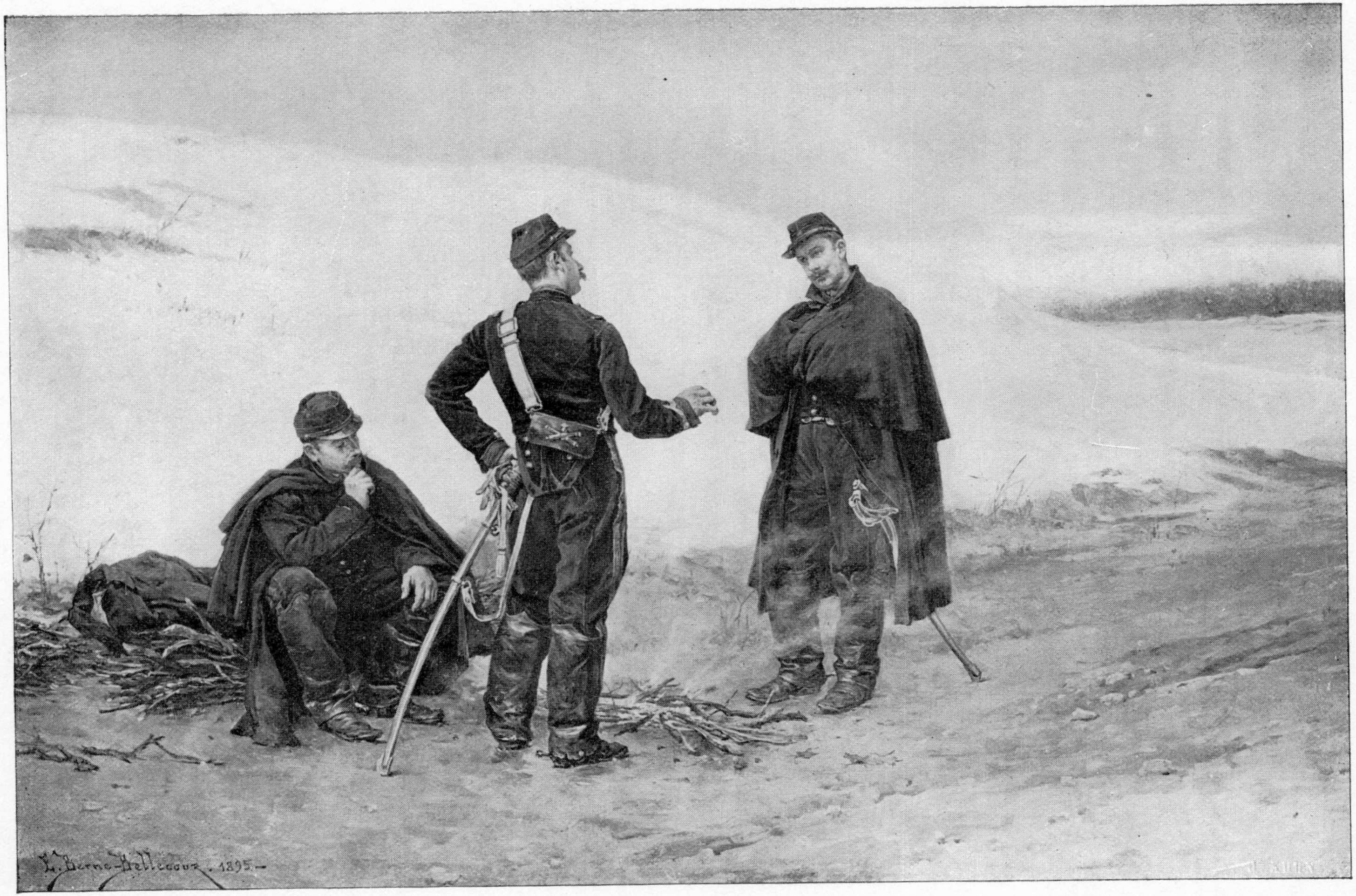

ACCOUNT OF THE BATTLE

Duke of Bourbon, who presently fell into disgrace and was dismissed from the court when, in 1726, at the age of sixteen, Louis took the reins of government into his own hands. The young king did not trust himself to rule absolutely, however, but made his tutor, Cardinal Fleury, his Minister, and that mild and amiable ecclesiastic gave France for a time a peaceful government. Fleury found the finances of the country in desperate disorder and the whole nation, indeed, on the verge of ruin. By his wisdom and uprightness he accomplished wonders, and restored a large measure of prosperity and honor to the stricken country.

But Fleury was an old man, and though he lived almost to the century mark the end had to come at last. After seventeen years of beneficent rule he died, and in that hour fate seemed to set its seal of woe against France. Freed from the good influence of Fleury, the king showed how well he had learned the lessons of the infamous Regent. He gave himself up to such debaucheries as Europe had scarcely seen since the days of Tiberius and Heliogabalus. He allowed his mistresses to rule the kingdom as they pleased, while he spent his time in his harem. He plundered the nation to get funds for the gratification of his vices and the extravagant whims of his herd of paramours. He even engaged in the scandalous traffic of a monopoly of corn, raising the price of bread and driving many of his subjects to starvation in order to maintain his vicious court in luxury.

France soon became involved in war with Austria and England, over the succession to the Austrian and Polish thrones and over the French colonies in America. In 1743 the French were badly beaten at Dettingen by the English under King George II. Two years later the French won a victory at Fontenoy over the English, being greatly assisted by a brigade of Irish exiles. The war went on with varying results until 1748, when a peace was made which was little to the advantage of France. That country was indeed almost bankrupt and in a state of utter wretchedness, and the people began to think of revolution as the only means of saving themselves from complete destruction.

## "After Us the Deluge!"

A losing war was waged in North America, the net result of which was that all of Canada was lost to France. In India the genius of two great commanders secured a splendid empire from the falling Moguls, but it too was lost in the battle of Plassey, in 1757, when Clive made British arms supreme in those regions. But the detestable king was past all sense of duty or of shame. He only abandoned himself the more to sensual pleasures, while Pompadour, Du Barry, and the other creatures who surrounded him merely said, " After us, the deluge ! " and went on in the road to ruin, carrying the kingdom with them.

The sole advantages gained by France in these times were the conquests of Lorraine and Corsica, the latter making a gallant but ineffectual struggle for freedom under the celebrated patriot, Pascal Paoli.

In 1765 the king's son and heir died. He had been a wise and virtuous prince, but for that very reason hated and ill-treated by the king. His son, the king's

25

grandson, then became heir to the throne, and succeeded to it when, in 1774, the worthless king died of smallpox.

### Spain and Portugal.

The history of Spain at this time was not particularly eventful. The kingdom was still on the down grade, though one or two fairly good kings did a little to retard the process of dissolution. Most of the West India islands were however lost— taken by the English.

Portuguese history was marked with the good work of Pombal, the great Minister, who reformed the government, and with the terrible earthquake at Lisbon in 1755, in which 30,000 people lost their lives.

In Italy the Duke of Savoy became King of Sardinia, and thus took another long step in the road which was in time to lead to a reunited and powerful Italy. The rest of the country remained, however, the prey of foreign powers.

### Frederick the Great.

The rise of Prussia was the leading feature of German history in the eighteenth century. Frederick William I. came to the throne of the new kingdom in 1713 and laid the foundations of its military greatness. He was a rude despot, but he formed a strong standing army of 83,000 men and made it the best equipped force in Europe. He also added considerably to the extent of Prussia by conquest from Sweden. In 1740 he died and was succeeded by Frederick the Great. In the same year the death of Charles VI. extinguished the male line of the Hapsburgs, rulers of Austria-Hungary, and plunged Europe into war over the succession to that throne.

The true heir to the throne was Maria Theresa, daughter of Charles. But her cousin, Charles Albert of Bavaria, was also a claimant, on the ground that a woman could not inherit it. There were also several other claimants. Frederick the Great offered to help Maria Theresa if she would let him have Silesia. She refused, whereupon he went to war against her, and got France, Spain, Bavaria, and Saxony to join him in it. In her extremity Maria Theresa made a personal appeal to the Hungarians, who responded to it with great enthusiasm. They soon conquered Bavaria and held the French in check at Prague. Then a compromise was made with Frederick, by which he received Silesia, whereupon he withdrew from the alliance against Maria Theresa. Then the intervention of England and the victory of Dettingen turned the scale so strongly in favor of Austria, that Frederick became alarmed, fearing Maria Theresa would become too strong and would demand Silesia back. Accordingly he again made war against her, with varying results, until the peace of 1748.

Thereafter he devoted himself to the peaceful development of his country for a time. Then the rapid rise of Prussia excited the jealousies of other powers, and Austria, France and Russia combined to crush her. Frederick did not wait to be attacked but assumed the aggressive at once. He first routed the Saxons and

Austrians and compelled the former to join him and fight on his side. Then Austria and Russia determined to divide his kingdom between them, with the aid of their allies, France and Sweden. But England took Frederick's part and gave him much assistance. After some disasters Frederick routed the French at Rossbach, and the Austrians at Leuthen, and then the Russians at Zorndorff, But as fast as one enemy was disposed of another appeared or was revived. With almost all Europe against him this wonderful king and warrior struggled on undismayed. At last peace came in 1763. Prussia did not gain any territory as a result of all her wars, but she won undisputed rank as one of the great powers. In the peace that followed Frederick showed himself as great an administrator as he was a soldier.

## The Hanoverians.

On the death of Queen Anne the British crown went to George, Elector of Hanover, and thus the Hanoverian dynasty in England was founded. The new king could not speak a word of English and was by no means popular, especially as he seemed inclined to subordinate the interests of England to those of Hanover. His short reign ended in 1727, and he was succeeded by his son, George II., whose military prowess made him more popular. In his reign the battle of Dettigen was won, as previously noted; Commodore Anson sailed around the world despoiling the treasure-ships of Spain; Clive drove the French from India and won an Empire there for England; Canada and other provinces were taken in America; Boscawen and Hawke almost annihilated the French navy; and Coote continued the work of Clive in India. The elder Pitt was the presiding genius of the Government, and he raised England to the summit of power and glory.

In 1760 the king died and was succeeded by his grandson, George III. The latter could speak English, which neither of his Hanoverian predecessors could do. His morals were irreproachable, and he was so good-hearted as to command much real affection. Unhappily he was also narrow, bigoted and stubborn, and not always wise in his choice of Ministers. Misgovernment was now alienating the American colonies, and the king would do nothing to stop the process. His Minister, Grenville, in 1765, secured the passage of the Stamp Act, a very obnoxious tax-law, and insisted upon the right to tax the colonies at will without giving them representation in the government. Against this suicidal course Pitt, Burke and other wise counsellors protested eloquently, but in vain. In 1770 the king found in Lord North a Minister willing to be even more despotic over the colonies. The natural result was soon apparent. The colonies rebelled and declared themselves independent.

In India, the Mogul and Mahratta powers steadily declined, and British influence increased. After the triumphs of Clive and Coote, Warren Hastings became Governor of British India. He conducted the government with marvellous ability through enormous difficulties, but was charged with many acts of oppression and injustice, for which he was called home and put on trial. After one of the most famous trials in history, in which the foremost Englishmen of the day were engaged, he was acquitted.

# CHAPTER IV.

---

## THE PRESENT ERA.

THE WAR BEGINS—THE AMERICAN CONSTITUTION—WAR OF 1812—THE FRENCH REVO-
LUTION—THE REIGN OF TERROR—RISE OF BONAPARTE—THE EMPIRE—FALL OF
BONAPARTE—BRITISH AFFAIRS—AMERICAN GROWTH—SOME MINOR STATES—
A REVOLUTIONARY ERA—ITALY—GERMANY—ENGLAND AND INDIA—
THE UNITED STATES—THE SLAVERY QUESTION—THE GREAT
REBELLION—FREEDOM AND VICTORY—THE RETURN OF
PEACE—THE FRENCH EMPIRE AND REPUBLIC—
THE TERRIBLE YEAR—GREAT BRITAIN—RUS-
SIA AND TURKEY—CHINA AND JAPAN
—CUBA—CLOSING YEARS.

---

## The Present Era.

THE last quarter of the eighteenth century was marked with two stupendous revolutions, one in each hemisphere, which produced greater changes in human affairs than any events that had occurred for ages. One was the War of the Revolution in America, the other was the French Revolution. The former was the earlier in date, and demands first consideration in this narrative.

The causes that led to it were persistent acts of injustice committed by the British Government. That the mass of the British people approved them is not to be believed. Many of the foremost and most representative British statesmen protested against them and urged a course of justice and conciliation. All was in vain. The King was stubborn and his Ministers fatuous. The American colonies were subjected to burdensome taxation and denied the right of representation in the Government that taxed them. Open rebellion soon showed itself in the New England colonies and spread through them all. In 1773 several cargoes of taxed tea were thrown overboard at Boston by the colonists. The next year a Continental Congress met at Philadelphia and drew up a Bill of Rights.

## The War Begins.

The war for independence began in 1775, with the battles of Lexington and Concord, in Massachusetts. In May of that year George Washington of Virginia was made Commander-in-Chief of the forces of all the colonies. In June came the famous battle of Bunker's Hill. Thus far the colonists had little thought of actual independence, but aimed merely at securing reforms and concessions. But

TURKISH CAVALRY EVACUATING GREECE

now they saw their only course was to sever themselves entirely from the Old Country. Accordingly on July 4, 1776, the Congress adopted a Declaration of Independence, and thus made of the colonies a new nation among the powers of the world.

At first the war went against the Americans. Boston and New York were occupied by the British, and the Americans were put upon the defensive. But Washington and his aids, especially Green, displayed great ability and valor. The British were beaten at Trenton, Princeton and elsewhere. Their army under Burgoyne was captured at Saratoga. Then France recognized the independence of the colonies and gave them material aid. In 1780 Benedict Arnold, maddened by the unjust treatment given him by Congress, turned traitor and sought to betray the American posts on the Hudson River to the British. His treason was detected and baffled. He made his escape, but his chief aid, Major Andre, of the British army, was taken and hanged as a spy.

Thereafter the war went steadily against the British. In 1781 their principal commander, Lord Cornwallis, surrendered at Yorktown, Virginia, and the war was practically ended. Great Britain recognized the independence of the United States, as the colonies were now called, and concluded a treaty of peace with what was destined to become one of the greatest nations in the world.

## The American Constitution.

The confederation of the thirteen colonies was soon exchanged for a more stable form of government. A National Constitution was adopted, and in 1789 the first Federal Congress met at New York, and George Washington was chosen the first President of the United States. The growth of the nation in population, wealth and territory was steady and rapid. Vermont was admitted as the fourteenth state in 1791, Kentucky as the fifteenth in 1792, Tennessee as the sixteenth in 1796, and at the commencement of the next century, Ohio as the seventeenth. Then, in 1803, the Government purchased from France the whole vast territory between the Mississippi River and the Rocky Mountains, thus more than doubling the size of the country.

Washington was President for eight years, and was succeeded by John Adams for four years. Next came Thomas Jefferson, for eight years, and under his administration relations with England became strained over commercial rights. This culminated in another war in the administration of the next President, James Madison.

## War of 1812.

The war began in 1812, and lasted over two years. The Americans invaded Canada, but were beaten, and were generally unsuccessful on the land. The British invaded Maryland, and wantonly burned the City of Washington, which had been made the capital. But on the sea the Americans won a series of brilliant victories, as they also did on Lakes Champlain and Erie, thus for the first time successfully challenging the then almost undisputed supremacy of England as a sea power. The war ended with a brilliant American victory, won by General Jackson at New Orleans, which took place after the treaty of peace had been signed, but before the news of it reached this country.

## The French Revolution.

In the meantime great things were happening in Europe. Discontent in France increased in spite of the amiable intentions of Louis XVI., and the admirable work of his ministers, Turgot and Neckar. Financial troubles compelled the King to summon a Parliament, the first in two centuries, to consider the state of the country. That body soon manifested revolutionary tendencies, and an inclination to abolish the ancient privileges of the nobility, and to restrict the authority of the King with a Constitution. On July 14, 1789, the mob of Paris took affairs into its own hands. It stormed the great prison of the Bastile, and then marched to Versailles, and compelled the King and his family to return to Paris with them and make that city his capital.

The King was soon forced to accept a Constitution, which made a single Parliamentary chamber the practical ruler of the country. Then a disposition to abolish the monarchy was manifested. For a time this was kept in check by the personal influence of the great orator and statesman, Mirabeau. Unfortunately he died in 1791, and no check was left upon the passions of the revolutionists.

## The Reign of Terror.

Maximilien Robespierre, head of the Jacobin Club, now became the dominant force in the government. The King and royal family were made prisoners. This enraged the surrounding nations so that they joined in a war against France. The French armies defended the frontiers with marvellous courage and skill, while a Reign of Terror was established within the Kingdom. Under the administration of Robespierre, Danton, Marat, and others of like character, all who were even suspected of royalist principles were put to death, often with hideous tortures. The King was hurried through a mockery of a trial and beheaded. The Queen was similarly disposed of after being subjected to infamous physical outrages. The Princess Lamballe, a beautiful woman of saintly character, was thrown out to the mob in the street and there outraged to death and then her dead body further outraged and mutilated and even partly devoured. The Prince Royal, a lad of tender years, was slowly tortured to death.

All over France like infamies were perpetrated upon royalists and upon all whose property was coveted by the greedy tyrants. Churches were confiscated, the Christian religion proscribed under penalty of death, and a lewd woman from a brothel was set upon the altar of the cathedral in Paris and worshipped with obscene rites. At Nantes 15,000 innocent persons were butchered in three months. Marat, one of the most bloodthirsty of the tyrants, was put to death by the noble Charlotte Corday, who gave her own life to rid France of his. Then the bloody Junta began fighting among themselves. Danton and others were put to death by their old comrades. Finally there was a revolt against Robespierre himself. He was guillotined, and thus the Reign of Terror was ended, and the government passed into the hands of more moderate and humane men.

## Rise of Bonaparte.

The armies of France had been successful against the allied foes, thanks to the genius of Carnot, the great War Minister, and the leadership of Hoche, Jourdan, Moreau, and other generals. At the siege of Toulon a young artillery officer from Corsica, named Napoleon Bonaparte, won distinction, and he soon rose to prominence. In 1796 he was entrusted with the command of an army to invade Italy. He crossed the Alps, compelled the King of Sardinia to cede territory to France and become its ally, defeated the Austrians, who then possessed most of Italy, in a wonderful series of battles at Lodi, Arcola, Rivoli, and elsewhere, and finally dictated a peace under which France gained Belgium, the Ionian Islands and the left bank of the Rhine.

Bonaparte next planned an invasion of England, but finally set out for the East instead, intent on seizing the British possessions in Asia. He invaded Egypt and conquered it. But the British fleet under Nelson followed and destroyed his fleet in the great battle of the Nile, in 1798. Bonaparte then marched into Syria, and after an indecisive campaign, made his way back to France, leaving his army to its own devices. In France affairs had been going badly. The Government was incompetent and the armies were falling back before the hosts of allied Europe. Bonaparte quickly made a coup d'etat, under which he was made military dictator under the guise of Consul. He soon concluded a peace on terms advantageous to France, and then set about reorganizing the domestic government, which he did in a manner on the whole admirable.

## The Empire.

At first Bonaparte was Consul for ten years. But in 1802 he proclaimed himself Consul for life, and two years later he proclaimed himself Emperor, and compelled the Pope to come to Paris, and crown him as such. The next year he horrified Europe by murdering the young duke of Enghien, a descendant of the Condes, and war was declared against him by England, Austria, Russia, and Sweden, while Spain sided with France. In the battle of Ulm the French routed the Austrians, but in the sea-fight of Trafalgar the British, under Nelson, annihilated the fleets of France and Spain combined. At Austerlitz Napoleon again crushed the allied armies and then made peace with Austria and Prussia, gaining great accessions of territory. The next war was with Prussia and Russia. Napoleon vanquished the former at Jena and the latter at Friedland, and dictated peace on his own terms. His brothers were made kings of Holland, Naples and Westphalia, and he himself was Protector of the Rhine Provinces. All Europe was now at his side, or his feet, except England, which stubbornly held out against him. Accordingly he entered upon a campaign for the destruction of that power.

He declared a blockade of all English ports, which he was, of course, unable to make effective. Portugal and Spain demurred at so senseless an order, whereupon he sent an army against the one, and made his brother King of the other. A British army, under the Duke of Wellington, baffled him in Portugal, and then, advancing into Spain, defeated his ablest Marshals, and finally expelled the entire French forces, inflicting upon them a loss of more than 400,000 men.

## Fall of Bonaparte.

Another war with Austria ended in the battle of Wagram, in which the Austrians were crushed. Meanwhile Napoleon divorced his wife, Josephine, to whom he owed much of his success, and wedded in her place Maria Louisa, daughter of the Austrian emperor, who bore him a son, called the King of Rome. The Emperor was now, in 1811, at the summit of his power. But his fall was near. Out of wanton desire to control the whole continent, he began war against Russia, and invaded that country in 1812 with half a million men. He crushed a Russian army at Borodino, and captured Moscow. But the Russians burned that city over his head, and, deprived of shelter and supplies, his army was forced to retreat in midwinter. Its sufferings were indescribable, it was harassed by the Cossacks, and scarcely a regiment of the great host ever got back to France.

With almost superhuman energy he raised another army and faced the allied foes who now closed in around him. England was the head of the league and supplied money for all. Russia, Prussia, Sweden, and at last Austria, were her allies. Napoleon defeated their armies at Lutzen and Bautzen, and at Dresden, his last great victory. At Leipzic in October, 1813, was fought the "Battle of the Nations," in which he was utterly routed. Further conflicts ensued, but early in 1814 the allies entered France, captured Paris, and compelled him to abdicate. The Island of Elba was given to him for a realm, and he was allowed to retain his imperial title. The Bourbons were restored to the throne of France, the King being Louis XVIII., brother of Louis XVI., the Dauphin who had been murdered in the Reign of Terror being reckoned Louis XVII. A Congress of the Powers restored most of the European states to the condition they were in before Napoleon disturbed them.

But they were not yet through with the Corsican. He escaped from Elba and landed at Cannes early in 1815. His old soldiers flocked to him and he entered Paris in triumph. For a hundred days he ruled France again. But Europe rose against him as the common enemy. He raised a great army and marched into Belgium. There he met and defeated at Ligny, on June 16, a German army under Blucher. Twelve days later he hurled himself against a composite army, the central portion of which was an English force under Wellington. The Battle of Waterloo ensued, in which the French were utterly routed. Napoleon fled, surrendered to the British, and was sent to the island of St. Helena as a prisoner for life. He died there in 1821.

## British Affairs.

The history of nearly all the rest of Europe is included in that of France during the period of which we have just been speaking. Great Britain had, however, other troubles than those with France and America. In 1791 an association called the United Irishmen, strove to separate Ireland from England. The insurrection was suppressed, and after ten years of agitation the Irish Parliment was abolished and the present union with England formed. Another Irish rebellion under Robert Emmett was suppressed in 1803. In 1806 the greatest British Minister of the age, William Pitt, died, but his policy was ably continued by his pupil, George Canning. About this time the British slave trade was abolished. It is also interesting to observe that in the midst of all this storm and stress, in 1788, the first English colony in Australia was planted, at Port Jackson, now Sydney.

## American Growth.

After the War of 1812 the United States rapidly grew in all directions. In 1815 a fleet under Commodore Decatur was sent to the Mediterranean to suppress Algerine piracy which had long been the scourge of Europe. Two years later James Monroe became President, and in time put forth his famous "Doctrine" to the effect that no further conquests of American soil must be attempted by European powers. A war with the Seminole Indians followed, and General Jackson pursued them into the swamps of Florida. That territory still belonged to Spain, but Jackson ignored the Spanish authorities, and Florida was presently ceded to the United States. Mississippi, Illinois, Alabama, and Maine were successively taken into the Union, and then the slavery question began to cause trouble. When Missouri applied for admission, the free states objected because she would be a slave state. Finally the "Missouri Compromise" was made, under which it was agreed that no slave state should thereafter be made north of the parallel of 36 deg. 30 min. N. lat. Then Missouri was admitted as the twenty-fourth state.

John Quincy Adams succeeded Monroe, and Andrew Jackson came after him. Under Jackson the "spoils system" in politics was established. South Carolina objected to the protective tariff and threatened to secede, declaring the law was null and void. Jackson coerced her into submission. There were Indian wars in Florida and Wisconsin, and Arkansas and Michigan were added to the Union.

## Some Minor States.

Under Napoleon, Holland and Belgium were a part of France. After his fall they were made an independent kingdom under the Prince of Orange, who became William I. In 1831 the Belgians seceded and established a separate kingdom of their own.

Sweden was compelled in 1809 to give up Finland to Russia. In 1814 Sweden and Norway were united under a common King, though each retained its own Parliament and Ministry. Bernadotte, formerly one of Napoleon's Marshals, became King, and established a new dynasty in 1818.

Poland, which had first been partitioned among Russia, Prussia and Austria in 1772, and again in 1794–5, finally disappeared as even a nominal kingdom in 1832, when, after ruthless suppression of an insurrection, it was incorporated fully into the Russian empire.

The British settlement of Australia and New Zealand proceeded apace. Western Australia was founded in 1829, South Australia in 1834, and Victoria in 1835. In 1851 gold was discovered near Sydney, and thereafter the growth of the colonies was more rapid than that of any other community in the world.

In South America the Spanish provinces revolted one after another in the early part of the century, until all became independent republics, excepting British, Dutch and French Guiana, and the Empire of Brazil, which became independent of Portugal, its founder, in Napoleonic times.

## A Revolutionary Era.

The revolution of 1848 in France, which expelled Louis Philippe, was the beginning of an era of revolutions throughout Europe. The French established a republic, and elected as their President Louis Napoleon, a nephew of Napoleon Bonaparte who, during the preceding reign had made two futile attemps to get himself declared Emperor. In December, 1851, he committed the great crime known as the Coup d'Etat, arbitrarily imprisoning the chief republican statesmen and making himself Dictator. Next he compelled the people to elect him President for ten years, and then Emperor, under the title of Napoleon III., the son of Napoleon who died in boyhood without reigning being reckoned Napoleon II. To give military glory to his ill-won crown, he soon involved himself in war with Russia, on the pretext that the latter was about to seize Constantinople. England became his ally, and the Crimean war was fought, in 1854-6. Notable battles were fought at the Alma River, Balakava, and Inkermann, and after a hard siege Sebastopol was captured and then peace was made. An Anglo-French war against China followed in 1858-60, in which Pekin was taken and sacked.

In 1859 the French Emperor began a war against Austria ostensibly to aid Italy in securing her independence. Italy had already risen to regain Lombardy and Venice. At Magenta and Solferino the Austrians were defeated and a treaty of peace was concluded by which Lombardy was given to Sardinia and Venice left to Austria, while France seized Savoy and Nice.

## Italy.

Joseph Mazzini was the first leader of the Italian revolution, and Charles Albert, King of Sardinia, was looked to as the coming sovereign of a reunited Italy. But Mazzini was impractical, and Charles Albert was not able to hold his own against the superior power of Austria. Little was therefore gained until Charles Albert's son, Victor Emanuel, came to the throne with Count Cavour as his chief Minister. Then with the aid of France, Lombardy was regained. Naples was groaning under the oppression of the tyrant Ferdinand, and rebellion became rampant there. Ferdinand died in 1859, and then the country arose against his son, Francis II., under the lead of Giuseppe Garibaldi, a daring soldier who had already distinguished himself in the war with Austria. With a thousand followers Garibaldi went from Genoa to Sicily and quickly freed it and then Naples from Francis's rule. Francis fled, and his kingdom was annexed to Sardinia, and all Italy, except Rome and its environs, was united under Victor Emmanuel.

## Germany.

Simultaneously with the Revolution of 1848 in France, a spirit of revolt against absolutism was manifested in Germany, together with a strong desire for reunion of the various states into one empire. Violent outbreaks occurred here and there, which were sternly repressed. But the net result was that Prussia and other states were compelled to adopt constitutional forms of government.

The most serious outbreak occurred in Hungary, against the tyranny and re-action of the Austrian Emperor. Under the lead of Louis Kossuth the Hungarians proclaimed their independence and established a republic. They were at first suc-cessful in the field, driving the Austrians before them and forcing the Emperor to abdicate in favor of his nephew, the present Emperor. The aid of Russia was then sought and given, and the Hungarians were crushed with great barbarity, and for years their land was treated as a conquered province.

## England and India.

Great Britain was meanwhile increasing the extent of her Indian empire, though at much cost. In 1857 the insurrection known as the Sepoy Mutiny occurred, provoked by bad administration. It was marked by the hideous massacre of English women and children at Cawnpore, the heroic defence of Lucknow and its rescue by Outram and Havelock, and the capture of Delhi by the unrivalled hero, Nicholson.

## The United States.

Martin Van Buren became the eighth President of the United States in 1837. Four years later he was succeeded by W. H. Harrison, who died within a month and was succeeded by the Vice-President, John Tyler. In his administration the Northwest boundary dispute with England was settled, and Oregon and Iowa and the vast region between them became part of the national domain. Texas also, which had won its independence from Mexico, was annexed.

Under the next President, James K. Polk, Iowa and Texas became states. An uncalled-for war with Mexico was then provoked, and under the lead of General Taylor the latter was subdued and compelled to relinquish much territory to the United States. In 1849 Wisconsin was admitted as a State, and General Taylor be-came President. He died a year later and was succeeded by the Vice-President, Millard Fillmore. At this time the discovery of gold in California caused an enor-mous rush of settlers to that territory.

## The Slavery Question.

The question of African slavery in the United States, long troublesome, now became acute. Anti-Slavery organizations were formed in the North, for the purpose of aiding runaway slaves to escape. The South on the other hand strove by legislation to force the North to return slaves to their masters. The struggle resolved itself into a fight for the control of Congress. In 1852 Franklin Pierce, a pro-slavery man, was elected President. Kansas and Nebraska were organized as territories and the question whether they were to be free or slave was left to their own people. The North then sought to colonize them with anti-slavery settlers, and succeeded, but the South, by provoking a practical state of civil war, forcibly prevented them from organizing on a free basis. In 1856 another pro-slavery President, James Buchanan, was elected. John Brown, the leader of the anti-slavery party in Kansas, after having his son murdered by the pro-slavery men and finding that the National government was not disposed to protect the rights of free men in Kansas, came to Harper's Ferry, Virginia, and organized a rebellion of slaves against slavery. This was in 1859. He was captured and hanged, but the incident startled the whole country and revealed the imminence of the final struggle between freedom and slavery. In this administration Minnesota and Oregon were added to the Union. They were sure to be free states. Then in 1860 an anti-slavery man, Abraham Lincoln, was elected President, and the slave states realized that they were beaten at last, and so resolved to secede from the Union.

## The Great Rebellion.

Without waiting for Lincoln to be installed and to reveal his policy, South Carolina seceded and was followed by nearly all the other slave States. Delegates were sent to Montgomery, Alabama, and a provisional government formed, under the style of the Confederate States of America. Jefferson Davis was chosen President. The government was afterward made permanent in character and removed to Richmond, Virginia. In April, 1861, the Confederate troops fired upon Fort Sumpter, in the harbor of Charleston, South Carolina, and thus one of the greatest wars of modern times was begun.

President Lincoln called for volunteers and declared the ports of the rebel states to be in a state of blockade. Great Britain, France and Spain promptly recognized the insurgents as belligerents, and permitted much aid to be given to them by the fitting out of privateers to prey upon United States commerce. A pretty effective blockade was soon established along the whole coast. In the first battles on land the insurgents were successful, and at Bull Run the Federal army was routed. In 1862 the Federals captured Fort Henry and Fort Donelson, in Tennessee, and won the great battle of Pittsburg Landing. These victories were chiefly owing to the genius of General U. S. Grant. Meantime Commodore Farragut captured New Orleans with his fleet. The chief Federal army under General McClellan was unable to make any headway against the Confederates under Robert E. Lee and

"Stonewall" Jackson, in Virginia. Indeed the national capital itself was on several occasions menaced by the Confederates.

### Freedom and Victory.

On January 1, 1863, President Lincoln issued a proclamation emancipating all the slaves. The following summer Lee invaded Pennsylvania, and at the beginning of July a great three-days' battle was fought between his army and the army of the Potomac—formerly commanded by McClellan, but now by George G. Meade—at Gettysburg. This was the greatest battle of the whole war, and resulted in the utter defeat of the Confederates, who retreated to Virgina. At the same time Grant captured Vicksburg and thus opened the Mississippi River to Federal traffic and broke the power of the rebellion in that part of the country. The next year Grant was called to the east and made commander-in-chief of the whole Federal army, taking personal charge of the Army of the Potomac in Virginia and making Richmond and Lee's army his objective points. William T. Sherman was left in charge in the west. Grant fought a series of tremendous battles with Lee around Richmond while Sherman marched southeast through Georgia, to Atlanta and to the sea at Savannah, reaching the latter at the end of 1864. Sherman then marched northward to join Grant, but before he reached him, on April 9, 1865, Grant surrounded Lee and compelled him to surrender with his whole army, at Appomattox Courthouse, Virginia. That was practically the end of the war. A few days later President Lincoln was assassinated by one Booth, a revengeful Southerner. Jefferson Davis was captured as he was trying to flee from the country, and was kept in prison for some time, and then released. A general amnesty was declared, slavery was forever abolished, the negroes were admitted to citizenship, and in time the lately rebellious states were taken back into the Union as before.

### The Return of Peace.

After the war the United States entered upon a career of great prosperity. The Vice-President, Andrew Johnson, succeeded to the Presidency on the murder of Lincoln. Nevada and Nebraska were admitted as states. The great territory of Alaska was purchased from Russia in 1867, for $7,000,000. In 1869 General Grant became President, and under his administration the serious disputes with Great Britain growing out of the war were submitted to arbitration, and thus the example of peaceful settlement of international disputes was set to the world.

In 1876 the centennial anniversary of the Declaration of Independence was celebrated with a world's fair at Philadelphia, the largest exhibition of its kind ever held in the world down to that time. The Presidential election of that year was closely contested and for months the result was in doubt, charges of fraud being freely made on both sides. At last a special commission to which the case had been referred decided that Rutherford B. Hayes had been elected, and he was accordingly installed. Near the close of his administration the use of gold as currency, which had been suspended in the war, was successfully resumed. In

1880 James A. Garfield was elected President, but was assassinated a few months after taking office and was succeeded by the Vice-President, Chester A. Arthur. The next President was Grover Cleveland, in 1885. Then came Benjamin Harrison, in 1889, for four years, then Cleveland again for four years, and then the latest, William McKinley, elected in 1896 and installed in 1897.

## The French Empire and Republic.

The Empire of Louis Napoleon began to decline soon after the war in Italy. In the hope of preserving prestige, Napoleon persuaded Maximilian, the brother of the Austrian Emperor, to go to Mexico, and set up an empire there under French protection. That enterprise seemed to prosper as long as the United States was convulsed with civil war. But in 1865 the United States Government compelled the French army to be withdrawn from Mexico. The fall of the Empire followed, and Maximilian was put to death. This brought much reproach upon Napoleon, and he sought to divert attention from his disgrace by other enterprises. He accordingly picked a quarrel with Prussia in 1870 over the succession to the Spanish throne. Prussia was not at all reluctant to fight. Indeed, she rather courted the conflict. The other German states joined Prussia, and thus another great war began.

War was declared on July 19, 1870. In one or two small engagements the French were successful. But it soon became clear that France was utterly unprepared for war, while Germany was perfectly prepared. The Germans poured across the Rhine in three enormous armies and defeated the French in a number of great battles. In a few weeks the French Emperor, with an army of 90,000 men, was captured at Sedan. He was sent to Germany as a prisoner, and afterward to England, where he died a few years later. On his fall the French declared the Empire abolished and established a republic.

## The Terrible Year.

But the war went on, through what the French well call the "Terrible Year." The Germans pressed on irresistibly. Strasburg was besieged, and after a heroic defence was taken. Metz was besieged, and soon captured with its garrison of 180,000 men, betrayed, it was believed, by a false commander. Paris itself was besieged, bombarded, and captured. Then peace was made on hard terms for France. She was compelled to cede Alsace and most of Lorraine to Germany, and to pay Germany $1,000,000,000. This immense sum she quickly paid, in spite of the exhaustion caused by the war, her people setting an example of patriotic devotion unsurpassed in history.

The new French republic was soon firmly established. It was at first fiercely resisted by the Communists, who seized possession of Paris and revived there the horrors of the Reign of Terror. They were at last suppressed. The first President of the Republic was Adolphe Thiers. He resigned and was succeeded by Marshal MacMahon, a gallant soldier, who was a friend of the Bonaparte family, and was suspected of wishing an Imperialist restoration. He too resigned, and was succeeded by Jules Grevy, who served a full term, and was elected to a second, but soon thereafter was compelled to resign on account of the political corruption of his son-in-law. Sadi Carnot, grandson of the Carnot of the Revolution, was next chosen, but near the end of his term of office was assassinated by an Italian Anarchist. To him succeeded Casimir-Perier, who resigned after a few months and was succeeded by Felix Faure.

## Great Britain.

The salient points of British history in these years may be briefly noted. An uprising of "Fenians" in Ireland was suppressed in 1867, and a successful expedition was dispatched to Abyssinia to rescue some British subjects held as prisoners. Between 1868 and 1874 a new Reform act was passed, the Irish Church was disestablished, the system of purchasing places in the army was abolished, and the secret ballot was introduced. These were largely Mr. Gladstone's work. Then Mr. Disraeli became Premier, a controlling interest in the Suez Canal was purchased, and in 1876 the Queen was proclaimed Empress of India. Wars with the Zulus, the Boers, and the Afghans followed, in 1879-81. Then a serious famine in Ireland was followed by political disturbances and a vigorous Parliamentary campaign for separation from England. A native rebellion in Egypt made British interference necessary, Alexandria was bombarded in 1882 and a British army soon dispersed the insurgents. The illustrious Charles Gordon was sent to Khartoum to hold that place and was there basely abandoned to his death by the Gladstone Government. Later, in 1896-7 a British expedition was sent to retake Khartoum and reconquer the Soudan which had been given up to the rebels.

In the summer of 1897 the sixtieth anniversary of the Queen's coronation was celebrated with imposing ceremonies, her reign then having lasted longer than that of any other British sovereign.

## Russia and Turkey.

Serious disturbances arose in the Balkan States in 1876, which led to a declaration of war against Turkey by Russia. A great Russian Army of invasion was sent down, but was at first defeated by the Turks. Finally with the aid of the Roumanians the Russians were successful, and would have captured Constantinople itself had not Great Britain interfered in the interest of the balance of power. The net results of the war were that Montenegro and Servia were enlarged and made independent, Bulgaria was made autonomous, Bosnia and Herzegovina were given to Austria, Roumania was much strengthened, Russia got an indemnity and much territory in Armenia, and England got the island of Cyprus.

In 1882 the Czar Alexander II. was assassinated by Nihilists, and a bitter campaign against them followed. Russia steadily pressed on in Central Asia, absorbing country after country until she possessed nearly all the continent not held by India, China and Persia.

The Turkish Government in 1895 entered upon a general massacre of Armenian Christians, and put more than 250,000 of them to death. The European powers protested but did not venture to interfere. Russia now posed as the ally of Turkey and virtually protected that power. Turkish aggression led to a war with Greece in 1897, in which Greece was beaten and robbed of much territory.

## China and Japan.

The empire of Japan about 1885 entered upon a career of marked expansion and progress. Universal suffrage and representative government were established and the country began to rank with Europe and America in civilization. A war broke out with China in 1894, in which the Chinese were badly beaten and great advantages won for Japan, although European powers interfered to rob Japan of some of the fruits of victory. Soon afterward China gave Russia the right to occupy and build railroads in Manchuria and Mongolia, and practically placed herself under Russian protection.

## Cuba.

The island of Cuba, long dissatisfied with Spanish rule, has often risen in revolt. A ten years' war was fought from 1868 to 1878, marked with great severities on the Spanish side, but ended indecisively. In the early part of 1895 the Cubans again took up arms and proclaimed their independence of Spain. An enormous army was sent to suppress them, by far the largest ever sent across the ocean by any power. Under the command of General Weyler, popularly called "The Butcher," it committed acts of incredible cruelty and savagery, and killed or starved to death scores of thousands of women and children, and laid much of the island waste. The Cubans proved unconquerable, however. Weyler was recalled in the fall of 1897, and a more humane man was put in his place to try to effect a compromise with the insurgents.

## Closing Years.

The four hundredth anniversary of the discovery of America by Columbus was magnificently celebrated in the United States in 1892–3, with a World's Fair at Chicago, and other demonstrations. In 1897 New York and its neighbors were consolidated into a single city, the largest in the world save London.

Of the vast achievements of science, in which the United States has borne a leading part, space will not permit us to treat at length. Every year brings forth some new triumph of mind over matter, for the betterment of the conditions of human life. There is no occasion to lament the "lost arts" of the past. The present is the best age that has yet dawned upon the world. And in it our own country may without boasting be reckoned

" . . . The heir of all the ages, in the foremost files of time."